Thirteenth Edition

A STAR ATLAS

AND REFERENCE HANDBOOK

(EPOCH 1950)

FOR STUDENTS AND AMATEURS

Covering the whole Star Sphere, and showing over 9000 Stars, Nebulæ, and Clusters; with Descriptive Lists of Objects mostly suitable for Small Telescopes; Notes on Planets, Star Nomenclature, &c.

BY

ARTHUR P. NORTON, B.A.

The Reference Handbook by

J. GALL INGLIS, F.R.A.S., AND A. P. NORTON

London:

GALL AND INGLIS, 12 NEWINGTON ROAD, EDINBURGH 9

AND LONDON

1957

Contents:

Made and Printed in Great Britain

Preface

The first Edition of this Atlas was published in the year 1910. The work was primarily designed for those amateur telescopists whose instruments are mounted either on alt-azimuth stands or as equatorials without graduated circles. It was also intended to be used as a companion to Webb's invaluable "Celestial Objects for Common Telescopes," and Smyth's admirable "Cycle of Celestial Objects," both now out of print, and unobtainable except in astronomical libraries. Practically all the objects contained in the latest editions of these two works, down to and including stars of the seventh magnitude, are shown in the maps, also several fainter objects of particular interest.

Owing to the plan and arrangement of the maps, and also on account of the large overlap, a view of about one-fifth of the entire heavens is shown on one folio, and no constellation is inconveniently broken up. The distortion is slight considering the large area represented. Altogether the charts indicate the positions of over 8,400 stars and 600 nebulæ. Bright variable and red stars are indicated by a small "V" and "R" respectively, but double stars could not be similarly lettered without sacrificing the clearness of the maps. For particulars of these objects, reference should be made to the lists on the back of the maps and to "Webb" and "Smyth."

The underlying idea has been to furnish both the amateur observer and the general reader with a reference book to which he can turn for an explanation of unfamiliar terms—observational terminology especially being very inadequately dealt with in text-books. These explanations are necessarily much compressed, but it is hoped they are sufficiently complete for the required purpose. Sources of fuller information are often given.

The Constellation boundaries used are those prepared by Mons. E. Delporte, and adopted by the International Astronomical Union in 1930. The epoch of Mons. Delporte's boundaries is 1875, and by 1950 the change of their positions in R.A. and Dec., due to 75 years of precession, is appreciable. With respect to the stars themselves the positions of the boundaries always remain unaltered.

The 9th and subsequent editions contain completely re-drawn charts for the new standard epoch 1950. The Index Maps and Galactic Charts which, having R.A. and Dec. lines as well as galactic co-ordinates, will be helpful in galactic studies.

All the main features of the 1920 epoch maps have been retained, but with certain alterations:—

(*a*) Stars from the Revised Harvard Photometry down to magnitude 6·35 have been charted. In the original edition of this work, the star places were taken mainly from Houzeau's "Uranométrie Générale." A careful comparison of the magnitudes of Houzeau's fainter naked-eye stars with the same stars included in the H.R. and its Supplement, showed that many of his stars are placed at a lower, sometimes a much lower magnitude than 6·35 on the Harvard scale. Such stars have now generally been omitted. On the other hand, many Harvard stars, not in Houzeau, have been inserted, as well as several additional double stars from various sources.

(*b*) All nebulæ, except those of Messier and those classed by Herschel (see p. 55), have now received the N.G.C. numbers.

(*c*) Variable stars which reach at their maximum brightness the 6th or 7th magnitude, have been indicated in the maps by small circles.

(*d*) The Galactic Equator and Poles now adopted are those recommended by the International Astronomical Union, and differ slightly in position from those which have appeared in the earlier maps.

The Milky Way is in many places extremely complex, varying much in brightness, with cloudy wisps of light, dark spaces and dark winding lanes. No single-tint representation, such as is used in this atlas, can satisfactorily represent it; but the outline of Proctor has been followed, for it does at least indicate the general position of the Milky Way and also suggests its complexity.

(*e*) The Abbreviation List printed in the margins of the 1920 maps was necessarily limited. It has been superseded by the complete List of Abbreviations given on page 55, preceding the charts.

Mr. Arthur P. Norton died in 1955, and this edition contains several changes which have been made on the suggestion of Dr. E. A. Baker, F.R.S.E., late of the Royal Observatory, Edinburgh. He has rewritten p. vi, and supplied new notes and corrections, as well as the short note relative to Radio Astronomy on p. 13.

INDEX TO CONTENTS.

STANDARD SOURCES OF REFERENCE.

(For contractions see p. vii).

With the progress of astronomy the standard reference sources quoted below may at any time be superceded and new recognised contractions appear. Such changes are forecast in the triennial Tr. I.A.U.: a more concise account of advances in astronomy is given in the *Annual Report*, M.N.R.A.S. (*February*).

Bibliography.—Summaries of astronomical publications are given in *Physics Abstracts* (formerly *Science Abstracts*) (from 1899): *Bulletin Astronomique* (from 1884); and *Astronomische Jahresbericht* (from 1899). The last named continues the summaries in V.J.S. (from 1866). For publications prior to 1882 Houzeau's *Vade mecum d'astronomie* is useful. Very early works are sometimes referred to by their numbers in Lalande's *Bibliographie Astronomique* (1803).

Star Positions.—Catalogues of the positions of stars may be divided into (*a*) Star Lists or *Durchmusterungen*, like the B.D, the C.D. and the C.P.D., serving purely for identification; (*b*) Catalogues formed from observations near a single epoch, e.g., the A.G. (or A.G.K.1) and the A.Z.; and (*c*) General Catalogues, formed from observations extending over many decades, giving both positions and proper motions, as the G.C. and the A.G.K.2. From 1940 positions and proper motions have been referred to the system of the F.K.3—the apparent places of the F.K. 3 stars are published annually in *Apparent Places of Fundamental Stars*. Many of these places also appear in the various national ephemerides. This fundamental system may soon be replaced.

Proper Motions.—Those given in General Catalogues are collected to 1935 in the E.B.L. A *Catalogue of Stars with Proper Motions exceeding* 0″.5 *per annum* was published at Lund in 1955.

Magnitudes and Colours.—The standard *North Polar Sequence* (photo) visual and photographic magnitudes (H.A. 76) are known to be appreciably in error. Proposed interim values are given in Tr.I.A.U., 8, 375, 1952.

Spectral Types.—The Draper classification (p. 19) has been developed farther at the Yerkes Observatory. The standard spectra are given as photographic illustrations in an *Atlas by Morgan, Keenan and Kellman* and do not lend themselves to verbal description. A system of classification has also been developed at D.A.O. based on the measured strengths of selected lines and is referred to as the Victoria system.

Trigonometrical Parallaxes.—Yale *General Catalogue of Trigonometrical Stellar Parallaxes, 1952.*

Absolute Magnitudes and Spectroscopic Magnitudes. The Yerkes and Victoria spectral types give estimated absolute magnitudes, and hence, with an allowance for the absorption of light in space, the corresponding spectroscopic parallaxes. See also pp. 14, 17.

Radial Velocities.—Wilson's *General Catalogue of Radial Velocities.* (Mt. W. *Papers*, 8, 1953.)

Double Stars.—The A.D.S. and the S.D.S. are likely to be replaced by a general catalogue based on the card catalogues of double stars at the Lick and Johannesburg Observatories. Moore and Neubauer's *Fifth Catalogue of Spectroscopic Binaries* (1947) is also likely to be replaced shortly by a Sixth Catalogue in preparation at D.A.O.

Variable Stars.—Kukarkin and Parenago's *General Catalogue of Variable Stars, 1948* is being kept up to date by the issue of supplements. Schneller's *Geschichte und Literatur der Veranderlichen Sterne* gives references to observations. With the introduction of photoelectric methods, work on *eclipsing binaries* is progressing rapidly, and reference must be made to the reports of Commission 42 of the I.A.U.

Nebulæ and Clusters.—The most prominent are listed in N.G.C., supplemented by I.C. (I & II).

Plan of Selected Areas.—Information about the fainter Stars is obtained by taking samples, a process begun by Sir W. Herschel in his *Star Gauges* (Star Counts). Kapteyn's *Plan of Selected Areas* comprises a *Systematic Plan* of uniformly distributed areas, and a *Special Plan* of areas selected to cover unusual star distributions. The chief publications are *Durchmusterung of the Systematic Selected Areas* (H.A. 101-103); *Durchmusterung of the Special Areas* (Kapteyn Laboratory, 1952); *Mt. Wilson Catalogue of Photographic Magnitudes in Selected Areas 1-139; Stockholm Catalogue of the Selected Areas*, giving magnitudes and colours; and the *Bergedorfer* (Northern Areas) and *Potsdam* (Southern Areas) *Spektral Durchmusterung* giving spectral types.

Stellar Wavelengths.—Merrill's *Lines of the Chemical Elements in Astronomical Spectra*, Washingon, 1956.

Star Charts.—

Visual	Limiting Magnitude	Scale mm./deg.	Epoch	*Photographic*	Limiting Magnitude	Scale mm./deg.	Epoch
Norton	6·5	3·5	1950	Carte du Ciel	14	120	1900
Becvar	7·5	7·5	1950	Franklin-Adams	16	15	1900
Bonn	9·0	20	1855	Wolf-Palisa	16	37	1875
Cordoba	9·5	20	1875	Palomar (red)	20	54	1950
Hagen	14·0	160	1900	do. (blue)	21	54	1950

The charts by Norton, Becvar and Franklin-Adams cover the whole sky. The Bonn charts cover the Northern hemisphere, the Cordoba Charts from −22° to the South Pole, and the National Geographic Institute-Palomar Sky Survey charts from the North Pole to −27°. The Carte du Ciel (Astrographic Chart) was intended to cover the whole sky but is incomplete. Hagen's Atlas Stellarum Variabilium is designed for visual observations of selected variable stars. The Wolf-Palisa Charts are of 210 galactic areas.

The Solar System.—For the sources of the solar, lunar and planetary positions and surface co-ordinates the explanatory matter of a national annual ephemeris such as the N.A. or A.E. should be consulted.

Solar Spectrum.—A re-revision of *Rowland's Table* of solar wavelengths is in preparation. *Photometric Atlases*—Minaert, Mulders and Houtgast (Utrecht), λ3332-λ8771; McMath-Hulbert, λ8465-λ25242; Migeotte and others (Soc. Roy. Liege), 2μ-23·7μ.

Lunar Surface.—*Named Lunar Formations* (Müller and Blagg). A recent map is that of Wilkins and Moore.

Planetary Surfaces.—See B.A.A. Mems. and Reports of the Planetary Sections.

Comets.—Yamamoto's *General Catalogue of Comets* (with supplements). Swings and Haser's *Atlas of Representative Cometary Spectra.*

Minor Planets.—*Annual Ephemerides* by the Institute of Theoretical Astronomy, Leningrad. (English translation of the Russian Text by Minor Planet Centre, Cincinnati.)

Astronomical Societies, Publications, &c.—Contractions commonly used. Standard contractions are now being prepared. For a list of General Contractions, and those for Places., see Trans. I.A.U. 1928.

	Publication, or Society.
A.A.S.	American Astronomical Society.
A.A.V.S.O.	American Association of Variable Star [Observers.
A.E.	American Ephemeris.
A.G.	Astronomische Gesellschaft.
A.J.	Astronomical Journal.
A.N.	Astronomische Nachrichten.
Ap.J.	Astrophysical Journal.
A.S.P.	Astronomical Society of the Pacific.
B.	Bulletin (Prefixed).
B.A.	British Association.
"	Bulletin Astronomique.
B.A.A.	British Astronomical Association.
B.A.N.	Bulletin of the Ast. Inst. of the Netherlands
B.J.	Berliner Jahrbuch.
B.S.A.F.	Bulletin de la Société Astronomique de [France.
C.O.	Cincinnati Observatory.
C.R.	Comptes Rendus (Paris Acad. Sciences).
C.T.	Connaissance des Temps.
D.A.O.	Dominion Astrophysical Observ., Victoria, [B.C.
D.O.	Dominion Observatory (Ottawa).
E.B.	Encyclopedia Brittannica.
E.M.	English Mechanic.
H.A.	Harvard Observatory Annals.
H.B.	Harvard Bulletin.
H.C.	Harvard Circular (Harv. C.).
H.C.O.	Harvard College Observatory.
I.A.U., I.U.A., U.I.A.	Internat. Astron. Union.
J.	Journal. (prefixed to Society name, as *J.B.A.A.*).
J.O.	Journal des Observateurs.
L.O.B.	Lick Observatory Bulletin (Lick B.)
M.N.	Monthly Notices Royal Astron. Society.
Mt.W., M.W.	Mt. Wilson Observatory.
Nat.	Nature.
N.A.	Nautical Almanac.
Obs.	The Observatory.
P.	Publications, Proceedings. (prefixed to Society [name, as, *P.A.S.P.*).
P.A.	Popular Astronomy.
P.A.S.P.	Pub'ns of Astronomical Socy. of the Pacific.
Phil. Trans.	Philosophical Transactions of the Royal [Socy.
R.A.S.	Royal Astronomical Society.
R.A.S.C.	Royal Astronomical Society of Canada.
S.A.	Scientific American.
"	Selected Areas (*Kapteyn's*), p. vi.
U.O.C.	Union Observatory Circulars.
V.J.S.	Verteljahrsschrift der Astron. Gesellschaft.

	General.
An.	Annals.
App.	Appendix.
Ass.	Association.
B., Bull.	Bulletin.
Cat.	Catalogue.
Cir.	Circular.
Cont.	Contributions.
Edn.	Edition.
I.	International.
Ist., Inst.	Institute.
M., Mem.	Memoirs.
Mag.	Magazine.
O., Obs.	Observatory,
Pr.	Proceedings.
P., Pub.	Publications, or Published,
R.	Review.
Rp.	Report.
S., Socy.	Society.
S.	Smithsonian.
Tr.	Transactions.
Vol.	Volume.
Yb.	Yearbook.
Zs	Zeitschrift.

Astronomical Catalogues.—Contractions in ordinary use. The letters are often used without points. For Observers' symbols see p. 55.

Contraction.	*With number added, =Number in:—*
A.D.S.	Aitken's Double Star Catalogue, 1932 (see p. vi).
A.G., A.G.K.2.	Astronomische Gesellschaft Katalog (see p. vi).
A.Z.	Astrographic Catalogue,* to mag. 11 (in progress).
B.A.C.	British Association Catalogue, epoch 1850 (*Baily*, 1845).
B.D.	Bonn Durchmusterung (*Argelander*) to mag. 9, 1859-62,* extended by Schönfield (1886) to 23° South Dec.
B.G.C.	Burnham's General Cat. of Double Stars.
Br.	Auwer's reduction of Bradley's Observations.
Bris. or Br.	Sir T. Brisbane's Catalogue of Southern Stars, 1835.
B.S.	Schlesinger's Catalogue of Bright Stars.
C.D.	Cordoba Durchmusterung, 22° to 62° S. [(*Gould*) 1886,
C.G.A.	Catalogo General Argentino, 32,448 Southern Stars.
C.P.D.	Cape Photographic Durchmusterung, to mag. 9, 19° to 90° South Dec. (*Gill and Kapteyn*), 1896-1903.
C.Z.	Cordoba Zone Cat. of South Stars, Nos. in zones of Dec.*
E-B.	Espin's edition of Birmingham's Cat. of Red Stars, 1888.
E.B.L.	Eigenbewegungs Lexikon (*Hamburg Obs.*) of all known [proper motions.
FK 3	Dritter Fundamental Katalog (p. vi.).
G.C.	Boss's General Catalogue, epoch 1950.
G.F.H.	Geschichte des Fixsternhimmels, see p. vi.
Gr.	Groombridge's Cat. of Circumpolar Stars for 1810, 1838.
H.D.	Henry Draper Cat. 1918-24 (vols. 91-99, Harvard Annals),
H.P.	Harvard Photometry (*Pickering*), 1884. (*H.A.* vol. 14).,
H.R. (also R.H.P.).	Revised Harvard Photometry, 1908 (vol. 50. [*H.A.*).
I.C.	Index Catalogue, extension of N.G.C. 1904, 1908.
Lac.	Lacaille's Catalogue of Southern Stars, Epoch 1750 published by the British Association, 1847.
Ll. or Lal.	Lalande's Cat., Epoch 1800, pub. by the *B.A.*, 1837.
M.	Messier's Catalogue of 103 Nebulæ & Clusters, pub. 1784. Reprinted, *Obs.*, Aug. 1918; and *P.A.S.P.* Aug. 1917,
N.G.C.	New General Catalogue (of Sir J. Herschel's Nebulæ and Clusters, *Dreyer*), 1888. Vol. 49, Memoirs, R.A.S.
O.A.	Oeltzen's reduction of Argelander's Zone Observations,
P.D.	Potsdam General Cat. (Supplementary vols., P.P.D., &c.)
P.G.C.	Preliminary General Catalogue of 6188 stars (*Boss*), 1910.
Pi.	Piazzi's Star Cat., epoch 1800, 1803-14.†
S.D.S.	Southern Double Star Catalogue (*Innes*) 1927.
St.	Stone's Cape Catalogue for 1880, or Radcliffe Cat., 1890.
W.B.	Weisse's reduction of Bessel's Zones, equinox 1825; Nos. in [hrs. of R.A.
W.Z.C.	Washington Zodiacal Cat., 1900, 1920.
U.A.	Uranometria Argentina (*Gould*), 1879.
U.O.	Uranometria Nova Oxoniensis (*Pritchard*), 1885.

* In this case the zone is stated as well as the number: thus B.D. +13° 2302 means star No. 2302 in the 13° zone, north Dec., in the B.D.

† The numbering commences anew in each hour of R.A.: thus V^h 123 denotes star No. 123 in the zone of 5 h. R.A.

Bode's Law.—Taking Mercury as 4, adding 4 to each term of the geometrical series 3, 6, 12, 24, &c., gives the approximate distances of the planets up to Uranus, but not Neptune's: Pluto is near the position Neptune should occupy. No reason is known for this curious relation. Bode remarked that a planet was missing at the distance where the asteroids were discovered later.

Planet ..	Mercury	Venus	Earth	Mars	Asteroids	Jupiter	Saturn	Uranus	Neptune	Pluto	..	..	..
Geometrical Series	...	3	6	12	24	48	96	192	384	768	...	...	...
Add ...	4	4	4	4	4	4	4	4	4	4	...	...	...
Dist. fr. Sun, Bode	4	7	10	16	28	52	100	196	388	772	...	...	...
,, **Actual** ...	**3·9**	**7·2**	**10**	**15·2**	**27·4**	**52**	**95·4**	**192**	**301**	**395**	...	...	...

Albedo of the Planets. Russell's figures are for *Bond's Albedo* (somewhat different from Lambert's original definition on p. 7: see *Ap. J.*, vol. 43, 1916).

Albedo:—	Mercury	Venus	Earth	Moon	Mars	Jupiter	Saturn	Uranus	Neptune	Pluto		
(Zöllner, 1865) ...	·13	·50	...	·17	·27	·62	·52	·64	·46	0·17	...	Clouds ·65-·72
(Müller, 1897) ...	·14	·76	·20	·13	·12	·62	·72	·60	·52	(Kuiper	...	Snow
(Russell, 1916) ...	·07	·59	·45	·07	·15	·56	·63	·63	·73	1950)	...	·70-·78

Saturn's Rings.—Approximate date of Earth passing the ring-plane; and Saturn's heliocentric longitude. Dates not "0°" are minima: the Earth did not quite pass the plane of the ring in 1936, though extremely near doing so.

Date	*lat.*	*long.*	*Date*	*lat.*	*long.*	*Date*	*lat.*	*long.*	*Date*	*lat.*	*long.*
1907 Apr. 13.	0°	349°	1920 Nov. 7.	0°	167°	1936 Jun. 28.	(+0°)	346°	1949 Dec. 26.	−1°·5	311°
,, Oct. 4.	0°	354°	1921 Feb. 22.	0°	183°	1937 Feb. 21.	0°	354°	1950 Sept. 14.	0°	334°
1908 Jan. 7.	0°	358°	,, Aug. 2.	0°	189°	,, Nov. 28.	$-2\frac{1}{2}$°	4°	1951 May 25.	+1°·0	357°

Parallaxes:—Sun. Adopted at Paris Conference, 1911. 8″·80.*

Moon. Equatorial horizontal parallax, at mean distance, 57′ 2″·7.

Asteroids (approximate maximum). *Eros*, 52″. *Amor*, 73″. *1932 H.A.*, 4′. *Adonis*, $8\frac{1}{2}$′.

Stars. The parallaxes of several of these are given in the Tables of the Brightest and Nearest Stars on page 53.

Planetary Colour Indices, &c.—"Sun's Radiation" gives the amount received per unit of area.

	Mercury	Venus	Earth	Moon	Mars	Jupiter	Saturn	Uranus	Neptune	Pluto		
Colour Index (Sun 0·72)	+...	+0·91	...	+1·2	+1·45	+0·96	+1·22	+0·94	+...	0·67	...	...
Sun's Radiation ...	6·6	1·9	1·0	1·0	0·43	0·04	0·01	0·003	0·001	0·0006	...	...
Velocity of escape, km/secs.	3·6	10·2	11·2	2·4	5·0	60	36	21	23	3?	...	...

Stellar Colour Indices.—

Type of Star.		O	B0	A0	F0	G0	K0	M	M3	Nc	R	S
Colour Index, ...	Giants ...		−0·32	0·0	+0·38	+0·86	+1·48	+1·88	...	+5·5	...	...
do	Dwarfs ...		−0·32	0·0	+0·38	+0·72	+0·99	+1·76	...	...	...	...
Heat Index (average), in Magnitudes ...			−0·1	0·0	+0·3	+0·7	+1·2	+2·3	...	...	...	...
Surface Brightness, ,,	Giants ...		−3·2	−2·3	−1·0	+0·3	+2·3	+4·5	...	...	...	...
do ,,	Dwarfs ...		−3·2	−2·3	−1·0	0·0	+1·2	+3·8	...	...	...	...

Novæ.—Many so-called New Stars have been recorded in years previous to those given in the list below Thus the appearance of a new star about the year 150 B.C. is said to have led Hipparchus to make his catalogue of stars. But generally, the old records are vague and indefinite, and, in some cases, undoubtedly refer not to Novæ but to comets.

Modern Novæ.—Only the brighter Novæ are included in this List.

Year A.D.	Nova:—	Greatest Mag.	Approx. Long.	Galac. Lat.	Position 1950. R.A.		Dec.	
1572.	Cassiopeiæ (B)	>1	88°	+ 2°	0h.	22 m.	+63°	53′
1600.	Cygni No. 1 (P)	3·5	43	+ 0	20	16	+37	52
1604.	Ophiuchi No. 1	>1	332	+ 5	17	28	−21	27
1670.	Vulpeculæ (11)...	3	31	− 0	19	46	+27	11
1848.	Ophiuchi No. 2	5·5	335	+16	16	57	−12	48
1860.	Scorpii (T) ...	7	321	+18	16	14	−22	31
1866.	Coronæ (T) ...	2	10	+47	15	57	+26	4
1876.	Cygni No. 2 (Q)	3	58	− 8	21	40	+42	34
1885.	Andromedæ (S)	7	89	−21	0	40	+40	59
1887.	Persei No. 1 (V)	9·2	100	− 4	1	58	+56	29
1891.	Aurigæ (T) ...	4·5	145	− 0	5	29	+30	25
1893.	Normæ (R) ...	7	295	+ 4	15	26	−50	25
1895.	Carinæ (RS) ...	8	259	− 1	11	6	−61	40
1895.	Centauri (Z) ...	7	283	+29	13	37	−31	23
1898.	Sagittarii No. 1	4·7	350	−10	18	59	−13	14
1899.	Sagittarii No. 3	8·5	335	− 6	18	17	−25	13
1899.	Aquilæ No. 1 ...	7	4	− 8	19	18	− 0	14
1901.	Persei No. 2 ...	0·0	119	− 9	3	26	+43	24
1903.	Geminorum No. 1	5·1	153	+13	6	41	+30	0
1905.	Aquilæ No. 2 ...	9	358	− 6	19	0	− 4	31
1910.	Sagittarii No. 2	7·5	331	− 3	17	57	−27	33
1910.	Lacertæ No. 1	5·0	71	− 5	22	33	+52	22

Year A.D.	Nova:—	Greatest Mag.	Approx. Long.	Galac. Lat.	Position 1950. R.A.		Dec.	
1910.	Aræ	6·0	302°	− 5°	16h.	37m	−52°	20′
1912.	Geminorum No. 2	3·3	152	+16	6	52	+32	12
1913.	Sagittæ ...	7·2	25	− 9	20	5	+17	32
1917.	Ophiuchi No. 5	6·5	321	+ 8	16	50	−29	33
1918.	Aquilæ No. 3	−0·7	1	− 1	18	46	+ 0	32
1919.	Ophiuchi ...	7·5	7	+12	18	11	+11	35
1919.	Lyræ ...	6·5	27	+11	18	51	+29	9
1920.	Cygni No. 3 ...	1·8	55	+12	19	57	+53	29
1925.	Pictoris (RR) ...	1·1	240	−25	6	35	−62	36
1934.	Herculis ...	1·3	40	+25	18	7	+45	51
1936.	Lacertæ ...	2·0	70	− 1	22	14	+55	23
1936.	Aquilæ ...	7·0	5	− 6	19	15	+ 1	38
1936.	Sagittarii ...	4·5	325	− 8	18	5	−34	21
1936.	Aquilæ ...	5·0	11	− 6	19	24	+ 7	30
1942.	Puppis ...	0·4	221	+ 0	8	10	−35	13
1946.	Coronæ (T) ...	3·1	...	(See	yr.	1866	above)	
1950.	Lacertæ ...	6·0	73	− 5	22	48	+53	2
...	...	...	...	...	...		...	
...	...	...	...	...	...		...	

* From observations of Eros around the opposition of 1931, the value is 8″·790 ± 0″·001 (see B.A.A. Handbook for 1942).

Nomenclature of Minor Planets, Variable Stars, Novæ, &c.—Systems that answered well in the early stages of discovery inevitably tend to become inadequate or unwieldy as discoveries increase, and from time to time they have to be revised. The following modifications have been made in the original systems.

Minor Planets. Each new discovery, before the number and name is given (p. 35), is temporarily assigned distinctive Roman letters, as not infrequently, a supposed new asteroid proves to be identical with one already known. Originally a single letter sufficed, and the year; but in 1893, the double form AA to AZ, BA to BZ, &c., was introduced (I being omitted), this new series being continued right on until ZZ was reached, instead of beginning the alphabet afresh each year. A second alphabet was begun in 1907, with the year (1907 AA, &c.), and a third in 1916—terminated with UA., Dec. 31, 1924, when a new system was started to enable belated discoveries to be inserted in approximately their proper place.

Under the present system of temporary nomenclature, the double alphabet begins afresh each year; the discoveries of Jan. 1-15 are AA, AB, AC, &c.; of Jan. 16-31, BA, BB, BC, &c.; of Feb. 1-15, CA, CB, &c., the year being added in each case; if more discoveries than 25 in half a month, AA_1, AB_1, &c. Minor planets are in the care of the Rechen-Institut of Berlin, which attends to the numbering, &c. When unnumbered, the orbit is not sufficiently certain, as 1932 HA, but a name may be given, as it is more convenient for reference. (Annual summary in *M.N.*, February).

Jan. A,B ; Feb. C,D ; Mar. E,F; Apr. G,H ; May J,K ; June L,M ; July N,O ; Aug. P,Q ; Sept. R,S ; Oct. T,U ; Nov. V,W ; Dec. X, Y.

Variable Stars. Argelander designated those not otherwise lettered or numbered, in any constellation, by the Roman capital letters, R, S, T, U, V, W, X, Y, Z. After Z, the double form RR to RZ, SS to SZ, TT to TZ, and so on to ZZ, was used, which provided for 54 variable stars in any constellation. As that number proved insufficient, AA to AZ, BB to BZ, and so on, was employed, J being omitted. The simplest system, which denotes the variables of each constellation by the letter V, followed by a number—thus V1 = R; V2 = S; V54 = ZZ, &c., is to be used from V^{335}, when QZ is reached. Letters are assigned when the variability is confirmed; provisionally, Novæ and ordinary variables are now designated by a number, year, and constellation, Nova Aquilæ 1918 being 7.1918 Aquilæ, in the 'variable' discoveries of 1918.

Novae. The older Novæ are designated by the constellation and year in which they appeared, thus, *Nova* Scorpii, 134 B.C.: some having also a 'popular' name, as *Kepler's Star*, *Tycho's Star*, &c. Modern Novæ were similarly designated till 1925: if more than one appeared in a constellation, they were numbered successively *Nova* I., *Nova* II., and so on, of that constellation, in order of discovery, disregarding the Novæ before 1572. As many Novæ were only discovered years after their appearance, when comparing star photographs of the same region taken at different times, this sometimes resulted in the numbers being out of order as regards date of *appearance*: the nomenclature was therefore altered to constellation and year, with the date in tenths of a year, if more than one in a year.

Primary and Secondary Stars.—The brightest star is A, the companion or companions B, C, &c., as *Sirius A* and *B*.

Comets.—Entirely new comets are usually named after the discoverer, adding the year, as Donati's comet, 1858.

Comet a, *Comet b*, &c., denotes the first, second, ... comet *discovered* that year, whether new or already known.
Comet I, *Comet II*, &c., „ „ „ „ *arriving at perihelion* that year, ditto

---

Some Terms occurring in Astronomical Papers.

Errors of Observation.—These are of two kinds: *Systematic Errors* and *Accidental Errors* (see page 7, *Equation*). The former are detected by observations repeated with different instruments, &c., or by comparison with results obtained by other methods; the latter errors are erratic, but can be estimated by analysis of the small discrepancies between the individual observations of a series, or between observed and calculated values—which discrepancies or differences are known as *Residuals*.

The Probable Error (P.E.), of a series of observations is a value derived mathematically from these residuals; it affords an index to the reliability of the figures given, and is prefixed by the sign ±, which means that it is an even chance whether, by the amount of the probable error, the value given is greater, or less. The smaller the probable error, the greater the reliability.

Method of Least Squares.—A method used to ascertain the most probable mean value derivable from a number of different observations. It is based on the principle that the 'weights' (degree of accuracy) of observations, with different probable errors, are inversely proportional to the squares of their probable errors.

Interpolation; Extrapolation.—*Interpolation* is the process of finding values for dates, hours, quantities, &c., intermediate to those given in a Table. For ordinary purposes, the proportional amount of the difference between the figures for the two nearest dates, quantities, &c., usually suffices, it being assumed, for simplicity, that the change in the interval is uniform; a more accurate result, useful when maximum or minimum occurs between the dates, is obtained by plotting on squared paper several successive dates, or figures, on each side of the one not given, and drawing a curve through these points.

Extrapolation, a similar process, extends a series of figures beyond the limit of the last figure actually known; there being only one limiting figure, however, it is less simple than interpolation.

Contracted Notation employs the factor '10,' with small index figures, to express large numbers in a small space. The index figures may be taken as indicating the number of ciphers to be added after the 1. A *minus* before the index figures indicates a fractional number, viz., 1 divided by that number; thus 10^{-6} = 1/1,000,000th or ·000001, from which it appears that *minus* index figures show the position, *after* the decimal point, of the first significant figure of the decimal fraction, the number of ciphers before the 1 being *one less* than the index number. The following are examples with decimal factors:—

$1{\cdot}23 \times 10^6 = 1{\cdot}23 \times 1{,}000{,}000$ or $123 \times 10^4 = 1{,}230{,}000$. $1{\cdot}23 \times 10^{-6} = 1{\cdot}23 \times {\cdot}000001$ or $123 \times 10^{-8} = 123 \times {\cdot}00000001 = {\cdot}00000123$.

Note to make the index of the 10 such that the figure before the decimal in the other factor is *1 to 9 only*; thus $1{\cdot}23 \times 10^6$ is correct, not the 123×10^4 illustrating the working: the index of 10 (both + and −) is then the 'characteristic' of the logarithm of the No.

10^1 = 10 ... ... =	1 with 1 cipher after it	10^{-1} = 0·1 ... ... =	1 in the 1st place after decimal point.
10^3 = 1000	1 „ 3 ciphers „	10^{-2} = 0·01 (1/100th) „	„ 2nd „ „ „
10^6 = 1 million	1 „ 6 „ „	10^{-6} = 0·000001 (1/millionth)	„ 6th „ „ „
10^7 = 10 millions	1 „ 7 „ „	10^{-7} = 0·0000001 (1/10-millionth)	„ 7th „ „ „
10^9 = 1 billion (U.S.A., &c.)	1 „ 9 „ „	10^{-9} = 1/billionth (U.S.A.)	„ 9th „ „ „
10^{12} = 1 billion (British) ...	1 „ 12 „ „	10^{-12} = „ (British)	„ 12th „ „ „

Magnitudes and Relative Brightness of the Sun, Planets, and Principal Stars, (1st magnitude star taken as 1·00).

Name of Star, &c.	H.R. Mag.	Brightness	Name of Star	H.R. Mag.	Relative Brightness	Name of Star	H.R. Mag.	Relative Brightness	Name of Star	H.R. Mag.	Relative Brightness
Sun ...	−26·6	{ 109,650 millions	Achernar ...	0·60	1·45	ε Canis Major.	1·63	0·56	δ Canis Major.	1·98	0·41
Moon (Full)	−12·2	190,550	β Centauri ...	0·86	1·14	ε Ursæ Major.	1·68	0·53	β Canis Major.	1·99	0·40
Venus (max.)	−4·28	129·4	Altair	0·89	1·11	γ Orionis ...	1·70	0·52	Magnitude	2·00	0·40
Jupiter* ...	−2·25	19·95	Betelgeuse ...	0·92	1·08	α^2Centauri ...	1·70	0·52	Polaris ...	2·12	0·36
Mars* ...	−2·25	19·95	Magnitude	1·00	1·00	λ Scorpii ...	1·71	0·52	Magnitude	2·50	0·25
Mercury (max)	−1·8	13·18	Aldebaran ...	1·06	0·95	ε Carinæ ...	1·74	0·51	" ...	3·00	0·16
Sirius ...	−1·58	10·77	Spica	1·21	0·82	ε Orionis ...	1·75	0·50	" ...	3·50	0·10
Saturn* ...	{ −0·18 +0·89	3·00 1·11	Pollux	1·21	0·82	β Tauri ...	1·78	0·49	" ...	4·00	0.06
Canopus ...	−0·86	5·55	Antares ...	1·22	0·82	β Carinæ ...	1·80	0·48	" ...	4·50	0·04
Magnitude	0·00	2·51	Fomalhaut ...	1·29	0·77	α Triang. Aust.	1·88	0·44	" ...	5·00	0·03
Vega ...	0·14	2·21	Arided ...	1·33	0·74	α Persei ...	1·90	0·44	" ...	5·50	0·02
Capella ...	0·21	2·07	Regulus ...	1·34	0·73	η Ursæ Major.	1·91	0·43	" ...	6·00	0·01
Arcturus ...	0·24	2·01	β Crucis ...	1·50	0·63	ζ Orionis ...	1·91	0·43	Uranus* ...	5·8	0·01
α^1 Centauri	0·33	1·85	α^1 Crucis ...	1·58	0·59	γ Geminorum	1·93	0·42	Magnitude	6·50	0·006
Rigel ...	0·34	1·84	Castor	1·58	0·59	ε Sagittarii ...	1·95	0·42	Neptune* ...	7·7	0·003
Procyon ...	0·48	1·61	γ Crucis ...	1·58	0·60	α Ursæ Major.	1·95	0·42	Pluto*	(14·5)	·000002

Ratio of Brightness, fainter or brighter, for a difference in magnitude ("Diff.") of :—

Diff.	Ratio	Diff.	Ratio	Diff.	Ratio	Diff.	Ratio	Diff.	Ratio	Diff.	Ratio	Diff.	Ratio	Diff.	Ratio	Diff.	Ratio	Diff.	Ratio
0·1	1·10	0·5	1·58	0·9	2·29	1·3	3·31	1·75	5·01	3·0	15·85	5·5	158·49	8·0	1584·9	10·5	15,849	13·0	158,490
0·2	1·20	0·6	1·74	1·0	2·51	1·4	3·63	1·8	5·25	3·5	25·12	6·0	251·19	8·5	2511·9	11·0	25,119	13·5	251,190
0·25	1·26	0·7	1·91	1·1	2·75	1·5	3·98	1·9	5·75	4·0	39·81	6·5	398·11	9·0	3981·1	11·5	39,811	14·0	398,110
0·3	1·32	0·75	2·00	1·2	3·02	1·6	4·37	2·0	6·31	4·5	63·10	7·0	630·96	9·5	6309·6	12·0	63,096	14·5	630,960
0·4	1·45	0·8	2·09	1·25	3·16	1·7	4·79	2·5	10·00	5·0	100·00	7·5	1000·00	10·0	10,000·0	12·5	100,000	15·0	1,000,000

Distance and Magnitude :—Increase of distance ("Dist.") for a difference ("Diff.") of 1 to 20 magnitudes. Thus a Mag. 5 star placed 100 times further away would be 10 magnitudes fainter, or Mag. 15. (Mag.-diff. × 0·2 = logarithm of distance-increase).

Diff.	Dist.	Diff.	Dist.	Diff.	Dist.	Diff.	Dist.	Diff.	Dist.	Diff.	Dist.	Diff.	Dist.	Diff.	Dist.	Diff.	Dist.	Diff.	Dist.	Diff.	Dist.
½	1·26	2	2·51	4	6·31	6	15·85	8	39·81	10	100·0	12	251·2	14	631·0	16	1585	18	3981	19	6310
1	1·59	3	3·98	5	10·00	7	25·12	9	63·10	11	158·5	13	398·1	15	1000	17	2512	18½	5012	19½	7943
																				20	10000

Mean Refraction *(Bessel)*.—For 50° F. (10° C.), and barometer 29·6 ins. (752 mm). Other Temperatures, add 1% per 5° F. (2·8° C.) if lower, deduct if higher : Pressures, add 3½% per inch (25·4 mm.) if higher, deduct if lower; = abt. 1% ℔ ¼ inch, or ℔ 6mm.

Alt.	Refraction.	Alt.	Refraction.	Alt.	Refraction.	Alt.	Refraction.	Alt.	Refraction.	Alt.	Refraction.	Alt.	Refraction.	Alt.	Refraction.	Alt.	Refraction.	Alt.	Refraction.
0°	34′ 54″	¾°	26′ 35″	3°	14′ 15″	6°	8′ 23″	9°	5′ 49″	12°	4′ 25″	15°	3′ 32″	25°	2′ 3″	40°	1′ 9″	65°	0′ 27″
¼	31 50	1	24 25	4	11 39	7	7 20	10	5 16	13	4 5	16	3 19	30	1 40	45	0 58	80	0 10
½	29 3	2	18 9	5	9 47	8	6 30	11	4 49	14	3 47	20	2 37	35	1 22	50	0 48	90	0 0

Light-Years equivalent to Parsecs.—Multiples by 10, 100, shift point one, two, places to rt. P., parsecs ; L/y., light-yrs.

P.	L/y.	P.	L/y.	P.	L/y.	P.	L/y.	P.	L/y.	P.	L/y.	P.	L/y.	P.	L/y.	P.	L/y.	P.	L/y.	P.	L/y.
1	3·259	6	19·554	11	35·85	16	52·14	21	68·44	26	84·73	31	101·03	36	117·32	41	133·62	46	149·91	60	195·54
2	6·518	7	22·813	12	39·11	17	55·40	22	71·70	27	87·99	32	104·29	37	120·58	42	136·88	47	153·17	70	228·13
3	9·777	8	26·072	13	42·37	18	58·66	23	74·96	28	91·25	33	107·55	38	123·84	43	140·14	48	156·43	80	260·72
4	13·036	9	29·331	14	45·63	19	61·92	24	78·22	29	94·51	34	110·81	39	127·10	44	143·40	49	159·69	90	293·31
5	16·295	10	32·590	15	48·89	20	65·18	25	81·48	30	97·77	35	114·07	40	130·36	45	146·66	50	162·95	100	325·90

Parsecs and Light-years equivalent to any parallax (π). ·0001, ·0002, &c., move parsec or light-yr. decimal one place to rt.

π	Parsecs	Light-yrs.	π	Parsecs	Light-yrs.	π	Parsecs	Light-y.	π	Parsecs	Light-y.	π	Parsecs	Light-y.	π	Parsecs	Light-y.
·001″	1000	3259·0	·021″	47·62	155·19	·041″	24·39	79·49	·061″	16·39	53·43	·081″	12·35	40·24	·12″	8·33	27·16
·002	500·0	1629·5	·022	45·45	148·14	·042	23·81	77·61	·062	16·13	52·57	·082	12·20	39·75	·14	7·14	23·28
·003	333·3	1086·3	·023	43·48	141·69	·043	23·26	75·79	·063	15·87	51·74	·083	12·05	39·26	·15	6·67	21·73
·004	250·0	814·74	·024	41·67	135·79	·044	22·73	74·06	·064	15·63	50·92	·084	11·90	38·80	·16	6·25	20·37
·005″	200·0	651·79	·025″	40·00	130·36	·045″	22·22	72·43	·065″	15·38	50·14	·085″	11·76	38·34	·18″	5·56	18·11
·006	166·7	543·16	·026	38·46	125·35	·046	21·74	70·84	·066	15·15	49·39	·086	11·63	37·90	·20	5·00	16·30
·007	142·9	465·56	·027	37·04	120·70	·047	21·28	69·34	·067	14·93	48·64	·087	11·49	37·46	·22	4·55	14·81
·008	125·0	407·37	·028	35·71	116·39	·048	20·83	67·91	·068	14·71	47·93	·088	11·36	37·03	·24	4·17	13·58
·009	111·1	362·11	·029	34·48	112·38	·049	20·41	66·51	·069	14·49	47·24	·089	11·24	36·62	·25	4·00	13·04
·010″	100·0	325·90	·030″	33·33	108·63	·050″	20·00	65·18	·070″	14·29	46·56	·090″	11·11	36·21	·26″	3·85	12·54
·011	90·91	296·27	·031	32·26	105·13	·051	19·61	63·90	·071	14·08	45·90	·091	10·99	35·82	·28	3·57	11·64
·012	83·33	271·58	·032	31·25	101·84	·052	19·23	62·68	·072	13·89	45·27	·092	10·87	35·42	·30	3·33	10·86
·013	76·92	250·69	·033	30·30	98·76	·053	18·87	61·49	·073	13·70	44·65	·093	10·75	35·04	·35	2·86	9·31
·014	71·43	232·79	·034	29·41	95·85	·054	18·52	60·35	·074	13·51	44·04	·094	10·64	34·67	·40	2·50	8·15
·015″	66·67	217·27	·035″	28·57	93·11	·055″	18·18	59·25	·075″	13·33	43·45	·095″	10·53	34·31	·45″	2·22	7·24
·016	62·50	203·69	·036	27·78	90·53	·056	17·86	58·20	·076	13·16	42·88	·096	10·42	33·95	·50	2·00	6·52
·017	58·82	191·70	·037	27·03	88·08	·057	17·54	57·17	·077	12·99	42·33	·097	10·31	33·60	·55	1·82	5·92
·018	55·56	181·05	·038	26·32	85·76	·058	17·24	56·20	·078	12·82	41·78	·098	10·20	33·26	·60	1·67	5·43
·019	52·63	171·53	·039	25·64	83·56	·059	16·95	55·23	·079	12·66	41·26	·099	10·10	32·92	·65	1·54	5·01
·020″	50·00	162·95	·040″	25·00	81·47	·060″	16·62	54·32	·080″	12·50	40·74	·100″	10·00	32·59	·70	1·43	4·66
															·75″	1·33	4·35

* Mean opposition magnitudes : star magnitudes only are from the H.R.

Parsecs or Light-years equivalent to Km/seconds Velocities, at 500 km/seconds (310·69 mile/secs.) per megaparsec; or 153·42 km./secs. (95·33 mile/secs.) per megalight-year. For per km/ or mile/ day, or year, multiply by 86,400, or $31\frac{1}{2}$ millions.

km/secs.	Millions of: Pcs.	L/y.	km/secs.	Millions of: Pcs.	L/y.	km/secs.	Millions of:— Pcs.	L/y.	km/secs.	Millions of— Pcs.	Ly.	km/secs.	Millions of:— Pcs.	L/y.	km/secs.	Millions of:— Pcs.	L/y.	km/secs.	Millions of:— Parsecs	Light-yrs
100	0·2	0·7	1500	3·0	9·8	4500	9·0	29·3	9000	18·0	58·7	15,000	30·0	97·8	21,000	42·0	136·9	35,000	70·0	228·1
200	0·4	1·3	2000	4·0	13·0	5000	10·0	32·6	10,000	20·0	65·2	16,000	32·0	104·3	22,000	44·0	143·4	40,000	80·0	260·7
300	0·6	2·0	2500	5·0	16·3	5500	11·0	35·8	11,000	22·0	71·7	17,000	34·0	110·8	23,000	46·0	149·9	45,000	90·0	293·3
400	0·8	2·6	3000	6·0	19·6	6000	12·0	39·1	12,000	24·0	78·2	18,000	36·0	117·3	24,000	48·0	156·4	50,000	100·0	325·9
500	1·0	3·3	3500	7·0	22·8	7000	14·0	45·6	13,000	26·0	84·7	19,000	38·0	123·8	25,000	50·0	163·0	55,000	110·0	358·5
1000	2·0	6·5	4000	8·0	26·1	8000	16·0	52·1	14,000	28·0	91·3	20,000	40·0	130·4	30,000	60·0	195·5	60,000	120·0	391·1

Kilometres converted into Miles:—Multiples by 10, 100, 1000, shift decimal point one, two, three places to the right.

km.	=miles	km.	=miles	km.	=miles	km.	=miles	km.	=miles	km.	=miles	km.	=miles	km.	=miles	km.	=miles	km.	=miles	km.	=miles
1	0·621	6	3·728	11	6·835	16	9·942	21	13·049	26	16·156	31	19·263	36	22·369	41	25·476	46	28·583	60	37·282
2	1·243	7	4·350	12	7·456	17	10·563	22	13·670	27	16·777	32	19·884	37	22·991	42	26·098	47	29·204	70	43·496
3	1·864	8	4·971	13	8·078	18	11·185	23	14·292	28	17·398	33	20·505	38	23·612	43	26·719	48	29·826	80	49·710
4	2·485	9	5·592	14	8·699	19	11·806	24	14·913	29	18·020	34	21·127	39	24·233	44	27·340	49	30·447	90	55·923
5	3·107	10	6·214	15	9·321	20	12·427	25	15·534	30	18·641	35	21·748	40	24·855	45	27·962	50	31·069	100	62·137

Centigrade Degrees converted into Degrees Fahr. (nearest 100, after 1000°). For any temperature (under 0°, use *lower* + or −: **°F.** = °C. × 9 ÷ 5 ± 32; **°C** = (°F. ∓ 32) × 5 ÷ 9. *For the °K equivalent*:—**If above 0° C.** *add*, **if below** subtract from, 273° C. **10 C.° = 18 F.°**

°C.	=°F.	°C.	=°F.	°C.	=°F.	°C.	=°F.	°C.	=°F.	°C.	=°F.	°C.	=°F.	°C.	=°F.	°C.	=°F.	°C.	=°F.	°C.	=°F.
−273	−460	−80	−112	10°	50	110°	230	210°	410	310°	590	410°	770	750°	1382	5500°	9900	11000°	19800	21000°	37800
250	418	70	94	20	68	120	248	220	428	320	608	420	788	1000	1832	6000	10800	12000	21600	22000	39600
200	328	60	76	30	86	130	266	230	446	330	626	430	806	1500	2700	6500	11700	13000	23400	23000	41400
150	238	50	58	40	104	150	284	240	464	340	644	440	824	2000	3600	7000	12600	14000	25200	24000	43200
140	220	40	40	50	122	150	302	250	482	350	662	450	842	2500	4500	7500	13500	15000	27000	25000	45000
130	202	30	22	60	140	160	320	260	500	360	680	460	860	3000	5400	8000	14400	16000	28800	26000	46800
120	184	20	−4	70	158	170	338	270	518	370	698	470	878	3500	6300	8500	15300	17000	30600	28000	50400
110	166	−10	+14	80	176	180	356	280	536	380	716	480	896	4000	7200	9000	16200	18000	32400	30000	54000
100	148	0	32	90	194	190	374	290	554	390	734	490	914	4500	8100	9500	17100	19000	34200	35000	63000
−90	−130	+5	+41	100	212	200	392	300	572	400	752	500	932	5000	9000	10000	18000	20000	36000	40000	72000

'K' Degrees converted into Centigrade and Fahrenheit Degrees (to nearest 100°, after 1000°). **100 K.° = 100 C.° = 180 F.°**

°K.	=°C.	=°F.	°K.	=°C.	=°F.	°K.	=°C.	=°F.	°K.	=°C.	=°F.	°K.	=°C.	=°F.	°K.	=°C.	=°F.
0	−273	−460	500	227	441	4000	3700	6700	7500	7200	13,000	14,000	13,700	24,700	25,000	24,700	44,500
100	−173	−280	1000	727	1341	4500	4200	7600	8000	7700	13,900	15,000	14,700	26,500	30,000	29,700	53,500
200	−73	−99	1500	1200	2200	5000	4700	8500	9000	8700	15,700	16,000	15,700	28,300	35,000	34,700	62,500
255	−18	0	2000	1700	3100	5500	5200	9400	10,000	9700	17,500	17,000	16,700	30,100	40,000	39,700	71,500
273	0	+32	2500	2200	4000	6000	5700	10,300	11,000	10,700	19,300	18,000	17,700	31,900	45,000	44,700	80,500
300	+27	+81	3000	2700	4900	6500	6200	11,200	12,000	11,700	21,100	19,000	18,700	33,700	50,000	49,700	89,500
400	+127	+261	3500	3200	5800	7000	6700	12,100	13,000	12,700	22,900	20,000	19,700	35,500	60,000	59,700	107,500

The Greek Alphabet. The small letters are on the left, the capitals on the right.

Letter	Name		Letter	Name		Letter	Name		Letter	Name		Letter	Name		Letter	Name	
α	Alpha	... A	ε	Epsilon	... E	ι	Iota	... I	ν	Nu	... N	ρ	Rho	... P	φ	Phi	... Φ
β	Beta	... B	ζ	Zeta	... Z	κ	Kappa	... K	ξ	Xi	... Ξ	σ	Sigma	... Σ	χ	Chi	... X
γ	Gamma	... Γ	η	Eta	... H	λ	Lambda	... Λ	ο	Omicron	... O	τ	Tau	... T	ψ	Psi	... Ψ
δ	Delta	... Δ	θ	Theta	... Θ	μ	Mu	... M	π	Pi	... Π	υ	Upsilon	... Υ	ω	Omega	... Ω

Degrees equivalent to Right Ascension Hours and Minutes:— See Table on page 43. **Decimals of a Degree,** p. xv.

No. of Seconds of Arc: in 360°, 1,296,000″; in 1°, 3600″. **No. of Seconds of Time: in 1 day,** 86,400 sec.; in 1 hour, 3600s.

Velocities of Gases in Km./sec. *H*, hydrogen; *He*, helium; H_2O, water; *N*, nitrogen; *O*, oxygen; CO_2, carbonic acid.

	−200°C.	−150°	−100°	−50°	0°C.	+50°	100°	200°	300°	400°
H.	0·95	1·33	1·46	1·66	**1·84**	2·00	2·15	2·42	2·67	2·89
He.	0·68	0·88	1·04	1·18	**1·31**	1·42	1·53	1·72	1·90	2·06
H_2O	0·32	0·42	0·49	0·56	**0·62**	0·67	0·72	0·82	0·90	0·97

	−200°	−150°	−100°	−50°	0°C.	+50°	+100°	200°	300°	400°
N.	0·25	0·33	0·39	0·44	**0·49**	0·53	0·57	0·64	0·71	0·77
O.	0·24	0·31	0·37	0·42	**0·46**	0·50	0·54	0·61	0·67	0·72
CO_2	0·20	0·26	0·31	0·35	**0·39**	0·42	0·46	0·51	0·57	0·61

Ionisation Potentials.—The second value is the voltage required to remove a second electron; it differs widely. Potassium, volts, 4·3, 22; Sodium, 5·1, 30; Lithium, 5·4, 68; Calcium, 6·1, 12; Titanium, 6·8, 14; Magnesium, 7·6, 15; Iron, 8·2, 13; Silicon, 8·2, 16; Sulphur, 10·3, ...; Carbon, 11·3, 24; Hydrogen, 13·5; Oxygen, 13·6, 35; Nitrogen, 14·2, 30; Helium, 24·4, 54 (see p. 24).

Sunset and Sunrise.—The time varies slightly from year to year, but the Sunset Table opposite will give the Apparent or True (Sundial) time of both Sunset or Sunrise within a few minutes, in both Northern and Southern latitudes.

To find the Mean Time equivalent, add or subtract the Equation of Time *(E)* given in small figures. A further correction is required for longitude, of 4 minutes for each degree W. or E. of the Standard meridian—added if W., subtracted if E.

Sunrise.—Subtract the time of Sunset from 12 hrs. 0 min., and adjust for Equation of Time, and longitude, as for Sunset. Thus sunrise on May 25, lat. 45°N., long. 4° W. of Std. meridian, is at 4·38 (12h. – 7h. 35m., – 3m. Equation, +16m. for longitude).

Earliest and Latest Sunrise and Sunset, in different N. Latitudes. There are two 'earliests' and 'latests' in low latitudes.

Latitude	0°	0°	10°	10°	20°	30°	35°	40°	45°	50°	55°	60°
Rising. Earliest:— a.m.	Nov. 4 5.40	May 16 5.53	May 30 5.37	Oct. 11 5.48	June 7 5.20	June 11 4.58	June 14 4.45	June 15 4.30	June 17 4.12	June 18 3.50	June 19 3.20	June 19 2.35
„ Latest:— a.m.	Feb. 12 6.11	July 28 6.03	Aug. 24 5.51	Jan. 27 6.23	Jan. 18 6.38	Jan. 11 6.57	Jan. 8 7.09	Jan. 6 7.22	Jan. 3 7.39	Jan. 1 7.59	Dec. 29 8.26	Dec. 28 9.04
Setting. Earliest— p.m.	Nov. 2 5.47	May 14 6.0	Nov. 17 5.35	Apr. 10 6.10	Nov. 26 5.19	Dec. 3 5.0	Dec. 6 4.48	Dec. 8 4.35	Dec. 11 4.18	Dec. 13 3.58	Dec. 15 3.32	Dec. 17 2.53
„ Latest:— p.m.	Feb. 10 6.18	July 25 6.10	July 12 6.25	Mar. 17 6.11	July 5 6.43	July 2 7.5	June 30 7.18	June 28 7.33	June 27 7.51	June 26 8.13	June 25 8.43	June 24 9·28

Sun's Longitude, Right Ascension, and Declination, at 0h. Intermediate dates: for R.A. add 4 minutes ℔ day.

Date	Long.	R.A.	Dec.	Date	Long.	R.A.	Dec.	Date	Long.	R.A.	Dec.	Date	Long.	R.A.	Dec.	Date	Long.	R.A.	Dec.
Jan. 1	280°	...	–23°	Mar. 5	344°	23h	–6°	May 22	60°	...	+20°	Aug. 2	130°	...	+18°	Oct. 13	200°	...	–7°
„ 5	284	19h	23	„ 11	350	...	–4	„ 23	61	4h	20	„ 5	132	9h	17	„ 24	210	...	11
„ 11	290	...	22	„ 21	0	24h	0	June 1	70	...	22	„ 13	140	...	15	„ 29	215	14h	13
„ 18	297	20h	21	„ 31	10	...	+4	„ 7	76	5h	23	„ 21	147	10h	12	Nov. 3	220	...	15
„ 20	300	...	20	Apr. 6	16	1h	6	„ 11	80	...	23	„ 24	150	...	11	„ 10	227	15h	17
„ 30	310	...	18	„ 10	20	...	8	„ 22	90	6h	23½	Sept. 3	160	...	8	„ 13	230	...	18
Feb. 2	312	21h	17	„ 20	30	...	11	July 2	100	...	23	„ 7	163	11h	6	„ 23	240	...	20
„ 9	320	...	15	„ 23	32	2h	12	„ 6	103	7h	23	„ 13	170	...	+4	„ 25	242	16h	21
„ 17	327	22h	12	May 1	40	...	15	„ 13	110	...	22	„ 24	180	12h	0	Dec. 3	250	...	22
„ 19	330	...	12	„ 8	47	3h	17	„ 21	118	8h	21	Oct. 3	190	...	–4	„ 8	255	17h	23
Mar. 1	340	...	–8°	May 11	50	...	+18°	July 23	120	...	+20°	Oct. 10	196	13h	–6°	„ 12	260	...	–23
																Dec. 22	270	18h	23½

Equation of Time.—Mean Time ± the minutes in the Table = True or 'sundial' time. Clock before Sun – ; after, +.

Date	Eqn.	Date	Eqn.	Date	Eqn.	Date	Eqn.	Date	Eqn.	Date	Eqn.	Date	Eqn.	Date	Eqn.	Date	Eqn.
Jan. 1	–3m.	Jan. 29	–13m.	Mar. 20	–8m.	Apr. 25	+2m.	Jun. 24	–2m.	Aug. 22	–3m.	Sep. 22	+7m.	Nov. 4	+16⅓	Dec. 11	+7m.
„ 3	4	Feb. 4	14	„ 23	7	May 2	3	„ 29	3	„ 26	2	„ 25	8	„ 11	16m.	„ 13	6
„ 5	5	„ 12	14⅓	„ 26	6	„ 7	3½	July 4	4	„ 29	–1	„ 28	9	„ 18	15	„ 16	5
„ 7	6	„ 20	14	„ 29	5	„ 15	3¾	„ 10	5	Sep. 2	0	Oct. 1	10	„ 22	14	„ 18	4
Jan. 9	7	„ 24	13½	Apr. 2	4	„ 23	3½	„ 14	5½	„ 5	+1	„ 4	11	„ 26	13	Dec. 20	3
„ 12	8	„ 27	13	„ 5	3	„ 28	3	„ 19	6	„ 8	2	„ 7	12	„ 29	12	„ 22	2
„ 15	9	Mar. 4	12	„ 8	2	Jun. 4	2	„ 27	6⅓	„ 11	3	„ 11	13	Dec. 1	11	„ 24	+1
„ 18	10	„ 8	11	„ 12	–1	„ 10	+1	Aug. 5	6	„ 14	4	„ 15	14	„ 4	10	„ 26	0
„ 21	11	„ 12	10	„ 16	0	„ 15	0	„ 13	5	„ 17	5	„ 20	15	„ 7	9	„ 28	–1
Jan. 24	–12	Mar. 16	– 9	Apr. 20	+1m.	Jun. 19	–1m.	Aug. 18	–4m.	Sep. 19	+6m.	Oct. 27	+16	Dec. 9	+8	Dec. 30	–2m.

Angular Distances on the Star Sphere.—The following approximations are convenient for rough estimates; others can easily be made up from the star charts: the degrees are those of a 'great circle,' as of Declination, or those on the Celestial equator.

½° = the angular diameter of the Moon (approx.).
1¼° = δ to ε Orionis: or β to λ Crucis „
2° = α to γ Aquilæ; or α to σ Scorpii. „
2½° = α to β Aquilæ; or α to δ Reticuli ... (approx.).
4° = α to β Canis Minoris; or α to β Crucis „
5° = α to β Ursæ Majoris; or α to β Centauri „

The Star Sphere contains 41,253 square degrees.

Approximate Galactic Longitude and Latitude of certain Stars:—

Long.	Lat.	Star
3°	+21°	α Ophiuchi
9°	+52°	α Coronæ
16°	–10°	α Aquilæ (*Altair*)
20°	+39°	ζ Herculis
31°	+12°	γ Lyræ
35°	+18°	α Lyræ (*Vega*)
46°	+ 1°	γ Cygni
52°	+ 1°	α Cygni (*Deneb*)
59°	+40°	η Draconis
65°	+65°	η Ursæ Maj.
79°	+41°	β Ursæ Min.
78°	+62°	ζ Ursæ Maj. (*Mizar*)
87°	+61°	ε Ursæ Maj.
88°	–81°	β Ceti
90°	+27°	α Ursæ Min. (*Polaris*)
91°	– 2°	γ Cassiopeiæ
98°	+60°	δ Ursæ Maj.
109°	+52°	α Ursæ Maj. (*Dubhe*)
121	+47°	υ Ursæ Maj.
130°	+ 6°	α Aurigæ (*Capella*)
132°	+64°	ψ Ursæ Maj.
135°	+12°	β Aurigæ
149°	–19°	α Tauri (*Aldebaran*)
155°	+24°	α Geminorum (*Castor*)
160°	+25°	β Geminorum (*Pollux*)
165°	–15°	γ Orionis (*Bellatrix*)
167°	– 7°	α Orionis (*Betelgeuse*)
177°	–24°	β Orionis (*Rigel*)
182°	+15°	α Canis Min. (*Procyon*)
195°	+50°	α Leonis (*Regulus*)
195°	– 8°	α Canis Maj. (*Sirius*)
205°	+66°	θ Leonis
210°	+30°	α Hydræ (*Alphard*)
210°	– 5°	η Canis Maj.
222°	+72°	β Leonis (*Denebola*)
228°	–25°	α Carinæ (*Canopus*)
230°	– 7°	γ Velorum
240°	+61°	β Virginis
250°	–13°	α Volantis
256°	–59°	α Eridani (*Achernar*)
268°	– 1°	α Crucis
279°	+ 1°	β Centauri
284°	– 1°	α Centauri
285°	+50°	α Virginis (*Spica*)
289°	–16°	α Trianguli Aus.
300°	– 9°	ζ Aræ
313°	–59°	β Gruis
317°	–54°	α Gruis
320°	+14°	α Scorpii (*Antares*)
321°	+22°	β Scorpii
327°	–11°	ε Sagittarii
343°	+68°	α Boötis (*Arcturus*)
348°	–66°	α Pisc. A. (*Fomalhaut*)
355°	+ 4°	η Serpentis

Apparent (Sundial) Time of Sunset.—To obtain Mean Time of Sunset, see opposite. *E.* = Equation of Time.

Northern Latitudes Date	*E.*	Date	*E.*	0° h. m.	10° h. m.	20° h. m.	30° h. m.	35° h. m.	40° h. m.	45° h. m.	50° h. m.	52° h. m.	54° h. m.	56° h. m.	58° h. m.	60° h m.	Southern Latitudes Date	*E.*	Date	*E.*
Dec. 21	-2	Dec. 21	-2	6 04	5 46	5 28	5 06	4 54	4 40	4 23	4 02	3 52	3 41	3 28	3 14	2 56	Jun. 21	+1	Jun. 21	+1
„ 24	-1	„ 19	3	6 04	5 47	5 28	5 07	4 55	4 40	4 23	4 03	3 53	3 42	3 29	3 14	2 57	„ 24	2	„ 18	1
„ 27	+1	„ 16	5	6 04	5 47	5 28	5 07	4 55	4 40	4 24	4 03	3 54	3 43	3 30	3 15	2 58	„ 27	3	„ 16	0
„ 30	2	„ 14	6	6 04	5 47	5 28	5 07	4 55	4 41	4 25	4 04	3 55	3 44	3 31	3 16	2 59	„ 30	3	„ 13	0
Jan. 1	3	„ 11	7	**6 04**	**5 47**	**5 29**	**5 08**	**4 56**	**4 42**	**4 26**	**4 05**	**3 56**	**3 45**	**3 33**	**3 18**	**3 01**	July 3	4	„ 10	-1
„ 4	5	„ 8	8	6 04	5 47	5 29	5 08	4 57	4 43	4 27	4 07	3 57	3 46	3 35	3 21	3 04	„ 6	4	„ 7	2
„ 7	6	„ 5	10	6 04	5 47	5 30	5 09	4 58	4 44	4 28	4 09	4 00	3 49	3 38	3 24	3 08	„ 9	5	June 3	2
„ 10	7	Dec. 2	11	6 04	5 48	5 31	5 11	4 59	4 46	4 30	4 12	4 03	3 53	3 41	3 28	3 13	„ 12	5	May 31	3
„ 13	8	Nov. 29	12	6 04	5 48	5 32	5 12	5 01	4 48	4 33	4 15	4 06	3 56	3 45	3 33	3 18	„ 15	6	„ 28	3
„ 16	10	„ 26	13	**6 04**	**5 48**	**5 32**	**5 13**	**5 02**	**4 50**	**4 36**	**4 17**	**4 09**	**3 59**	**3 49**	**3 37**	**3 23**	„ 19	6	„ 25	3
„ 19	11	„ 23	14	6 04	5 49	5 33	5 15	5 04	4 52	4 39	4 21	4 13	4 03	3 54	3 42	3 29	„ 22	6	„ 22	4
„ 22	11	„ 20	15	6 04	5 50	5 34	5 17	5 07	4 55	4 42	4 25	4 18	4 08	3 59	3 48	3 36	„ 25	6	„ 19	4
„ 25	12	„ 17	15	6 04	5 50	5 35	5 19	5 09	4 58	4 45	4 29	4 22	4 14	4 05	3 54	3 42	„ 28	6	„ 15	4
„ 28	13	„ 14	16	6 04	5 51	5 36	5 20	5 11	5 01	4 48	4 33	4 26	4 19	4 10	4 00	3 49	„ 31	6	„ 12	4
„ 31	13	„ 11	16	**6 04**	**5 51**	**5 38**	**5 22**	**5 14**	**5 04**	**4 52**	**4 38**	**4 31**	**4 24**	**4 16**	**4 07**	**3 56**	Aug. 3	+6	„ 9	4
Feb. 3	+14	„ 8	-16	6 04	5 52	5 39	5 24	5 16	5 07	4 56	4 43	4 36	4 30	4 22	4 13	4 04	„ 7	6	„ 6	3
„ 6	14	„ 5	16	6 04	5 52	5 40	5 27	5 19	5 10	5 00	4 48	4 42	4 36	4 28	4 20	4 12	„ 10	5	May 3	3
„ 9	14	Nov. 2	16	6 04	5 53	5 42	5 29	5 22	5 14	5 04	4 53	4 48	4 42	4 35	4 27	4 19	„ 13	5	Apr. 30	3
„ 12	14	Oct. 30	16	6 04	5 54	5 44	5 32	5 25	5 18	5 09	4 58	4 53	4 48	4 42	4 35	4 27	„ 16	4	„ 27	2
„ 15	14	„ 27	16	**6 04**	**5 55**	**5 45**	**5 34**	**5 28**	**5 21**	**5 13**	**5 03**	**4 59**	**4 54**	**4 48**	**4 42**	**4 35**	„ 19	4	„ 24	2
„ 18	14	„ 24	16	6 04	5 55	5 46	5 36	5 31	5 24	5 17	5 08	5 04	5 00	4 55	4 49	4 43	„ 22	3	„ 21	-1
„ 21	14	„ 21	15	6 03	5 56	5 48	5 39	5 34	5 28	5 21	5 14	5 10	5 06	5 01	4 56	4 51	„ 26	2	„ 18	0
„ 24	13	„ 18	15	6 03	5 56	5 50	5 42	5 37	5 32	5 26	5 19	5 16	5 13	5 08	5 04	4 59	„ 29	+1	„ 15	0
„ 27	13	„ 15	14	6 03	5 57	5 51	5 44	5 40	5 36	5 31	5 25	5 22	5 19	5 15	5 11	5 07	Sept. 1	0	„ 12	+1
Mar. 2	12	„ 12	-13	**6 03**	**5 58**	**5 53**	**5 47**	**5 43**	**5 40**	**5 36**	**5 30**	**5 28**	**5 26**	**5 22**	**5 19**	**5 15**	„ 4	-1	„ 9	2
„ 5	+12	„ 9	12	6 03	5 59	5 54	5 49	5 46	5 43	5 40	5 35	5 33	5 32	5 29	5 26	5 23	„ 7	2	„ 5	3
„ 8	11	„ 6	12	6 03	6 00	5 56	5 52	5 50	5 47	5 45	5 41	5 39	5 38	5 36	5 34	5 32	„ 10	3	Apr. 2	4
„ 11	10	Oct. 3	11	6 03	6 01	5 58	5 55	5 54	5 51	5 50	5 47	5 45	5 45	5 43	5 42	5 40	„ 13	4	Mar. 30	5
„ 14	10	Sep. 30	10	6 03	6 01	5 59	5 57	5 57	5 55	5 54	5 52	5 51	5 51	5 50	5 49	5 48	„ 16	5	„ 27	6
„ 17	9	„ 27	9	**6 03**	**6 02**	**6 01**	**6 00**	**6 00**	**5 59**	**5 59**	**5 58**	**5 58**	**5 57**	**5 57**	**5 57**	**5 56**	„ 19	6	„ 25	6
„ 20	8	„ 24	8	6 03	6 03	6 03	6 03	6 03	6 03	6 03	6 04	6 04	6 04	6 04	6 04	6 04	„ 22	7	„ 22	7
„ 23	7	„ 21	7	6 03	6 04	6 05	6 06	6 06	6 07	6 08	6 09	6 10	6 11	6 11	6 12	6 13	„ 25	8	„ 19	8
„ 26	6	„ 18	5	6 03	6 05	6 07	6 09	6 10	6 11	6 13	6 15	6 16	6 17	6 18	6 19	6 21	„ 28	-9	„ 16	9
„ 29	5	„ 15	4	6 03	6 06	6 08	6 11	6 13	6 15	6 18	6 21	6 22	6 24	6 25	6 27	6 29	Oct. 2	10	„ 13	10
Apr. 1	+4	„ 11	3	**6 03**	**6 06**	**6 10**	**6 14**	**6 16**	**6 19**	**6 22**	**6 26**	**6 28**	**6 30**	**6 32**	**6 35**	**6 38**	„ 5	11	„ 9	11
„ 4	3	„ 8	2	6 03	6 07	6 12	6 17	6 20	6 23	6 27	6 32	6 34	6 37	6 39	6 43	6 46	„ 8	12	„ 6	12
„ 7	2	„ 5	-1	6 03	6 08	6 13	6 20	6 23	6 27	6 32	6 38	6 40	6 44	6 46	6 50	6 54	„ 11	13	Mar. 3	12
„ 10	2	Sept. 2	0	6 03	6 08	6 14	6 22	6 26	6 31	6 36	6 43	6 46	6 50	6 53	6 57	7 02	„ 13	13	Feb. 28	+13
„ 13	+1	Aug 30	+1	6 03	6 09	6 16	6 24	6 29	6 35	6 41	6 48	6 52	6 56	7 00	7 05	7 10	„ 16	14	„ 25	13
„ 16	0	„ 27	2	**6 03**	**6 10**	**6 18**	**6 27**	**6 32**	**6 39**	**6 46**	**6 54**	**6 58**	**7 02**	**7 07**	**7 12**	**7 18**	„ 19	15	„ 22	14
„ 19	-1	„ 24	3	6 03	6 11	6 20	6 30	6 35	6 43	6 50	7 00	7 04	7 09	7 14	7 20	7 26	„ 22	15	„ 20	14
„ 22	1	„ 21	3	6 03	6 12	6 21	6 32	6 38	6 46	6 54	7 05	7 09	7 15	7 20	7 27	7 34	„ 25	16	„ 17	14
„ 25	2	„ 18	4	6 04	6 13	6 23	6 35	6 41	6 50	6 59	7 10	7 15	7 21	7 27	7 34	7 42	„ 28	16	„ 14	14
„ 28	2	„ 15	5	6 04	6 13	6 24	6 37	6 44	6 53	7 03	7 15	7 20	7 27	7 33	7 41	7 50	„ 31	16	„ 11	14
May 1	-3	„ 12	+5	**6 04**	**6 14**	**6 26**	**6 40**	**6 47**	**6 57**	**7 07**	**7 20**	**7 26**	**7 33**	**7 40**	**7 49**	**7 58**	Nov. 3	-16	„ 8	14
„ 4	3	„ 9	6	6 04	6 15	6 27	6 42	6 50	7 00	7 11	7 25	7 31	7 39	7 47	7 56	8 06	„ 6	16	„ 5	14
„ 7	3	„ 6	6	6 04	6 15	6 28	6 44	6 53	7 03	7 15	7 30	7 36	7 44	7 53	8 02	8 14	„ 9	16	Feb. 2	14
„ 10	4	Aug. 3	6	6 04	6 16	6 31	6 46	6 56	7 07	7 19	7 35	7 42	7 50	7 59	8 09	8 22	„ 12	16	Jan. 31	13
„ 13	4	July 31	6	6 04	6 17	6 32	6 48	6 58	7 10	7 23	7 39	7 47	7 55	8 05	8 16	8 29	„ 15	15	„ 28	13
„ 16	4	„ 28	6	**6 04**	**6 18**	**6 33**	**6 50**	**7 01**	**7 12**	**7 26**	**7 43**	**7 52**	**8 00**	**8 11**	**8 22**	**8 36**	„ 17	15	„ 25	12
„ 19	4	„ 25	6	6 04	6 18	6 34	6 52	7 03	7 15	7 30	7 47	7 56	8 05	8 16	8 28	8 43	„ 20	15	„ 22	11
„ 22	4	„ 22	6	6 04	6 19	6 35	6 54	7 05	7 18	7 33	7 51	8 00	8 10	8 21	8 34	8 50	„ 23	14	„ 19	11
„ 25	3	„ 19	6	6 04	6 19	6 36	6 55	7 06	7 20	7 35	7 54	8 04	8 14	8 26	8 39	8 56	„ 26	13	„ 16	10
„ 28	3	„ 16	6	6 04	6 20	6 37	6 57	7 08	7 22	7 38	7 58	8 08	8 18	8 30	8 44	9 01	„ 29	12	„ 14	9
„ 31	3	„ 13	5	**6 04**	**6 20**	**6 38**	**6 58**	**7 10**	**7 24**	**7 41**	**8 01**	**8 11**	**8 22**	**8 34**	**8 49**	**9 07**	Dec. 2	11	„ 11	8
June 3	-2	„ 10	5	6 04	6 20	6 38	6 59	7 11	7 26	7 42	8 03	8 14	8 25	8 38	8 53	9 12	„ 5	10	„ 8	6
„ 6	2	„ 7	5	6 04	6 21	6 39	7 00	7 13	7 27	7 44	8 05	8 16	8 28	8 41	8 57	9 16	„ 7	-9	„ 5	5
„ 9	-1	„ 4	4	6 04	6 21	6 39	7 01	7 13	7 28	7 46	8 07	8 18	8 30	8 44	9 00	9 19	„ 10	8	Jan. 2	+4
„ 12	-1	July 1	3	6 04	6 21	6 40	7 02	7 14	7 29	7 47	8 09	8 20	8 32	8 46	9 03	9 22	„ 13	6	Dec. 31	3
„ 15	0	Jun. 28	3	**6 04**	**6 21**	**6 40**	**7 02**	**7 15**	**7 30**	**7 48**	**8 10**	**8 21**	**8 33**	**8 48**	**9 04**	**9 24**	„ 16	5	„ 28	+1
„ 18	+1	„ 25	2	6 04	6 21	6 40	7 02	7 15	7 30	7 48	8 11	8 22	8 34	8 48	9 05	9 26	„ 19	3	„ 25	0
Jun. 21	+1	Jun. 21	+1	6 04	6 22	6 41	7 03	7 16	7 31	7 49	8 12	8 23	8 35	8 49	9 06	9 27	Dec. 21	-2	Dec. 21	-2

Duration of Twilight (Table I).—See Note on page 38. (For fuller Tables, see *Nautical Almanac*).

Latitude,	0°	10°	20°	30°	40°	45°	50°	55°	60°
Winter Solstice	$1^h\ 16^m$	$1^h\ 16^m$	$1^h\ 19^m$	$1^h\ 25^m$	$1^h\ 38^m$	$1^h\ 47^m$	$1^h\ 59^m$	$2^h\ 17^m$	$2^h\ 46^m$
Equinoxes ...	1 9	1 10	1 13	1 19	1 30	1 39	1 50	2 4	2 25
Summer Solstice	1 15	1 18	1 25	1 36	2 03	2 33	Lasts from	Sunset to	Sunrise.
Apex of glow above horizon, 1 hr. after sunset, Dec. 21, *about*					*7°*	*8°*	*9°*	*10°*	*12°*

Semi-diurnal Arcs (II), or Time between Rising or Setting, and Culmination. (Refraction not allowed for).

N. Hemisphere observers read the star's N. or S. Declination at the *top* of the column; those in the S. Hemisphere, at the *foot*.

N. Hemisphere:—STARS WITH NORTH DECLINATION.

Observ. Lat.	30° h.	m.	25° h.	m.	20° h.	m.	15° h.	m.	10° h.	m.	5° h.	m.	0° h.	m.
5°	6	11	6	8	6	7	6	5	6	4	6	2	6	0
10	6	23	6	19	6	15	6	11	6	7	6	4	6	0
15	6	36	6	29	6	22	6	16	6	11	6	5	6	0
20	6	49	6	39	6	30	6	22	6	15	6	7	6	0
25	7	2	6	49	6	39	6	29	6	19	6	9	6	0
30	7	19	7	2	6	49	6	36	6	23	6	12	6	0
35	7	35	7	16	6	59	6	43	6	28	6	14	6	0
40	7	55	7	32	7	11	6	52	6	34	6	17	6	0
45	8	18	7	51	7	25	7	2	6	41	6	20	6	0
50	8	53	8	15	7	43	7	14	6	49	6	24	6	0
55	9	39	8	47	8	5	7	30	6	58	6	29	6	0
60°	11	22	9	35	8	36	7	51	7	11	6	35	6	0

S. Hemisphere:—STARS with SOUTH DECLINATION.

N. Hemisphere:—STARS WITH S. DECLINATION.

Observer's Lat.	5° h.	m.	10° h.	m.	15° h.	m.	20° h.	m.	25° h.	m.	30° h.	m.	Observ. Lat.
5°	5	58	5	56	5	55	5	53	5	52	5	49	5°
10	5	56	5	53	5	49	5	45	5	41	5	37	10
15	5	55	5	49	5	44	5	38	5	31	5	24	15
20	5	53	5	45	5	38	5	30	5	21	5	11	20
25	5	51	5	41	5	31	5	21	5	11	4	58	25
30	5	48	5	37	5	24	5	11	4	58	4	41	30
35	5	46	5	32	5	17	5	1	4	44	4	25	35
40	5	43	5	26	5	8	4	49	4	28	4	5	40
45	5	40	5	19	4	58	4	35	4	9	3	42	45
50	5	36	5	11	4	46	4	17	3	45	3	7	50
55	5	31	5	2	4	30	3	55	3	13	2	21	55
60°	5	25	4	49	4	9	3	24	2	25	0	38	60°

S. Hemisphere:—STARS with N. DECLINATION.

Rising or Setting of Stars, &c.—From the R.A., find culmination-time (Table III), then for *Rising* Subtract, for *Setting* Add the semi-diurnal arc for the Dec. and observer's latitude. *Ex.* Rising of Leo on Nov. 13, in lat. 55 °N.; R.A. 10h., Dec. 20° N.? On Nov. 14 (after midnight, 13th), as R.A. 9½h. souths at 6 a.m., 10h. souths at 6.30 a.m. Semi-diurnal arc for Dec. 20° N. and 55° N. is 8h. 5m., which subtracted from 6.30 a.m. gives 10.25 p.m. on Nov. 13th as the rising-time of Leo.

When does Mars rise on Mar. 28 in lat. 45° N.?; R.A. 13½h., Dec. 5° S. *(a)* Proceed as above. Or *(b)* Find in the *N.A.* the time of meridian passage on Mar. 28, say 1 a.m. (29th), from which subtract the semi-diurnal arc 5 h. 40 m. Answer, 7.20 p.m.

To find when a Star is on the Meridian.—(The R.A. Central Meridian of each Chart is given at the side).

When will the constellation Taurus be south at 10 p.m.? From the Index of Constellations (last page) Taurus is in Map **5**: the central meridian of Taurus is R.A. 4 h. (see also at side). In Table III below, Sidereal Time, in the column headed 10 p.m., and in line with R.A. 4 h., is the date required, Dec. 21.

What constellations are in the south at 8 p.m. on March 22nd? In Table III find March 22; in the column headed 8 p.m., in same line, is the answer R.A. 8 h., contained in Maps 7-8:—Gemini, Cancer, &c.

When will R.A. 6h. culminate on March 7? *Answer* (Table III), **7** p.m.—March 7 line, above R.A. **6**h.

Central Maps	Meridian = R.A.
3-4	24 h.
5-6	4 h.
7-8	8 h.
9-10	12 h.
11-12	16 h.
13-14	20 h.

Sidereal Time (III), or Hour of R.A. on the Meridian.—If time is after midnight, add 1 day to the date at the side.

Intermediate Dates. Add to the R.A. for the previous date the requisite No. of minutes from the **7**- or **8**-day-interval Table below.

7 Days Interval:—	1 day	2 dys.	3 dys.	4 dys.	5 dys.	6 days.
Add minutes,	4 m.	9 m.	13 m.	17 m.	21 m.	26 m.

8 Days Interval.	1 day	2 dys.	3 dys.	4 dys.	5 dys.	6 dys.	7 dys.
Add minutes,	4 m.	8 m.	12 m.	15 m.	19 m.	23 m.	26 m.

Intermediate Minutes of Mean Time. Add the same No. of R.A. minutes to the previous R.A. hour. Thus Apr. 6 at 5.9 p.m. = R.A. **6 h. 9m.**

Hour of R.A. on the Meridian at:—

Date	5 p.m.	6p.	7p.	8p.	9p.	10p.	11p.	12a.	1a.	2a.	3a.	4a.	5a.	6a.
Jan. 5	0h.	1h.	2h.	3h.	4h.	5h.	6h.	7h.	8h.	9h.	10	11	12	13
13	½	½	½	½	½	½	½	½	½	½	½	½	½	½
21	1	2	3	4	5	6	7	8	9	10	11	12	13	14
28	½	½	½	½	½	½	½	½	½	½	½	½	½	½
Feb. 5	2	3	4	5	6	7	8	9	10	11	12	13	14	15
13	½	½	½	½	½	½	½	½	½	½	½	½	½	½
20	3	4	5	6	7	8	9	10	11	12	13	14	15	16
28	½	½	½	½	½	½	½	½	½	½	½	½	½	½
Mar. 7	4	5	6	7	8	9	10	11	12	13	14	15	16	17
15	½	½	½	½	½	½	½	½	½	½	½	½	½	½
22	5	6	7	8	9	10	11	12	13	14	15	16	17	18
29	½	½	½	½	½	½	½	½	½	½	½	½	½	½
Apr. 6	6	7	8	9	10	11	12	13	14	15	16	17	18	19
14	½	½	½	½	½	½	½	½	½	½	½	½	½	½
22	7	8	9	10	11	12	13	14	15	16	17	18	19	20
29	½	½	½	½	½	½	½	½	½	½	½	½	½	½
May 7	8	9	10	11	12	13	14	15	16	17	18	19	20	21
15	½	½	½	½	½	½	½	½	½	½	½	½	½	½
22	9	10	11	12	13	14	15	16	17	18	19	20	21	22
30	½	½	½	½	½	½	½	½	½	½	½	½	½	½
June 6	10	11	12	13	14	15	16	17	18	19	20	21	22	23
14	½	½	½	½	½	½	½	½	½	½	½	½	½	½
22	11	12	13	14	15	16	17	18	19	20	21	22	23	0
Jun. 29	½	½	½	½	½	½	½	½	½	½	½	½	½	½

Hour of R.A. on the Meridian at:—

Date	5 p.m.	6p.	7p.	8p.	9p.	10p.	11p.	12a.	1a.	2a.	3a.	4a.	5a.	6a.
Jul. 7	12	13	14	15	16	17	18	19	20	21	22	23	0h.	1h
15	½	½	½	½	½	½	½	½	½	½	½	½	½	½
22	13	14	15	16	17	18	19	20	21	22	23	0	1	2
30	½	½	½	½	½	½	½	½	½	½	½	½	½	½
Aug. 6	14	15	16	17	18	19	20	21	22	23	0	1	2	3
14	½	½	½	½	½	½	½	½	½	½	½	½	½	½
22	15	16	17	18	19	20	21	22	23	0	1	2	3	4
29	½	½	½	½	½	½	½	½	½	½	½	½	½	½
Sept. 6	16	17	18	19	20	21	22	23	0	1	2	3	4	5
13	½	½	½	½	½	½	½	½	½	½	½	½	½	½
21	17	18	19	20	21	22	23	0	1	2	3	4	5	6
29	½	½	½	½	½	½	½	½	½	½	½	½	½	½
Oct. 6	18	19	20	21	22	23	0	1	2	3	4	5	6	7
14	½	½	½	½	½	½	½	½	½	½	½	½	½	½
21	19	20	21	22	23	0	1	2	3	4	5	6	7	8
29	½	½	½	½	½	½	½	½	½	½	½	½	½	½
Nov. 6	20	21	22	23	0	1	2	3	4	5	6	7	8	9
13	½	½	½	½	½	½	½	½	½	½	½	½	½	½
21	21	22	23	0	1	2	3	4	5	6	7	8	9	10
28	½	½	½	½	½	½	½	½	½	½	½	½	½	½
Dec. 6	22	23	0	1	2	3	4	5	6	7	8	9	10	11
14	½	½	½	½	½	½	½	½	½	½	½	½	½	½
21	23	0	1	2	3	4	5	6	7	8	9	10	11	12
Dec. 29	½	½	½	½	½	½	½	½	½	½	½	½	½	½

Decimals of a Degree.—For valuing minutes and seconds of arc to the nearest 1/100th of a degree, and *vice versa.* (The *exact* equivalent of ·01 degree is 36″). Take the decimal equivalent just *less* than the value to be converted; or *vice versa*, the Tabular value *plus* 18″, which gives the exact value of 100ths of a degree. Thus 33′ 48″ = 0°·56 approx.; ·0°·43 = 25′ 48″.

·01	0′ 18″	·11°	6′ 18″	·21°	12′ 18″	·31°	18′ 18″	·41°	24′ 18″	·51°	30′ 18″	·61°	36′ 18″	·71°	42′ 18″	·81°	48′ 18″	·91°	54′ 18″
·02	0 54	·12	6 54	·22	12 54	·32	18 54	·42	24 54	·52	30 54	·62	36 54	·72	42 54	·82	48 54	·92	54 54
·03	1 30	·13	7 30	·23	13 30	·33	19 30	·43	25 30	·53	31 30	·63	37 30	·73	43 30	·83	49 30	·93	55 30
·04	2 6	·14	8 6	·24	14 6	·34	20 6	·44	26 6	·54	32 6	·64	38 6	·74	44 6	·84	50 6	·94	56 6
·05	2 42	·15	8 42	·25	14 42	·35	20 42	·45	26 42	·55	32 42	·65	38 42	·75	44 42	·85	50 42	·95	56 42
·06	3 18	·16	9 18	·26	15 18	·36	21 18	·46	27 18	·56	33 18	·66	39 18	·76	45 18	·86	51 18	·96	57 18
·07	3 54	·17	9 54	·27	15 54	·37	21 54	·47	27 54	·57	33 54	·67	39 54	·77	45 54	·87	51 54	·97	57 54
·08	4 30	·18	10 30	·28	16 30	·38	22 30	·48	28 30	·58	34 30	·68	40 30	·78	46 30	·88	52 30	·98	58 30
·09	5 6	·19	11 6	·29	17 6	·39	23 6	·49	29 6	·59	35 6	·69	41 6	·79	47 6	·89	53 6	·99	59 6
·10°	5′ 42″	·20°	11′ 42″	·30°	17′ 42″	40°	23′ 42″	·50°	29′ 42″	·60°	35′ 42″	·70°	41′ 42″	·80°	47′ 42″	·90°	53′ 42″	1°	59′ 42″

Decimals of a Day.—The decimals of a minute for columns 2-10 are the same as those, *in the same line*, of the 1st column.

Dec.	h.	m.	Dec.	h.	m.	Dec.	h.	m.	Dec.	h.	m.	Dec.	h.	m.	Dec.	h.	m.	Dec.	h.	m.	Dec.	h.	m.	Dec.	h.	m.	Dec.	h.	m.	Dec.	min.
·01	0	14·4	·11	2	38	·21	5	2	·31	7	26	·41	9	50	·51	12	14	·61	14	38	·71	17	2	·81	19	26	·91	21	50	·001	1·44
·02	0	28·8	·12	2	52	·22	5	16	·32	7	40	·42	10	4	·52	12	28	·62	14	52	·72	17	16	·82	19	40	·92	22	4	·002	2·88
·03	0	43·2	·13	3	7	·23	5	31	·33	7	55	·43	10	19	·53	12	43	·63	15	7	·73	17	31	·83	19	55	·93	22	19	·003	4·32
·04	0	57·6	·14	3	21	·24	5	45	·34	8	9	·44	10	33	·54	12	57	·64	15	21	·74	17	45	·84	20	9	·94	22	33	·004	5·76
·05	1	12·0	·15	3	36	·25	6	0	·35	8	24	·45	10	48	·55	13	12	·65	15	36	·75	18	0	·85	20	24	·95	22	48	·005	7·20
·06	1	26·4	·16	3	50	·26	6	14	·36	8	38	·46	11	2	·56	13	26	·66	15	50	·76	18	14	·86	20	38	·96	23	2	·006	8·64
·07	1	40·8	·17	4	4	·27	6	28	·37	8	52	·47	11	16	·57	13	40	·67	16	4	·77	18	28	·87	20	52	·97	23	16	·007	10·08
·08	1	55·2	·18	4	19	·28	6	43	·38	9	7	·48	11	31	·58	13	55	·68	16	19	·78	18	43	·88	21	7	·98	23	31	·008	11·52
·09	2	9·6	·19	4	33	·29	6	57	·39	9	21	·49	11	45	·59	14	9	·69	16	33	·79	18	57	·89	21	21	·99	23	45	·009	12·96
·10	2	24·0	·20	4	48	·30	7	12	·40	9	36	·50	12	0	·60	14	24	·70	16	48	·80	19	12	·90	21	36	1·0	24	0	·010	14·40

Hours and Minutes as Decimals of a Day.

Hrs.	½ hr.	1 h.	1½ h.	2 h.	2½ h.	3 h.	3½ h.	4 h.	4½ h.	5 h.	5½ h.	6 h.	6½ h.	7 h.	7½ h.	8h.	8½ h.	9h.
=	·0208 dy	·0417	·0625	·0833	·1042	·1250	·1458	·1667	·1875	·2083	·2292	·2500	·2708	·2917	·3125	·3333	·3542	·3750
	9½ h.	10 h.	10½ h.	11 h.	11½ h.	12 h.	12½ h.	13 h.	14 h.	15 h.	16 h.	17 h.	18 h.	19 h.	20 h.	21 h.	22 h.	23 h.
=	·3958 dy	·4167	·4375	·4583	4792	·5000	·5208	·5417	·5833	·6250	·6667	·7083	·7500	·7917	·8333	·8750	·9167	·9583
Minutes:—	1 m.	2 m.	3 m.	4 m.	5 m.	6 m.	7 m.	8 m.	9 m.	10 m.	11 m.	12 m.	13 m.	14 m.	15 m.	16 m.	17 m.	
Decimal =	·0007 dy	·0014	·0021	·0028	·0035	·0042	·0049	·0056	·0062	·0069	·0076	·0083	·0090	·0097	·0104	·0111	·0118	
	18 m.	19 m.	20 m.	21 m.	22 m.	23 m.	24 m.	25 m.	26 m.	27 m.	28 m.	29 m.	30 m.	35 m.	40 m.	45 m.	50 m.	55 m.
=	·0125 dy	·0132	·0139	·0146	·0153	·0160·	·0167	·0174	·0181	·0187	·0194	·0201	·0208	·0243	·0278	·0313	·0347	·0382

PRECESSION TABLES

Precession in R.A. for 10 Years. For Northern objects use the upper line of R.A. Hours; for Southern objects, the lower. The ± signs are added algebraically to the catalogue positions, like signs being added, unlike signs subtracted.
For reckoning backwards, to an earlier date, reverse the + or − signs.

	Hours of Right Ascension for NORTHERN Objects.													
Dec.	0, 12	1, 11	2, 10	3, 9	4, 8	5, 7	6	18	19, 17	20, 16	21, 15	22, 14	23, 13	Dec.
80°	+0·51m	+0·84m	+1·14m	+1·40m	+1·60m	+1·73m	+1·77m	−0·75m	−0·70m	−0·58m	−0·38m	−0·12m	+0·19m	80°
70°	0·51	0·67	0·82	0·94	1·04	1·10	1·12	−0·10	−0·08	−0·02	+0·08	+0·21	0·35	70°
60°	0·51	0·61	0·70	0·78	0·84	0·88	0·90	+0·13	+0·14	+0·18	+0·24	+0·32	0·41	60°
50°	0·51	0·58	0·64	0·70	0·74	0·77	0·78	+0·25	+0·26	+0·28	+0·32	+0·38	0·44	50°
40°	0·51	0·56	0·61	0·64	0·67	0·69	0·70	+0·33	+0·33	+0·35	+0·38	+0·42	0·46	40°
30°	0·51	0·54	0·58	0·60	0·62	0·64	0·64	+0·38	+0·39	+0·40	+0·42	+0·45	0·48	30°
20°	0·51	0·53	0·55	0·57	0·58	0·59	0·59	+0·43	+0·43	+0·44	+0·45	+0·47	0·49	20°
10°	0·51	0·52	0·53	0·54	0·55	0·55	0·55	+0·47	+0·47	+0·48	+0·48	+0·49	0·50	10°
0°	+0·51m	+0·51m	+0·51m	+0·51m	+0·51m	+0·51m	+0·51m	+0·51m	+0·51m	+0·51m	+0·51m	+0·51m	0·51m	0°
Dec.	0, 12	23, 13	22, 14	21, 15	20, 16	19, 17	18	6	5, 7	4, 8	3, 9	2, 10	1, 11	Dec.
	Hours of Right Ascension for SOUTHERN Objects.													

Precession in Declination for 10 Years for objects having N. Declination. S. Declination, reverse the + or − signs.

Hours	0, 24	1, 23	2, 22	3, 21	4, 20	5, 19	6, 18	7, 17	8, 16	9, 15	10, 14	11, 13	12
	+3′·3	+3′·2	+2′·9	+2′·4	+1′·7	+0′·9	0	−0′·9	−1′·7	−2′·4	−2′·9	−3′·2	−3′·3

Example:—**The Star α Ursæ Majoris is placed in 1920 in R.A. 10h. 58·9m., Declination +62° 11′; find its approximate position in 1950.**

Turn to the column headed by the nearest R.A. hour, 11. In this column the 10-year R.A. correction for 60°N. is +0·61m., for 70°N. it is +0·67m., giving about +0·62m. for the intermediate Dec. of the Star.

R.A. of α Ursæ Majoris for 1920	is	10h. 58·9m.
Correction for 30 years (+0·62 × 3)	„	+ 1·9m.
R.A. for 1950		11h. 0·8m.

The Star's Declination for 1920	is	62° 11′
Correction for 30 years (−3′·2 × 3)	„	−10′
Dec. for 1950		62° 1′

Astronomical Signs or Symbols (occasionally-used symbols in brackets) :—

Signs of the Zodiac.	Aries	Taurus	Gemini	Cancer	Leo	Virgo	Libra	Scorpius	Sagittarius	Capricornus	Aquarius	Pisces
Symbol.	♈	♉	♊	♋	♌	♍	♎	♏	♐	♑	♒	♓

Sun, &c.—	Sun	Mercury	Venus	Earth	Moon	Mars	Minor planet	Jupiter	Saturn	Uranus	Neptune	Pluto	Comet	Star
Symbol.	☉ (○)	☿	♀	⊕ (♁)	☽	♂	⑨	♃	♄	♅, ⛢	♆	♇	☄	✶

Other Signs.	1st of Aries,	Conjunction,	Quadrature,	Opposition.	Node (longit. of).	**Moon's Phases**:—	New,	1st qr.,	Full,	3rd qr.
Symbol. ...	♈	☌	□	☍	☊ ascending	...	●	☽	○	☾
	Longit. fr. Sun, = 0°		90°	180°	☋ descending.	Longit. from Sun, =	0°	90°	180°	270°

Symbols of Elements.—*A*, Argon ; *Al*, Aluminium ; *Be*, Beryllium ; *C*, Carbon ; *Ca*, Calcium ; *Cr*, Chromium ; *Fe*, Iron ; *H*, Hydrogen ; *He*, Helium ; *K*, Potasssium ; *Li*, Lithium ; *Mg*, Magnesium ; *Mn*, Manganese ; *N*, Nitrogen ; *Na*, Sodium ; *Ne*, Neon ; *O*, Oxygen ; *P*, Phosphorus ; *Rb*, Rubidium ; *S*, Sulphur ; *Sc*, Scandium ; *Si*, Silicon ; *Sr*, Strontium ; *Ti*, Titanium ; *Zr*, Zirconium.

Significance of + and −. **For Direction,** + indicates (*a*) northwards; (*b*) 'direct' or 'positive' motion—*i.e*, to the left, or eastwards, when looking south : − indicates (*a*) southwards ; (*b*) 'retrograde' or 'negative' motion—*i.e.*, to the right, or westwards when looking south. **Variable Stars:** + indicates that a maximum or minimum is later than the predicted date; −, that it is earlier. **Comets:** as for Variable stars, + later, − earlier, to indicate departure from the ephemeris, or the elements.

Earth's Areo-, and Zenographic Dec.—When +, the planet's North pole is presented to the Earth; when −, the South pole.

Declination :—
+ = North of Celestial eqr.
− = South „ „

Latitude :—
+ = N. } of Ecliptic, or of
− = S. } Earth's or Galact. [eqr.

Longitude :—
+ = W. } of Greenwich.
− = E. }

Libration ; mean centre :—
+ = Displaced to E. (longit.)
− „ „ W. „
+ = Displaced to S. (lat.)
− „ „ N. „
(see note, p. 29)

Magnitude :—
+ = Fainter than mag. 0·0
− = Brighter „ „ 0·0

Position Angle Sun's Axis :—
+ = N. Pole, E. } of the Hr.
− = „ W. } Circle.

Proper Motion, Precession :—
+ = Northwards (in Dec.)
− = Southwards „
+ = Direct (in R.A.)
− = Retrograde „
Light-time. + later, − earlier.
(see pp. 6, 11)

Radial Velocity :—
+ = Recession from Sun.
− = Approach to „

Saturn's Rings :— (p. 32).
+ = Earth N. of ring-plane.
− = „ S. „ „

Sun's Equator :— (p. 40).
+ = S. of centre of disc.
− = N. „ „

Astronomical Contractions.—Those for Astronomical Societies, Publications, Star catalogues, &c., are given on pp. vi-vii.

Æ	Right Ascension
A.U.	Astronomical Unit
„	Angstrom Unit
C.I.	Colour index
C.M.	Central Meridian
Dec.	Declination
Eqr.	Equator
Gal.	Galactic
G.E.	Greatest elongation
G.C.T.	Greenwich Civil Time
G.M.A.T.	„ Mean Astron. Time
G.M.N.	Greenwich Mean Noon
G.M.T.	„ „ Time
H.I.	Heat Index
H.P.	Horizontal parallax
I.A.	International Angstrom
J.D., J.P.,	Julian Day & Period
J.A.D.	„ Astr. Day, p. 9.
K.	Kelvin (Abs. temp., p. 17).
Lat.	Latitude
Long.	Longitude
Mag.	Magnitude
N.P.D.	North Polar Distance
N.P.S.	„ „ Sequence
O. − C.	Observed − calculated
P.A.	Position Angle
P.E.	Probable error
P.M.	Proper Motion
R.A.	Right Ascension
U.T., T.U.*	Universal Time
S.D.	Semi-diameter
Z.D.	Zenith distance
nf	North following.
np	„ preceding.
sp	South preceding.
sf	„ following.

(see p. 39)

d, days ; *h.*, hours; *m.*, minutes; *s.* seconds. *mm.*, millimetres ; *cm.*, centimetres ; *km.*, kilometres. *l/y*, light-years.

Astronomical Symbols for Positions, Magnitudes, Parallaxes, &c. (fuller list facing front cover). (I.A.U. proposed, 1935).

α	Right Ascension
δ	Declination
β	Latitude (celestial), geocent.
λ	Longitude „ „
G	Galactic longitude
g	„ latitude
b	Heliocentric latitude
l	„ longitude
ϕ	Geographical latitude: ϕ' geocentric
L	„ longitude, + W.
Az	Azimuth, h Altitude
z	Zenith Distance
H or t	Hour Angle
π	Parallax, annual, in ″.
P_0	„ equatorial horizontal
p	Annual precession (general)
p	Position angle, p. 5.
μ	Proper motion (total annual)
R, T, W,	Velocity,† radial (receding +), tangential, spatial.
λ	Wave-length, in Angstroms, p. 22
μ	Micron, = 1/1000th mm. = λ10,000
$\mu\mu$	1/millionth mm. = λ10
ϵ	Obliquity of Ecliptic
P	Orbital period
E	Time, Equation of
t	„ of observation
t_m	„ mean : t_v True time.‡
θ	„ sidereal: θ_0 at mean midnight
M	Magnitude, absolute
m	„ apparent
m_v	„ „ visual
m_{pv}	„ „ photovisual
m_{pg}	„ „ photographic
m_{ipg}	„ „ internat. pg.
m_{bol}	„ „ bolometric
m_{rad}	„ „ radiometric
m_{pr}	„ „ photo-red
m_{pir}	„ „ infra-red

Constellation Abbreviations. Three- and four-letter contractions (Int. Astr. Union, 1922, -32). (Malus replaced by Pyxis.

And	Andromeda	Andr
Ant	Antlia	Antl
Aps	Apus	Apus
Aql	Aquila	Aqil
Aqr	Aquarius	Aqar
Ara	Ara	Aræ
Arg	Argo	Argo
Ari	Aries	Arie
Aur	Auriga	Auri
Boo	Boötes	Boot
Cae	Caelum	Cæl
Cam	Camelopard.	Caml
Cap	Capricornus	Capr
Car	Carina	Cari
Cas	Cassiopeia	Cass
Cen	Centaurus	Cent
Cep	Cepheus	Ceph
Cet	Cetus	Ceti
Cha	Chamæleon	Cham
Cir	Circinus	Circ
CMa	Canis Maj.	C Maj
CMi	Canis Min.	C Min
Cnc	Cancer	Canc
Col	Columba	Colm
Com	Coma Ber.	Coma
CrA	Corona Aus.	Cor A
CrB	Corona Bor.	Cor B
Crt	Crater	Crat
Cru	Crux	Cruc
Crv	Corvus	Corv
CVn	Canes Ven.	C Ven
Cyg	Cygnus	Cygn
Del	Delphinus	Dlph
Dor	Dorado	Dora
Dra	Draco	Drac
Equ	Equuleus	Equl
Eri	Eridanus	Erid
For	Fornax	Forn
Gem	Gemini	Gemi
Gru	Grus	Grus
Her	Hercules	Herc
Hor	Horologium	Horo
Hya	Hydra	Hyda
Hyi	Hydrus	Hydi
Ind	Indus	Indi
Lac	Lacerta	Lacr
Leo	Leo	Leon
Lep	Lepus	Leps
Lib	Libra	Libr
LMi	Leo Minor	L Min
Lup	Lupus	Lupi
Lyn	Lynx	Lync
Lyr	Lyra	Lyra
(Malus = Pyxis)		...
Men	Mensa	Mens
Mic	Microscop'm	Micr
Mon	Monoceros	Mono
Mus	Musca	Musc
Nor	Norma	Norm
Oct	Octans	Octn
Oph	Ophiuchus	Ophi
Ori	Orion	Orio
Pav	Pavo	Pavo
Peg	Pegasus	Pegs
Per	Perseus	Pers
Phe	Phœnix	Phœ
Pic	Pictor	Pict
PsA	Piscis Aust.	Psc A
Psc	Pisces	Pisc
Pup	Puppis	Pupp
Pyx	Pyxis	Pyxi
Ret	Reticulum	Reti
Scl	Sculptor	Scul
Sco	Scorpius	Scor
Sct	Scutum	Scut
Ser	Serpens	Serp
Sex	Sextans	Sext
Sge	Sagitta	Sgte
Sgr	Sagittarius	Sgtr
Tau	Taurus	Taur
Tel	Telescop'm	Tele
TrA	Triang. Aus.	Tr Au
Tri	Triangulum	Tria
Tuc	Tucana	Tucn
UMa	Ursa Major	U Maj
UMi	Ursa Minor	U Min
Vel	Vela	Velr
Vir	Virgo	Virg
Vol	Volans	Voln
Vul	Vulpecula	Vulp

* Germany, W.Z. Weltzeit. † Relative to the Sun. ‡ From mean and true midnight.

A STAR ATLAS

AND REFERENCE HANDBOOK

I.—NOTES ON STAR NOMENCLATURE, &c.

The Constellations.—The origin of most of the constellation names is lost in antiquity. COMA BERENICES was added to the old list (though not definitely fixed till the time of Tycho Brahé), about 200 B.C.; but no further addition was made till the seventeenth century, when Bayer, Hevelius, and other astronomers, formed many constellations in the hitherto uncharted regions of the southern heavens, and marked off portions of some of the large or ill-defined ancient constellations into new constellations.* Many of these latter, however, were never generally recognised, and are now either obsolete or have had their rather clumsy names abbreviated into more convenient forms. Since the middle of the 18th century, when La Caille added thirteen names in the southern hemisphere, and sub-divided the unwieldy Argo into Carina, Malus (now Pyxis), Puppis, and Vela, no new constellations have been recognised. Originally, constellations had no boundaries, the position of a star in the 'head,' 'foot,' &c., of the figure answering the needs of the time; the first boundaries were drawn by Bode in 1801. For List of Constellations, see last page.

Star Nomenclature.—The star names given on the last but one page have, for the most part, been handed down from classical or early mediæval times, but only a few of them are now in use, a system devised by Bayer in 1603 having been found more convenient, viz., the designation of the bright stars of each constellation by the small letters of the Greek alphabet, α, β, γ, &c., the brightest star being usually made α, the second brightest β—though sometimes, as in Ursa Major, sequence, or position in the constellation figure, was preferred. When the Greek letters were exhausted, the small Roman letters, a, b, c, &c., were employed, and after these the capitals, A, B, &c.—mostly in the Southern constellations. The capitals after Q were not required, so Argelander utilised R, S, T, &c., to denote *variable* stars in each constellation, a convenient index to their peculiarity (see also p. ix).

The fainter stars are most conveniently designated by their numbers in some star catalogue. By universal consent, the numbers of Flamsteed's British Catalogue (published 1725) are adopted for stars to which no Greek letter has been assigned, while for stars not appearing in that catalogue, the numbers of some other catalogue are utilised. The usual method of denoting any lettered or numbered star in a constellation is to give the letter, or Flamsteed number, followed by the genitive case of the Latin name of the constellation: thus α of Canes Venatici is described as α Canum Venaticorum. These genitives are given in the list of constellations on the last page, facing the cover.

Flamsteed catalogued his stars by constellations, numbering them in the order of their 'Right Ascension'—that is, the number of hours and minutes they southed after the southing of a certain zero point among the stars (p. 2). Most modern catalogues are on this convenient basis (ignoring constellations), as the stars follow a regular sequence. But when Right Ascensions are nearly the same, especially if the Declinations (p. 3) differ much, in time 'precession' may change the order: Flamsteed's 20, 21, 22, 23 Herculis, numbered 200 years ago, now south in the order 22, 20, 23, 21.

For convenience of reference, the more important star catalogues are designated by recognised contractions: thus "B.A.C. 2130" is at once known by astronomers to denote the star numbered 2130 in the British Association Star Catalogue of 1845. In most star catalogues a number is assigned to each star included in them, whether it has a Greek or other letter, or not. Thus, *Vega* is α Lyræ, 3 Lyræ (Flamsteed's number), and (constellations ignored) Groombridge 2616. A list of some of the best-known catalogues, and their contractions, is given on p. vii.

Constellation Boundaries.—Bode's boundaries were not treated as standard, and charts and catalogues issued before 1930 may differ as to which of two adjacent constellations a star belongs. Thus Flamsteed numbered in Camelopardus several stars now allocated to Auriga, and by error he sometimes numbered a star in two constellations. Bayer, also, sometimes assigned to the same star a Greek letter in two constellations, ancient astronomers having stated that it belonged to both constellation figures: thus β Tauri $= \gamma$ Aurigæ, and α Andromedæ $= \delta$ Pegasi.

To remedy this inconvenience, in 1930 the International Astronomical Union standardised the boundaries along the Jan. 1, 1875, arcs of Right Ascension and Declination, having regard, as far as possible, to the boundaries of the best star atlases. The work had already been done by Gould on that basis for most of the S. Hemisphere constellations.

C * Antinous, added in A.D. 130 by the Emperor Adrian, was long combined with Aquila as 'Aquila et Antinous.'

The I.A.U. Boundaries.—These do not change their positions among the stars, thus objects can always be correctly located, though, owing to precession, the arcs of Right Ascension and Declination of to-day no longer follow the boundaries, and are steadily departing from them. After some 12,900 years, however, these arcs will begin to return towards the boundaries, and 12,900 years after this, on completing the 25,800-year precessional period (p.6) will approximate to them, but not exactly coincide.

II. NOTES ON ASTRONOMICAL TERMS.

The Star Sphere, a convenient term used in speaking of the heavenly bodies and their relative positions, derives its name from the appearance of the heavens to an observer: he seems to be at the centre of a vast hollow sphere (half of it unseen, beneath his feet), which revolves round the Earth once each day. The stars seem permanently fixed to the inside surface of this sphere—their vast distances practically nullify their actual rapid motions—and are known as *fixed stars*, in contrast to the 'wandering stars' or *planets*, which move among the others. Rather more than half the star sphere is seen at one time, as refraction adds a strip equal to the breadth of the Moon's disc in the sky.

The Celestial Poles and Equator.—The pivots, as it were, on which the star sphere revolves, are called the *Celestial Poles*; they are directly overhead at the Terrestrial Poles. Half way between them is the great circle of the *Celestial Equator* or *Equinoctial*, which passes directly overhead at every point on the Terrestrial equator.

Culmination: Southing.—A celestial object *culminates* when it reaches its highest point above the observer's horizon. In the N. Terrestrial hemisphere, *souths* is used in the same sense, as culmination is always at the instant when the object is due south of the N. Pole; in the S. Terrestrial hemisphere, objects culminate when due north of the S. Pole.

Rising and Setting of Stars.—At the Terrestrial Equator, the Celestial poles lie on the horizon; all the stars remain above the horizon for half a day, and their rising and setting are at right angles to the horizon. At the Terrestrial poles, on the other hand, the Celestial equator coincides with the horizon, parallel with which the stars move in circles, neither rising nor setting, the other half of the star sphere being never seen.

In intermediate latitudes there is every variety between these extremes, but always some stars never set (and a corresponding area round the opposite Pole never rises), also the paths in the sky cut the horizon obliquely—all in proportion to the observer's nearness to, or remoteness from, the Terrestrial Pole or Equator.

The stars which rise and set always do so at the same points on the horizon—unlike the Sun, Moon, and planets, which rise and set at different points on successive days. In temperate latitudes, especially, those of them nearest the observer's Celestial pole rise far north (S. hemisphere, *south*), and are above the horizon most of the twenty-four hours; as distance from the Celestial pole increases, they rise further and further south (or *north*), and their time above the horizon diminishes, till, for the stars furthest south (or *north*), they set again a very short time after rising. Stars on the Celestial equator rise due E., set due W., and are 12 hrs., above the horizon, all over the Earth—except at the Poles

Stars rise, 'south' or 'north', and set, at a given hour *only once a year*, always on or about the same date, for they culminate nearly four minutes earlier each day, and make 366¼ revolutions in 365¼ solar days. On one day in the year 'southing,' &c., occurs *twice*, for when a star souths at 12·1 a.m. it will south again at 11·57 p.m. the same day. This occurs with the Superior planets (p. 32) also—Mars, and the asteroids in general, about each second year—their mean daily motions being less than the Earth's. Mars and Venus, however, may not south at all on one day in the year.

The Stars that never set or rise.—Stars never set when their distance from the Celestial pole is less than the latitude of the observer on the earth. Or, stars with Declination (p. 3) greater than the observer's *Co-latitude* his latitude subtracted from 90°) never set; the corresponding area round the opposite Pole never rises.

The Ecliptic is another important great circle on the star sphere, which intersects the Celestial equator at an angle of 23½° (the *Obliquity of the Ecliptic**), and lies in a plane which passes through the centres of the Sun and the Earth: it represents the yearly path of the Sun's centre on the star sphere, as seen from the Earth, or the Earth's as seen from the Sun: it is shown in Maps 3-14. *The Ecliptic Poles*, the points on the star sphere 90° from the Ecliptic, (about 23½° from the Terrestrial poles), are at R.A. 18h., and 6h., and Dec. 66½° N., and S., respectively.

The Ecliptic and its poles are 'sensibly' (*i.e.*, for ordinary purposes) fixed on the star sphere, but change slightly in centuries. The former also represents (*a*) the central line of the Zodiac (p.3); (*b*) the average path of the Moon, Mercury, and Venus, on the star sphere (pp. 8, 33), but not those of the other major planets—though these are always *near* the Ecliptic, except Pluto.

The Vernal Equinox or **First Point of Aries**, the zero for the celestial measurements corresponding to terrestrial longitude, is the point of intersection on the star sphere, at any moment, of the Celestial Equator and the Ecliptic, at or near the point where the Sun crosses the former from S. to N., about March 21.

This point—the *True* or *Apparent Equinox*, or *The Equinox* of any date—moves westward on the Ecliptic 1/7th second of arc every day, but is nevertheless the most convenient point for the purpose, as the Sun's position in the sky, measured from it, remains practically the same on a given day of the year for thousands of years, by the leap year arrangements of the calendar, though those of the stars slowly change. 'Vernal Equinox,' *when used in connection with measurements*, always means this moving True Equinox, but the *literal* Vernal (Spring, p. 6) equinox is the instant when the Sun's centre actually crosses the Celestial equator.

The Mean Equinox, is the True Equinox corrected for the irregularity (max. ± 1¼ secs.) called nutation in Right Ascension (p. 7). Positions in star charts and catalogues are measured from it, at the time when the Sun's mean longitude is 280°, about Jan. 1: thus for 1950, the star positions are called 'mean places for 1950·0'—'·0' after a year always indicates the 280° start.

The position of the First Point of Aries is about nine moon-breadths W. of the end of a line drawn first from α Andromedæ to γ Pegasi (which form one side of the 'Square of Pegasus') then extended downwards for the same length.

*Mean, Jan. 1, 1950, 23° 26′ 45″ (annual decrease 0″·47), may vary 9″ from mean.

The Meridian is that great circle on the star sphere which passes through both Celestial poles, and through the zenith of the observer; it always meets the horizon due south and north of the Pole and the observer. *On the meridian, meridian passage, returns to the meridian*, have the same meaning as culmination, or transit (see below).

Transit.—A celestial object *Transits* when it crosses *(a)* the meridian of a place—*Upper Transit* = culmination: or *(b)* any selected line on the star sphere: The term is also used for a meridian or spot crossing the centre of a disc. *Lower Transit*, or *Lower Culmination*, of a 'circumpolar' star which never sets, is at the opposite side of the Pole, twelve sideral hours after upper transit, when the star is nearest the horizon.

Transit also denotes the passing, as a black circular spot, of *Mercury* and *Venus* across the Sun's disc; or of a satellite or its shadow (p. 34) across the disc of its primary. *Ingress* is the entrance on to the disc; *egress*, the departure.

Celestial Positions.—As the star sphere has an Equator and Poles, taking the meridian through the Vernal equinox as zero, the position of any object in the sky can be indicated in the way places on the Earth are located by their latitude N. or S. of the Equator, and their longitude from Greenwich. The corresponding astronomical terms, however, are *Declination* and *Right Ascension*, ancient astronomers having unfortunately (for similarity of nomenclature) used the terms latitude and longitude to denote measurements referred to the Ecliptic, instead of the Celestial equator.

Declination (contracted δ, or *Dec.*) corresponds to terrestial latitude; it is measured in degrees North or South of the Celestial equator. The International Astronomical Union recommend the use of + and − instead of N. and S.

North Polar Distance (contracted *N.P.D.* or *P.D.*), measured in degrees (0° to 180°) from the N. celestial pole, is sometimes used instead of Declination, as it obviates the use of negative signs, and all chance of error with N. and S.

Right Ascension (contracted α, *R.A.*, or Æ), corresponds to terrestial longitude, it is measured eastwards, or counter-clockwise, on the Celestial equator from the True equinox, sometimes in degrees (0°-360°), usually in sidereal hrs. (*h.*), minutes (*m.*), seconds (*s.*); 1 h. = 15°, 1° = 4 m. Every observatory has a clock regulated to this sidereal time (p.9); when it shows 0 hrs. the True equinox is on the observatory's meridian.

As the True Equinox culminates daily, it is easy to note how many hours, minutes, and seconds elapse from its culmination to that of any other object; this interval is the *Right Ascension* of the object. Objects that culminate at the same instant as the True Equinox have R.A. 0 hrs.; those culminating 1 hour later, R.A. 1 hr.; those 2 hrs. later, R.A. 2 hrs., and so on up to 24 hrs., the 0 hrs. of a new sidereal day: of course minutes and seconds are also used.

Right Ascension hours, &c., are very slightly shorter than those of ordinary mean time, the 24-hr. sidereal day being only 23 hrs. 56 min. 4 secs. mean time in length, or about four minutes shorter than the mean solar day. (See p. 8).

Hour and Declination Circles.—An *Hour Circle*, or a *Declination Circle*, is the great circle passing through a celestial object and the Celestial poles; the former term is preferable, as the latter is liable to be confused with 'Declination Parallels,' which are not great circles. These terms are also applied to the graduated circles on 'equatorial' telescopes (p. 46); the hour circle is graduated in R.A. hrs. and minutes, and the Declination circle in degrees.

Colures.—*The Equinoctial Colure* is the great circle of R.A. 0 hrs. and 12 hrs.; it passes through the Celestial Poles, the First Point of Aries, and 180° of celestial longitude. *The Solstitial Colure* is the great circle of R.A. 6 hrs. and 18 hrs.; it passes through both the Celestial and Ecliptic Poles, and through the *Solstitial Points**.

The Zodiac (literally 'circle of the animals,' most of the signs represent living creatures) is the belt of the sky 8-9° on each side of the Ecliptic, within which the Sun, Moon, and the planets known to the ancients are found.

Starting yearly at the First Point of Aries, it is divided into the twelve 'Signs of the Zodiac' (see symbols, p. xvi)—each 30° of longitude on the Ecliptic—which, however, do *not* coincide with the constellations of the same name, although they did so some 2300 years ago when the First Point was named, precession having carried them westwards some 30°, or a whole sign.

The Invariable Plane of the Solar System, passing through the System's centre of gravity, forms an unvarying reference plane, as it does not change its position in space owing to mutual planetary perturbations, as the Ecliptic does. Inclined 1° 35′ to the Ecliptic plane, 7° to Sun's equator; longitude of ascending node 106° 35′ (epoch 1850).

The Fundamental Plane, in occultations and eclipses, is that passing through the centre of the Earth at right angles to the line drawn from the star, or the centre of the Sun, through the centre of the Moon.

Alternative Reference Circles.—The Celestial Equator, though the most convenient for finding or recording positions on the star sphere, by R.A. and Dec., is an unsuitable reference circle for many purposes, and other great circles and reference planes are used instead. The position of an object is indicated, with respect to the :—

1.	Celestial Equator ...	by its	Declination, and Right Ascension, from the Vernal equinox	(p. 3)
2.	Ecliptic, (*a*) from the Earth's centre	„	Geocentric Latitude, and Longitude, „ „ „	(p. 4)
3.	„ (*b*) „ Sun's ...	„	Heliocentric „ „ „ „ „	(p. 4)
4.	Horizon of the observer ...	„	Altitude, and Azimuth, from the N. or S. point ...	„
5.	Meridian	„	Hour Angle from the meridian, and Declination from the Celest. Eqr.	„
6.	Hour Circle or Declination Circle	„	Position Angle, from the North Point	„
7.	Galactic Plane, or Milky Way ...	„	Galactic Latitude, and Longitude, from node on Celestial equator	(p. 4)
8.	Sun's Equator	„	Heliographic „ „ „ arbitrary zero ...	„
9.	Planet's or Moon's Equator ...	„	Planetographic „ „ (Seleno-, Zeno-, &c., -graphic, see p. 4)	
10.	Limb of the Sun, Moon, or Planet	„	Distance (*a*) from the North Point; (*b*) from the Vertex	(p. 5)

Thus there are several kinds of astronomical latitude and longitude. But unless qualified by an adjective, in astronomy these terms usually mean *Geocentric Latitude and Longitude*, referring objects to the Ecliptic and the Earth's centre.

* In Celestial longitude 90°, 270° (or R.A. 6h., 18h.), and Dec. 23½° N. and S.

Geocentric Positions.—All astronomical observations are necessarily *topocentric—i.e.*, made from a point on the Earth's surface—but for simplicity, the figures in Tables are always *geocentric*, that is, calculated as if bodies were observed from the Earth's centre. The reason is that the topocentric values differ with the position of the observer (except for stars—too distant for appreciable change), but are easily obtained for any place from the geocentric values.

Angular and linear distances are in general measured from centre to centre of the bodies concerned, and those calculated as seen from the Sun, or a planet, are also given for the centres (heliocentric, &c., values, see below).

Latitude and Longitude (unqualified by an adjective) refer celestial objects to the Earth's centre and the Ecliptic instead of to the Celestial Equator, and therefore do not correspond to geographical latitude and longitude. They are used for calculations involving angular distance from the Sun, as seen from the Earth, of planets and comets, —phase, opposition, &c.; the same definitions, but referred to the Sun's centre, instead of the Earth's, are termed *heliocentric* latitude and longitude. The Earth's heliocentric longitude is the Sun's geocentric longitude +180°.

The *Longitude* of a celestial object is the angle in degrees (0°-360°) measured eastwards, between the First Point of Aries (♈) and the foot of a perpendicular drawn from the object to the Ecliptic. Similarly, the *Latitude* of a celestial object is its distance in degrees N. or S. of the Ecliptic, measured on an arc at right angles to the Ecliptic.

Longitude and Right Ascension both start from the First Point of Aries, and both are measured eastwards, but the former is measured in degrees along the *Ecliptic*; the latter along the *Celestial Equator*, in hours, &c. (but 1 hour R.A. is exactly 15°, 4 minutes exactly 1°). As the plane of the Ecliptic lies at an angle to that of the Celestial Equator, however, a movement of 1° in longitude does not exactly correspond to 1° (*i.e.*, 1/15th hour, or 4 minutes) in R.A., because *(a)* the direction of measurement is different, and *(b)* the respective degrees may differ in length on the star sphere—as, for instance, where the 'great circle' degrees of the Ecliptic traverse the narrower R.A. degrees measured on the parallel of Dec. 20°. The 'precession' (p. 6) of the First Point of Aries continually changes longitudes, the longitude of the perihelion of each major planet increasing some 2° per century; but latitudes alter very little, as the Ecliptic is almost fixed on the star sphere (p. 2).

Latitude, similarly, differs from Declination. Both are measured on arcs of great circles on the star sphere, but whereas all Declination circles pass through the Celestial poles, all circles of Latitude pass through the Ecliptic poles, 23½° from the Celestial poles. The parallels of latitude, therefore, are always inclined to those of Declination, and a motion of 1° in latitude is never exactly 1° in declination—except along the Solstitial colure (p. 3), which intersects the Ecliptic and the Celestial equator at right angles, and passes through both the Celestial and Ecliptic poles.

Heliographic, Selenographic, and Planetographic latitude and longitude refer objects to the equators of the Sun, Moon, and planets, respectively—the equators with reference to the axis of rotation. They thus exactly correspond to geographical latitude and longitude, and positions are denoted by them in the same way—by latitude N. or S. of the equator in degrees, and by longitude on that equator from a zero meridian. Their chief use is for recording the positions of markings on the surface, such as spots, lunar craters, &c. *Areographic*, *Zenographic*, and *Saturnigraphic*, are the terms for Mars, Jupiter, and Saturn, respectively.

The zero meridian on the Moon is that of the 'mean centre' of the disc, and longitude is measured E. or W. of it in degrees; for Mars and Jupiter, see the *N.A.* On the Sun, Jupiter, and Saturn, there being no fixed markings, zero meridians can only be arbitrary. The Sun's is based on an assumed unvarying sidereal rotation period of 25·38 days (see p. 26); the longitude is measured (0° to 360°) from left to right looking south, across the non-inverted apparent disc—*i e.*, in the direction of the Sun's rotation.

Measured on the star sphere, instead of the body's surface, *helio-*, *seleno-*, &c., *-graphic* latitude and longitude correspond to solar, lunar, &c., Declination and R.A., but *heliocentric*, *areocentric*, &c., latitude and longitude are usually employed for this sense. They are used for indicating the position of the Sun's equator with reference to the centre of the disc, the amount of lunar libration, openness of Saturn's ring's, &c.—published annually in the *Nautical Almanac*.

Galactic latitude and longitude refer objects to the Galactic Plane (p. 10) or mean plane of the Milky Way—important for problems regarding the distribution of the stars on the star sphere. Galactic latitude is measured in degrees N. or S. of the Galactic Plane; Galactic longitude, along the Galactic plane (0° to 360°), from its intersection with the Celestial equator about R.A. 18h. 40m., and measured in the same direction as R.A. (but see note, p. 10).

Altitude, Azimuth, Meridian, &c.—These refer the positions of celestial objects to the observer's horizon. The *altitude* of a heavenly body is its vertical angular distance in degrees above the horizon; its *azimuth*, the horizontal angular distance in degrees between the observer's S. or N. point, and the foot of a perpendicular drawn from the object to the horizon. In the N. hemisphere, azimuth is usually measured from south (0°) westwards, *i.e.*, from the *meridian*, already defined as the great circle passing through the Celestial poles and the north and south points of the observer. The *zenith* and *nadir* are the points in the sky directly over the observer's head and below his feet, respectively, *i.e*, the poles of the horizon; the *prime vertical* is the great circle passing through the zenith and the observer's east and west points, corresponding to the Solstitial colure in R.A. and Declination. The *amplitude* is the arc of the horizon between the E. or W. point, and the foot of the vertical circle passing through the object. (Amplitude of variable stars, see p. 12).

Hour Angle.—The hour angle of a celestial object refers it to the *meridian* of the observer; it is used in calculating an object's altitude or azimuth, the time of its rising or setting, &c., and may be defined as the difference between its Right Ascension and the hour of R.A. on the meridian at the time of an observation, or the angle which the hour-circle passing through the object makes with the meridian—for most purposes expressed in hrs., &c., of sidereal time. It is measured westwards or clockwise from the meridian south of the Pole (S. Hemisphere, N. of the Pole).

Position Angle: North Point.—*The Position Angle* of a planet's axis, or of any line on the star sphere, is its inclination to the hour circle (p. 3) passing through the centre of the object. This circle is the most suitable one for reference, as, unlike the horizon, it is stationary with respect to the stars, and being perpendicular to the horizon at the instant of culmination, can be used for finding the inclination to the horizon at other times (see diagram, p. 39). *The North Point* is the point on the hour-circle nearest the N. Celestial pole, in the field of view.

(*a*). **Double Stars.** The position angle of a double star is the angle which the line joining the components makes with the hour-circle passing through the brighter star of the pair. This angle is measured from the *North Point* (or point on the hour-circle nearest the North Celestial Pole, in the field of view) from 0° to 360°, going round by E., S., and W. (See p. 39).

(*b*) **Sun's or Planet's axis.** The position angle is measured to it from the North Point on the disc. This varies throughout the year; but for the Sun, on the same date it is about the same every year (see the *N.A.*, and diagram on p. 40). The angle is measured from 0° to 360° for the Moon and planets, as in (*a*); but for the Sun, E. (+) or W. (−) of the hour circle.

Limb, Cusps, Vertex.—The *Limb* is the edge of the Sun's, Moon's, or a planet's disc; the *Cusps*, the horns of the crescent (less than half-illumined) Moon, Mercury, or Venus. The *Vertex*, sometimes used for occultations, is the point on the limb furthest above the observer's horizon; distances from the vertex are counted eastwards from 0° to 360°.

Opposition.—Mars, and the outer planets (p. 32), are in *Opposition* (symbol ☍), when 180° of longitude (or 12 hrs. R.A.) away from the Sun on the star sphere: this occurs annually (Jupiter, 1·1 yrs.), but biennially for Mars and most asteroids. They are then on the meridian about midnight, and nearer the Earth than when not in opposition.

An opposition is 'favourable' when the Earth and the planet are near the point where their orbits most closely approach, and as this point is always about the same longitude, favourable oppositions *always take place about the same date in the year* (given on pp. 32 to 34), and the favourableness or otherwise of any opposition can always be judged by its nearness to, or remoteness from, that date; the least favourable are six months later.

Conjunction: Syzygy.—A celestial object is in *conjunction* (symbol ☌) with another celestial body when their longitudes are the same, but the term may also denote equality in Right Ascension—as in *N.A.* 'Phenomena,' for some objects. Mercury and Venus are in *Inferior Conjunction* with the Sun, if the conjunction occurs when they are on the side of the Sun nearest the Earth: in *Superior Conjunction* if they are on the far side of the Sun, with the Sun between the planet and the Earth. The Moon is in *Syzygy* when in conjunction or opposition, *i.e.*, when New or Full.

Appulse.—An appulse is the near approach of one celestial body to another: the term is also used for approaching culmination, conjunction, &c.; as, the appulse of a star to the meridian, of the Moon to the Earth's shadow.

Orbital Motions.—The orbital motion of a planet or comet round the Sun, or of a satellite round its primary, is *Direct* when from W. to E.; *Retrograde*, when from E. to W.: similarly the seeming motions of the planets among the stars, as seen from the Earth. A planet is *Stationary* when its movement is reversing to the opposite direction.

A planet or comet is in *Perihelion* (π) when at the point in its orbit nearest the Sun; in *Aphelion*, when at the point most distant; in *Quadrature* (□), when 90° in longitude from the Sun. The Moon and the planets are in *Perigee* when at the point in their orbits nearest the Earth; in *Apogee*, when at the point most distant. *Pericentre* and *Apocentre* are the corresponding general terms for a satellite with respect to its primary: for Mars, Jupiter, Saturn, *Perimartium*, *Perijove*, and *Perisaturnium*, are used. A planet's *Elongation* from the Sun is the angular distance in degrees as seen from the Earth: the *Greatest Elongation* of Mercury and Venus is when that angular distance reaches a maximum—not necessarily the very greatest. A comet in *Recession* is moving away from the Sun, after perihelion.

Elliptical Orbits.—*The Major Axis* (symbol for semi-major axis, a) is the greatest length, usually expressed in Astron. Units; midway in it is the *Centre* of the ellipse. *The Minor Axis* (semi-minor, b) is the line drawn through the centre at right angles, the greatest breadth: *the Focus*—occupied by the Primary (p. 7)—one of two points, equidistant from the centre, such that the sum of their distances from the foci to any point on the orbit is constant, and equal to the major axis.

The Eccentricity (e) is the ratio, to the semi-major axis, of the focus-to-centre distance; *the Radius Vector* (r), the line joining the centre of a planet, comet, or satellite, to that of its primary, usually given in A.Us. *The Apsides* (plural of apsis) are the extremities of the major axis—the points of perihelion, aphelion, perigee, &c.; the *Line of Apsides*, that axis extended indefinitely.

The Nodes are the points where a planet's or comet's orbit intersects the Ecliptic on the star sphere—*i.e.*, when the object is in the Ecliptic plane:* where the object crosses from S. to N. is the *Ascending node* (☊), from N. to S. the *Descending node* (☋).

The Anomaly [*true*] (v) is the actual perihelion-focus-planet angle, measured in the direction of the planet's motion; the *Mean Anomaly* (M), that angle calculated for uniform, not actual, motion: the *Eccentric Anomaly* (μ) is derived from it, $M = \mu - e \sin \mu$.

The Elements of an Object are seven factors required to determine (*a*) Position in space of its orbit—1, the semi-major axis: 2, the eccentricity: 3, the inclination to the Ecliptic: 4, the longitude of the ascending node: 5, the longitude of the perihelion: (*b*) Position of the object at any time—6, the orbital period; 7, epoch (position at a known date); or, time of perihelion passage.

These are the *Heliocentric or Fixed Elements*—the object's relation to its primary, the Sun, ignoring other planets. *The Barycentric Elements* are those referred to the *Barycentre*, or centre of *mass* of the Solar System, instead of the Sun, which give a better average orbit—though the heliocentric one corrected for *perturbations* (disturbances) by the other planets is more accurate.

The Osculating Orbit is that which a planet or comet would pursue if, at some specified instant, the *Epoch of Osculation*, all the planets should cease to attract that body, and leave it free to move under the attraction of the Sun alone.

---

* In an elliptical orbit, the node-perihelion-node angle is always less, in degrees, than node-aphelion-node, but the difference is trifling if the eccentricity is small, as in the principal planets. Also a planet attains its maximum heliocentric latitude, above the plane of the Ecliptic, halfway between the nodes—at about 90° longitude, for the principal planets, which have nearly-circular orbits.

Planetary Periods.—The *Sidereal Period* of a planet, its true period of revolution round the Sun, is the time it takes to make a complete circuit round the star sphere, from star to star again, as seen from the Sun, not the Earth.

The *Synodic* or *Apparent Period* of a planet is the interval *as seen from the Earth's centre*, between successive oppositions (or conjunctions) with the Sun; or, for a satellite, between successive similar elongations or conjunctions with its primary. The *Anomalistic Period* is the interval from any point in a planet's orbit to the same point again —for instance between successive returns to perihelion or to aphelion; this period, and also that of successive returns to the same node, is practically the same as the planet's sidereal period.

The Synodic period determines the dates of opposition, conjunction, &c.; the Sidereal period, those of the opening and closing of Saturn's rings, also of the recurrence of a planet's greatest N. or S. latitude—important for observing Mercury.

Secular Acceleration.—An apparent shortening of the periods of Sun, Moon, and planets, as compared with those calculated on the basis of uniform motion—a shortening so minute as to be only detectable in 'secular' periods, *i.e.*, those of the order of a century; it is expressed by the number of seconds of arc per century the object is ahead of the uniform-motion position. It is simplest to suppose that the periods do not change, but that our day, the unit of measurement, is slowly lengthening (partly through tidal friction) by some 1/1000th of a second per century, on the average, so that after a century the number of days in a year is a fraction less than before. 6″ of the Moon's acceleration, however, is due to other causes than the lengthening day.

Secular acceleration of the Moon, about 10″ per century (1337 sidereal months); *of the Sun*, about 1″·5 per century.

Rotation Periods.—The *Sidereal* rotation period of the Sun, or of a planet or satellite, its true period of axial rotation, is the interval between a star's successive returns to the same meridian on the Sun's or planet's surface.

The *Synodic* or *Apparent* rotation period of the Sun, or of a planet, is the interval, as seen from the Earth's centre, between successive returns of a meridian on its surface to the centre of the disc. The apparent rotation periods of the Superior planets merely vary to and fro a very little on each side of the sidereal rotation periods.

The Sun and the planets—Uranus excepted—have actually the same 'direct' rotation as the Earth (from W. to E. looking south), but to us are seen revolving from E. to W., because the hemisphere we see faces in the opposite direction from our hemisphere.

The Equinoxes and Solstices.—*The Vernal and Autumnal Equinoxes* are two days in the year on which, everywhere on the Earth, day and night are equal, whence the name. The instant when the Sun crosses the Celestial equator into the N. Celestial hemisphere, on March 19-22, determines the Vernal or Spring equinox (also the solar year, p. 8); this instant may be distinguished as the *literal* Vernal equinox, in contrast to the moving conventional Vernal equinox used for R.A. The Autumnal equinox is on or about Sept. 23, when he recrosses into the S. Celestial hemisphere.

The Solstices are on the longest and shortest days of the year, on or about June 21 and Dec. 22, when the Sun attains his greatest angular distance N. or S. of the Celestial Equator,* and 'stands' for an instant before turning back; the Equinoxes and Solstices always keep to these dates, by the Leap year arrangements of the calendar. In the South terrestial hemisphere the seasons are reversed, Sept. 23 being the spring equinox, Dec. 22 the summer solstice.

Precession of the Equinoxes is the annual occurrence of the (literal) vernal equinox, about Mar. 21st, nearly 20½ minutes (1/25,800th year) before the Earth has made a *complete* orbital revolution round the Sun, so that each year, at that instant, he crosses the Celestial equator at a slightly different point. 25,800 years will elapse before he again crosses at that point. As the result of precession, every star—except those less than 23½° from the Ecliptic poles —passes through every hour of R.A. from 0h. to 24h., once every 25,800 years; also the Declinations, every 12,900 years, swing to and fro 47° (23½° × 2), greatly changing the stars visible at a given place, or season.

Precession is due to a continuous minute tilting of the Earth's axis by the Sun and Moon, which causes the Celestial poles and equator (always overhead at those of the Earth) to change their places continuously among the stars in harmony, so that each successive moment the Celestial equator intersects the Ecliptic at a slightly different point (in the opposite direction to the Earth's orbital motion) of the one it would occupy if left undisturbed. Thus precession is continuous, not a yearly jump.

The tilting is the result of the bulge at the Earth's equator, inclined considerably to the plane of her orbit round the Sun, and also to that of the Moon. Half of the bulge is above and half below the plane of the Earth's orbit, part of it considerably, and the Sun's and Moon's pull on the elevated (or depressed) portion nearest them is stronger than their pull on the more distant depressed (or elevated) portion opposite. This tends to tilt the Earth's axis towards the attracting body, and, by the gyroscopic law applicable to the rapidly-rotating Earth, causes the Earth's axis (which would otherwise always point to the same position on the star sphere) and the Celestial poles to rotate round the poles of her orbit (*i.e.*, those of the Ecliptic) in circles 23½° distant from them, and in a period of 25,800 years, displacing the Vernal Equinox in the opposite direction to her orbital motion.

The Amount of Precession.—Every day the Celestial equator intersects the Ecliptic at a point about 1/7th of a second of arc W. of the position the day before at the same hour, so that R.A. is measured from a slightly different point on the star sphere each day, and each March 19-22, the *literal* Vernal equinox is 50″·26 W. of its position a year before—about 3 seconds of R.A., or 1/37 of the angular breadth of the Moon, or 1° in 71·62 years, or 1°·396 per century. Thus the First Point of Aries—which some 2200 years ago was in the constellation of Aries—is now 30° to the west, in the constellation of Pisces. Star charts sooner or later cease to give reasonably accurate positions, owing to this change in the zero-point on the Ecliptic, amounting to a whole degree, or two Moon-breadths, in about 72 years.

In Star Catalogues the precession in R.A. and Declination represents the co-ordinates of the total annual linear precessional motion of each star along the Ecliptic. Near the Celestial poles, the figures make it seem very great, but as regards actual change on the star sphere they are misleading. Among the closely-crowded nearly-converged hour-circles of R.A. near the poles, a movement of many seconds in R.A., as measured along the very small Declination parallels, is only a few seconds when converted into Equatorial great-circle measure. In converting a star position for precession, *add like signs, subtract unlike signs*

* At the Solstitial Points, p. 3.

Nutation.—The precessional path traced on the star sphere by the Celestial Pole is a wavy line varying slightly from a true circle. This irregularity is called *Nutation*, being, as it were, a 'nodding' of the Celestial poles to and from from the Ecliptic Poles, and though minute—about 9″ on each side of the mean, or 18″ in $18\frac{2}{3}$ years—perceptibly modifies the precessional displacement in R.A. and Declination. The Earth's axis passes the mean position about 2800 times in the 25,800-year period. Nutation is due to the Moon's being sometimes above and sometimes below the Ecliptic, and so not always pulling on the Earth's equatorial protuberance in the same direction as the Sun.

The above figures for nutation give the *Nutation in Obliquity*—the total motion of the Celestial Poles to and fro from the Ecliptic poles. *Nutation in R.A.* is its co-ordinate measured along the Celestial equator; and *Nutation in Longitude*, or the *Equation of the Equinoxes*, its co-ordinate measured along the Ecliptic.

Variation of Latitude.—Star Declinations show minute irregular cyclic changes up to 0″·04, due to the Earth's Poles wandering round her mean rotation-axis counter-clockwise—the combined result of periods arising from (*a*) that axis differing from her axis of figure (432 dys.); (*b*) meteorological changes (1 yr.): max. departure from mean, 60 ft.

Primary, Satellite.—Two (or more) celestial bodies which revolve round a common centre of gravity are *physically connected*: the larger is the *Primary* (the Sun, for planets and comets), the smaller, the *Satellite*—or for stars the *Companion*, which implies visual proximity, but not necessarily physical connection. Stars with motions similar in amount and direction on the star sphere (Moving Clusters, p. 11), are also taken as being physically connected.

Phase denotes (*a*) the extent to which the disc of the Moon or a planet, as seen from the Earth, is illumined or not illumined by the Sun—in the latter case, its *Dark Phase*, or *Defect of Illumination*. (*b*) Appearance or configuration, as in the *N.A.* 'Phases of the eclipses of Jupiter's satellites'; *Aspect* is also used in this sense. (*c*) The stage of progress towards maximum or minimum of a variable star, + denoting the No. of days towards the former, − towards the latter. (*d*) In any periodic phenomenon, the fraction of its period which has elapsed since the last occurrence of a given aspect.

Dark Phase is greatest in the Superior planets when they are in *Quadrature* (□), *i.e.*, 90° longitude (or 6 h. R.A.). from the Sun, and therefore on the meridian about 6 a.m. or 6 p.m. As phase decreases with increasing distance from the Earth, it is only observable on Mars, which becomes *gibbous*—*i.e.*, not quite a full disc—and on Jupiter, to the extent of a slight shade along the limb furthest from the Sun. On the other outer planets it is wholly unmeasurable.

Albedo.—When sunlight falls on a planet, part is absorbed, the rest reflected: the *Albedo* of the planet is the ratio, to the total sunlight received, of the light it reflects in *all* directions: this cannot be determined from full phase alone, and different formulæ give rather different results in some cases, see the Table on p. viii.

Refraction.—All observations of position have to be corrected for atmospheric refraction, which raises a celestial object higher in the sky than its true position, by fully ½° at the horizon, decreasing to 0° at the zenith (Table p. x).

Aberration.—The velocity of light is not infinite compared with the Earth's orbital velocity, and the two velocities combined results in a small variable displacement (max. 20″·47 on each side) of celestial objects from their true positions; the Earth's rotation causes a lesser aberration. At the end of a sidereal year, however, a fixed star returns to its original place, so far as aberration is concerned.

Apparent: True.—In astronomy 'things are not what they seem,' in literal fact. Movements actually seen, and positions read off, by the observer, are in general not the real movements or positions, owing to refraction, aberration, Earth's orbital motion, &c., and are therefore called *Apparent* or observed movements or positions—Apparent Time, Noon, R.A., motion, &c. The *True* (real) values are 'reduced' from the apparent ones by eliminating the effects of refraction, and other factors modifying the actual values, but sometimes 'True' = 'Apparent,' as in True Time, True Equinox.

Epoch.—The date for which an astronomical catalogue, chart, or position, &c., has been calculated, as, sooner or later, precession, proper motion, &c., perceptibly change the positions given, and comparison at future epochs would be of little use without this date. The usual date is Jan. 1st of the year; that of 1950 is a standard one.

Ephemeris (plural Ephemerides). Any Table of calculated positions, &c., in connection with a celestial object. The *American Ephemeris* corresponds to the British *Nautical Almanac*, and has some Tables not given in the latter.

Equation.—A small correction on the figures actually observed, to eliminate instrumental, ocular, and other imperfections, grouped together as *Systematic Errors*—i.e., errors that always recur when the observations are repeated under the same conditions, and with the same instruments (*Accidental Errors* are those that do not recur, as from abnormal refraction, &c.). Also a similar correction for orbital irregularity, as in the *Equation of Time*, and *of the Equinoxes* (see above). For the errors of the eye in observing, see an interesting paper in the *J.B.A.A.*, vol. 39, p. 4.

The Personal Equation of the observer affects observations of every kind, and for refined work has to be found by experiment; the transit records of one observer are regularly late or early compared with those of another observer.

Colour and Magnitude Equation, see p. 17. Transits of the same star recorded in the hours after sunset and before sunrise, respectively, also seem to require an equation, a difference of some 0·06 second having been noted.

Fundamental or Clock Stars, are stars the positions, &c., of which have been measured with the utmost care, and which are used as reference points for finding the R.A. of other stars with less labour. The positions of these stars for each day is given in the *N.A.*; they are called 'clock stars' because they are used for regulating the clocks.

Dependencies: a short, and accurate method of measuring positions on star photographs from the *Dependence Centre*—an imaginary point, close to the image of an asteroid or planet, the position of which can be exactly calculated.

A Day is (*a*) the axial rotation-period of the Sun, Moon, or a planet; (*b*) the interval between successive returns of a celestial body to an observer's meridian. With respect to the Sun, or a star, three 'days' are used in astronomy:—

1. *The ordinary Solar Day* of 24 hours—strictly speaking the slightly irregular interval between successive transits of the real Sun, but in practice taken as the unvarying interval between those of an imaginary 'Mean Sun,' adjusted to the *average* solar day. The true solar day is variable to the extent of 51 seconds between the extremes, being 30 seconds over the mean solar day about Dec. 22, and 21 seconds under the mean about Sept. 17. A new day or date on the Earth begins on the *Date Line*—the meridian 180° E. of Greenwich, with deviations for geographical, &c., reasons. *Julian Day, p. 9.*

   The Longest and Shortest Days are at the Solstices, but owing to the difference between Sundial and Mean time (local), and to changes in it resulting from the varying hour of sunset or sunrise in different latitudes, the dates of earliest rising and setting vary from the actual solstices with the latitude. There are two earliests and latests in low latitudes (see p. xii).
2. *The Sidereal Day* (conventional) of 24 sidereal or R.A. hours, the interval between successive transits, *not* of a star but of the ever-moving True Equinox (23 h. 56 m. 4·0905 secs. mean time); it is really the *equinoctial* sidereal day, used in preference to (3) because the Sun's R.A.—being always 0ʰ about March 21—is always about the same on a given day of the year.
3. *The True Sidereal Day*, the interval between successive transits of a star (23 h. 56 m. 4·0996 secs. mean time), is the exact period of the Earth's axial rotation. Each year it falls behind (2) by 3·3 secs. mean time, or exactly 1 day in 25,800 years. As this is nearly 1 hour per 1000 years, the stars familiar to us now as winter, spring, &c, stars will in some 6000 years be those of autumn, winter, &c. The true sidereal day is (irregularly) lengthening about 1/1000th second per century, on the average; in harmony, therefore, the sidereal year, expressed in days, *shortens* about 1/3rd second per century.

A Lunar Day, the interval between successive meridian transits of the Moon, varies from 24 h. 38 m. to 25 h. 6 m., and averages 24 hrs. 51 m.; it determines the tide-interval from high water to high water, which is *half* a lunar day.

Our *Mean Time* (Mean Solar Time) is based on the mean solar day; *True*, or *Apparent Solar Time*, or sundial time—which varies slightly from day to day—on the Sun's actual southings; *Sidereal Time*, on the sidereal day.

The Year.—The *Solar*, *Equinoctial*, or *Tropical Year* (365·2422 solar or 366·2422 sidereal dys) in which the seasons recur, is determined by successive returns of the Sun to the same equinox; or to the same 'tropic' or 'solstitial point,' the point on the star sphere where he attains his greatest distance N. or S. of the Celestial equator, on mid-summer or mid-winter days: 'tropic' also denotes the Declination parallels on the star sphere passing through the solstitial points.

The *Sidereal Year* (365·2564 days) is the interval between successive conjunctions of the Earth with a star, as seen from the Sun; it is the true period of the Earth's orbital revolution round the Sun. (Solar year is 20½ min. less).

The *Anomalistic Year* (365·2596 days) is the mean interval between the Earth's returns to perihelion about Jan. 2; as it varies a day or two on each side of the mean, perihelion may occur twice in a calendar year, or not at all.

The *Julian Year*, used in our calendar, has exactly 365·25 (365¼) days: the fraction is adjusted by having *Calendar Years* of 365 or 366 days, the latter in every fourth year divisible by 4 (leap yr.). All years have been Julian since the Julian year was instituted in 45 B.C., except (*a*) 1582, which by the Gregorian revision of that year had only 355 days (Britain and its American colonies substituted 1752, which had only 355 days instead of 366), and (*b*) 1700, 1800, 1900, restricted to 365 days by the new Gregorian rule omitting leap year in century years not divisible by 400.

The *Lunar Year* (354·3670 days) of twelve lunations, used in the Mahommedan calendar, has twelve months of 29 or 30 days each, based on the *phasis*, or first observation, of each New Moon; it may have 354 or 355 days.

Bessel's Fictitious Year, used in the *N.A.* Mean Star Places, begins at the instant when the Sun's apparent mean longitude is 280°, on Dec. 31st civil date (in the *N.A.* 'Jan. 0,' to which it corresponds), or on Jan. 1st.

The *Eclipse Year* (346·6200 days), the interval between successive returns of the Sun to the same node of the Moon's orbit, is the period of possible recurrence of both solar and lunar eclipses, which can only take place when these bodies are within a small distance from the node. 19 eclipse years are 6585·78 days, almost exactly the same as the ancient 'Saros' cycle of 6585·32 days, (18·03 yrs.), the period after which the same eclipses occur regularly for centuries.

A Planet's Year denotes the period in which it completes one orbital revolution round the Sun.

Lunar Months.—*The Synodic Month* or *Lunation* (mean, 29·53059 days), the period from New Moon to New Moon, or between similar phases, varies between 29¼ and 29¾ days. New Moons recur on the same day of the year every 19 years (subject to leap-year disturbances)—the ancient *Metonic Cycle* of 235 lunations, or 6940 days. But four cycles were found to displace recurrence a whole day, as 235 lunations only amounted to 6939¾ days, so the more accurate *Callippic Cycle* of 6939¾ days × 4 was framed, which adjusted the error on the same principle as leap year.

The Anomalistic Month, from perigee to perigee, 27·55455 days on the average, is the period of the Moon's changes in angular diameter and luminosity, as seen from the Earth; it varies a day or two on each side of the mean.

The Sidereal Month (mean, 27·32166 days), the period in which the Moon circuits the star sphere from transit at the same instant as a star back to transit at the same time with it again, is also the short-term period (p. 38) in which an occultation may recur, or in which the Moon's close proximity will again hinder the observation of a star.

The Nodical Month, or *Draconitic Period* (mean, 27·212220 days), from a node back to the same node again, is also the period in which the Moon again attains her greatest distance N. or S. of the Ecliptic: it varies from about 27 to 27½ days. As the Moon's nodes travel westwards along the Ecliptic about 1½° per month, her path sweeps completely round the star sphere in about 18½ years: the Ecliptic therefore represents the Moon's *average* path on the star sphere.

The Tropical Month (mean, 27·32158 days), the Moon's period from conjunction with the True Equinox back to conjunction again with that Equinox, is the period after which the Moon has again the same longitude.

Sidereal Time, used for measuring R.A., is the interval, in sidereal hours, minutes, and seconds, since the preceding meridian passage, at a given place, not of a star but of the True Equinox or First Point of Aries; each sidereal hour is 1/24th of the average interval (see below), and 9·83 secs. mean time shorter than the mean solar hour, making the sidereal day 3m. 55·91s. (mean time) shorter than the mean solar day. Each observatory has a sidereal clock keeping this time, to give the hour of R.A. on the meridian at any time (Table p. xiv); at 0 hrs. by the clock, the True Equinox is on the observatory's meridian. As that Equinox is not directly observable on the meridian, the clock is regulated by observing transits of 'clock' stars (p. 7) of known position, given in the *N.A.*

Sidereal Time is thus a *local* sidereal time, measured from, and keeping step with, the True Equinox of date, but differing from the sidereal time of every other observatory not on the same meridian. Being measured by a clock it is a uniform time, but it is not *Actual Sidereal Time*, the interval between successive transits of the True Equinox being slightly irregular; the difference from the clock time, however, is too small to cause practical inconvenience.

Uniform or Mean Sidereal Time has the same relation to ordinary sidereal time as Mean Time has to True Time. It is measured from the *Mean* equinox of date, instead of the True equinox; the difference never exceeds ± 1·2 secs.

Mean Time, shown by ordinary clocks, is the interval since the preceding 'mean midnight,' or instant when, during the night, an ordinary clock, correctly regulated to the average length of the mean solar day from noon to noon, shows 12 hrs., or a 24-hour clock shows 24 hrs. *Mean Noon* is the instant when mean time clocks indicate XII, at mid-day. Each country has its own meridian for 0 hrs., (see below 'Standard Time'). *Local Mean Time*, see below.

Apparent Time or *True Time* (solar), is *Sundial* or *Local Time*, based on the observed interval (varies slightly, p. 8) between two successive transits of the Sun's centre at a given place. These differences, by accumulation, may mount up to ± 15-16 minutes from the mean interval, thus to obtain the true Local *Mean* Time, a correction called the *Equation of Time* has to be added to the True Time, or subtracted: this is given in almanacs, sometimes on the sundial (*Table*, p. xii). The Sun and clock agree, however, on or about April 15, June 14, Sept. 1, and Dec. 25.

Astronomical and Civil (Mean) Time.—Both begin at midnight, the former starting at 0 hrs., the latter at 12 a.m., and are the same till noon—in Civil Time 12 p.m., when the hours begin again with 'p.m.', till midnight. But Astronomical Time, to avoid confusion with a.m. and p.m., continues 13 hrs., 14 hrs., &c., to 24 hrs. or 0 hrs., midnight.

Interval between two Phenomena.—Till Dec. 31, 1924, the astronomical day ran from noon to noon, so that its last twelve hours were in the following civil day. As this caused confusion, on Jan. 1, 1925, the astronomical day beginning was put back twelve hours, to coincide with the civil day. Hence in finding intervals, one before and the other after midnight Dec. 31, 1924, to obtain the true interval, *12 hours must be deducted* from the apparent interval arrived at from the *N.A.* dates and hours.

The best way to find long intervals is to convert the dates into days of the Julian Period (see below) by the *N.A.* Tables.

Universal Time (U.T., T.U.), [Britain, *Greenwich Mean Time (G.M.T.)*; Germany, *Weltzeit*, World-time, *W.Z.*], denotes the Mean Time for the meridian of Greenwich, starting at midnight for both Civil and Astronomical Time. Outside Britain, *Greenwich Civil Time (G.C.T.)* was often used for this time till the I.A.U. adopted *U.T.*, 1935.

Noon to noon astronomical time, when required, is designated *G.M.A.T.*—Greenwich Mean Astronomical Time.

Standard Time is an international arrangement for facilitating inter-communication, whereby *(a)* Greenwich is taken as the universal zero of longitude and time, and *(b)* the official mean time of each country or large district differs from Greenwich time by an exact multiple of half an hour. For the various Standard Times see almanacs.

Local Mean Time, required for finding the clock time of sunrise, southing of the Sun, &c., is the true *mean* time of the meridian of a place. On the standard meridian, at a given hour, the local time is slow compared with that of places to the E., where the day begins sooner, but fast compared with that of places to the W.; hence to obtain local mean time, add to, or subtract from, the standard mean time, 4 minutes for each degree the place is E. or W., respectively, of the standard meridian. Thus if using, in other places, the Sunrise and Sunset Tables calculated for the local time of the standard meridian (see the *N.A.*), the longitude correction must be *subtracted* for E., *added* for W., as the phenomena take place earlier and later, respectively, than at the standard meridian.

Light-Time, the time taken by light to travel from a celestial body to the Earth at a given moment, has to be allowed for when computing true rotation periods, &c. For the Sun, at mean distance it is 498·58 secs. (8·31 min.); the maximum is about 8·4m., the minimum, 8·2m. The observed maxima and minima times of variable stars require a + or − light-time correction for the Earth's position, as periods are stated for the Earth at mean distance.

The Julian Period (J.P.), used to calculate the exact interval between dates at long intervals apart, starts on Jan. 1, 4713 B.C., at noon. The *Julian Day*, or *Julian Date* (contracted J.D.)* is the number of days that have elapsed since the beginning of the Julian Period; a Table in the *N.A.* gives the Julian Day corresponding to Jan. 1 of each fourth year from 1 B.C., which the Table calls 'A.D. 0'. In ordinary chronology, A.D. 1 is the year following 1 B.C., and as there is no zero year, when B.C. and A.D. years are added, the resulting period is one year too great; or, if subtracted, one year too little. Calling 1 B.C., 'A.D. 0 (astronomical)'; 2 B.C., '1 B.C. (astron.),' and so on, gets over the difficulty.

For astronomical purposes, decimals of a day are employed with the Julian Day, instead of hours and minutes, as addition and subtraction are easier; thus Jan. 1, 1926, 9 p.m., astronomical time, is stated as J.D. 2,424,517·375, reckoned from noon. But the Julian Period being still reckoned from noon, not midnight, note that all astronomical hours less than 12 h. 0 m. (or ·5 day), still belong to the Julian Day *preceding* the civil date. Thus Jan. 1, 1926, 9 a.m., astronomical time, is J.D. 2,424,516·875, *i.e.*, Dec. 31 1925, 21 hrs., of the Julian Period. (Decimals of a day, p. xv).

* Sometimes J.A.D.—Julian Astronomical Day.

III. THE GALAXY AND THE STARS

The Galactic System.—Though sagacious conjectures as to the structure of the Universe had been previously made, nothing was known from observation till 1785, when Sir W. Herschel concluded, from the distribution of the stars, and the relative magnitudes of the brightest and faintest stars seen in his 18¾-inch telescope, that the Galaxy was in the form of a thin lens-shaped disc, slit at one end lengthways where the Milky Way branches. Its length he stated as about six times its greatest breadth, and he believed that the Sun was near its centre, but as nothing was known of the distances of even the brightest and therefore presumably the nearest stars (except that they were greater than that corresponding to 1″ annual parallax), he could only state the dimensions in what he called *Siriometers*, the (unknown) distance of *Sirius* or an average first magnitude star; this could be converted into actual dimensions when the parallax became known. Expressed in modern units, Herschel's dimensions are 5950 light-years across, 1085 through.

When, however, the distances of the Magellanic Clouds (p. 13 and extra-galactic Nebulæ became known, our Universe was found to have definite limits, and to be merely an 'island universe'—one out of millions of similar systems separated by distances of millions of light-years. Our Galactic System—containing some 30-100,000 million stars, and perhaps larger than the others—seems to be in the form of a lens-shaped disc some 100,000 light-years in its greatest length, and some 6000-10,000 in its greatest thickness, with a spheroidal centre perhaps 15,000 light-years in diameter.* The stars are greatly condensed towards the galactic plane.

The Galaxy is in rotation round *The Galactic Centre*, some 30,000 light-years from the Sun, in the dense star-clouds near the junction of Sagittarius, Scorpius, and Ophiuchus, about galactic lat. 0° and longit. 325-330° (Map 12)—there is no evidence for a central Sun, once thought probable—and the rotation periods of its members decrease with distance from the centre, those near the Sun being about 225 million years, at a speed of some 275 km/secs. (171 m/secs.). *The Rotational Term* of the Galaxy is the rotational velocity round the Galactic centre corresponding to a given distance from that centre (but may be used of any term arising from galactic rotation): being proportional to the distance, it can be found by measuring the intensity of interstellar lines, (p. 23; see *Pub. D.A.O.*, vol. 5, 1933).

Novæ, Wolf-Rayet stars, Cepheid variables, Planetary nebulæ, the Gaseous nebulæ, stars of Types B and N, and eclipsing binaries, show an unusually strong preference for the Milky Way and its neighbourhood, while the Globular clusters and Extra-galactic nebulæ seem to avoid it—now believed to be largely the result of the opaque matter being distributed more thickly in the Galactic Plane, similar to what is seen in spiral nebulæ viewed edgeways.

It is probable that our System of stars, globular and open clusters, gaseous nebulæ, and dust clouds, is a spiral nebula, something like the Great Andromeda Nebula, with local condensations in its arms, in one of which the Sun is situated a little above the plane of the Galaxy—the Galaxy being a 'small circle' of 88° (Struve).

Metagalactic Space is space outside the limits of the Galaxy; *Anagalactic Space*, that within its limits.

Interstellar Matter.—The space intervening between the members of our System is not empty, as was once thought, but is occupied by matter of exceeding tenuity—which has been computed as being of the order of 3 ounces per 1000 cubic miles—rotating on the whole with the general System, and revealing its presence by 'interstellar lines' (p. 23), and—near the Galactic plane, where it is denser, though elsewhere mostly evenly distributed—by light-absorption, which reddens the stars (p. 22). There are also vast opaque clouds, probably minute dust particles, to which the irregular breadth and outline, and the rifts and gaps, of the Milky Way, also the dark patches elsewhere, are partly due.

The Galactic Plane, passing through the central line or equator of the Galaxy (Galactic lat. 0°), is of fundamental importance in stellar study, owing to the peculiar distribution of various classes of objects with respect to it (see above). This plane is completely defined by the position of its N. pole, but authorities vary (see below). The I.A.U. (1932) recommend as the Standard System for statistical purposes, R.A. 190°, Dec. + 28°, 1900 (Ohlsson, practically Argelander's). For *Selected Areas*, Harvard uses Gould's value; for Galactic Charts 17-18, the Standard is used.

The Galactic Equator.—Authorities differ somewhat as to its course, as is not unnatural owing to the very irregular outline of the Milky Way: reference to the rough outline in the star maps will show that in several places the Galactic equator comes near the edge of the visible Milky Way, the observed central line of which averages about 1° S. of the actual equator. Newcomb's position for its N. pole (see below) includes the 'branch.'

The North Galactic Pole is about **1° W. of 30** Comæ Ber. (Map 9), where the extra-galactic Nebulæ cluster thickly; the Table gives various estimates (dates not epochs): the *S. Galactic Pole* is near nebula H. VI 20 Sculptoris (20^6, Map 4).

Authority.	R.A.	= h. m.	Dec. N.	Authority.	R.A.	= h. m.	Dec. N.	Authority.	R.A.	= h. m.	Dec. N.
Herschel, ...	187¼°	(12 29)	31° 30′	Newcomb (1904)	191°	(12 44)	26° 48′	...	...		...
Argelander, ...	190°	(12 40)	28° 5′	Hertzsprung (1912)	190¾°	(12 43)	27° 12′	...	...		...
Marth (1872) ...	190°	(12 40)	30° 0′	Walkey ... (1914)	191¾°	(12 47)	27° 0′	...	...		...
Gould (*U.A.*, 1875)	190¼°	(12 41)	27° 21′	Graff ... (1920)	192¼°	(12 49)	26° 48′	...	...		...

Galactic Longitude.—The usual zero is the intersection of the Galactic Equator with the Celestial Equator about R.A. 18h. 40m. If, however, the galactic meridian passing through a star with almost no proper motion, as α Cygni, were adopted instead, as has been proposed, the precession of the equinoxes would not affect the galactic co-ordinates as it does at present—obviously a great advantage, unless epoch 1900, say, is kept as a permanent zero. If the galactic longitude of α Cygni is made 0° (I.A.U., 1925), about 51° must be deducted from the galactic longitudes measured from the node of the Galaxy on the 1900 Celestial equator. Charts 17, 18 of this Atlas give both Galactic and ordinary co-ordinates.

* Plaskett, Halley Lecture, 1935.

The Milky Way or Galaxy, composed of millions of minute stars, observationally forms a great ring extending right round the star sphere, inclined about 61° to the Ecliptic plane, and slit lengthways at one part. It is brightest in Cygnus and Aquila (N. Hemisphere), in Scorpius and Sagittarius (S. Hemisphere), and faintest in Monoceros.

Between Cygnus and Scorpius the Galaxy forms two narrow parallel bands for some 110°, then it is very much broken up and complex for a considerable distance, but brighter, especially in Sagittarius, where the individual stars in the star clouds are so densely packed as to be indistinguishable (not well seen in European latitudes, as they south low in mid-summer). In Argo, near Canopus (50°S.), the Milky Way is (visually) completely divided across for a short distance, but near Canis Major it again becomes a single, though fainter band, which narrows to about 5° in Taurus, and broadens out once more in Perseus and Cassiopeia; its very variable width averages 15°, but in places it is 20° or 30°.

The *Coal Sack*, a remarkable gap (starless to the naked eye) in the Milky Way, near the foot of Crux, appears like a dark abyss in the surrounding brightness—largely due to contrast, as, in a photograph, the area is much brighter than in the non-galactic regions in the vicinity. This gap, similar but smaller gaps in Cygnus and elsewhere, also the Great Rift in Argo, are believed to be due to dark nebulæ (p. 13), intervening between us and the Galaxy beyond.

Stellar Photographs taken on ordinary plates, differ in general from what is seen visually, owing to what may conveniently be termed colour index effect—*i.e.*, stars bluer than A0 being photographically brighter, those redder fainter, than they are visually (p. 16). Such photos show faint B stars bright, and bright M stars faint, making familiar visual groups unrecognisable.

Photographs of the Milky Way (sectional) are given in *H.A.*, vols. 72, 80; others are in *Die Milchstrasse* (Goos), Hamburg 1921, and in *Handbuch der Astrophisik*, vol. 5 (2).

Double Stars are stars which to the naked eye appear as a single point of light, but when viewed through a telescope are found to be composed of two stars—not necessarily physically connected, as they may simply happen to be in the same line of sight. *Triple Stars* have three, *quadruple stars* four, and *multiple stars* many components. Where one of the stars is of a much smaller magnitude than the other, it is often styled a *comes* (plural *comites*) or companion. The most interesting 'doubles,' &c., are indicated in the Notes appended to each star chart.

Binary Stars are double stars which are 'physically connected,' revolving round a common centre of gravity, and not merely chancing to be in the same line of sight. *Spectroscopic Binaries* are those found to be binary by the temporary doubling and displacement of the lines in their spectra, although too close together to be 'resolved,' *i.e.*, seen separate in the telescope. Visible binary stars have periods varying from two years to many centuries. If the plane of their orbit is in the line of sight from the Earth, they may be seen to approach closer and closer together, and at last appear to the eye as a single point for a considerable period, afterwards opening out again.

In a binary system, the motion of the companion is *direct* when the position angle is increasing in degrees, and *retrograde* when decreasing. The smaller star is sometimes said to be in *periastron* with the principal star, when actually (as distinct from apparently) nearest to it; and in *apoastron* when furthest from it.

Star Clusters are small groups of stars, crowded more or less closely together, which in the telescope are glorious sights (see Notes, Star Charts). *Star Clouds* differ in being portions of the Milky Way itself in which the stars are so closely packed as to appear as a continuous irregular bright cloud: they are most conspicuous in Sagittarius, in which the centre of the Galactic System seems to be situated. Star clusters, proper, are of two kinds.

Globular Clusters are globe-shaped, densely-packed masses of stars, thinning out rapidly at the edges of the central condensation, then slowly when the distances between individual stars has become considerable; M 13 in Hercules (N.G.C. 6205) is a typical specimen. Over 100 are known,* few nearer the Galactic Plane than about 10°, and all lie in the region between 149° and 41° Galactic longitude, which indicates considerable eccentricity with respect to the Sun. They also occupy a place opposite to the majority of the Spiral nebulæ, being mostly in Ophiuchus and Sagittarius.

Open Clusters have no central condensation, are more or less irregular in form, are often associated with nebulosity, and are most numerous opposite the region in which the Globular clusters predominate. The Præsepe in Cancer exemplifies one type, somewhat resembling an open Globular cluster; the Pleiades, in Taurus, represents another type, an irregular, yet well marked group, the components of which have a common motion.

Moving Clusters or *Star Groups* are not clusters in the ordinary sense, but groups of stars which have evidently some intimate relationship, as they are moving with similar velocities towards the same point on the star sphere. Proctor termed this phenomenon 'star-drift.' The individual stars may be in widely different parts of the star sphere. The best known are the Taurus, Perseus, and Ursa Major groups: the latter includes β, γ, δ, ε, ζ, of Ursa Major, and the apparently unconnected stars δ Leonis, Sirius, β Eridani, β Aurigæ, and α Coronæ Borealis.

The Local Cluster, inferred to exist from the study of parallaxes, magnitudes, &c., is believed to be a bun-shaped aggregation of stars, like a very open Globular cluster, to which our Sun appears to belong, and in which he is situated a little to the north of its central plane, and some distance to one side of its centre. Its central plane is inclined 10°-15° to the plane of the Galaxy, and its stars are relatively near us, compared with the Milky Way, and comparatively close together, while its diameter is of the order of 1000 parsecs, or 3000 light-years. The majority of the brighter B stars seem to belong to this cluster, and according to Shapley its apparent centre is in Carina.

* See List in *H.A.*, Vol. 76, and *H.C.O.* 776.

Variable Stars are those which wax and wane in brightness; there are many varieties, which afford a useful and interesting study for amateur observers. The *Amplitude* (*A*, visual, photographic, &c.) is the range of magnitude between maximum and minimum. The more important types are given below (See Notes on Observing, p. 42, and on Nomenclature, p. ix).

When a variable star is, for the time-being, a morning star, rising shortly before sunrise, its maximum or minimum is called a 'morning' one. Similarly, 'spring,' 'autumn,' maxima, &c., refer to the time of year at which they occur.

I. **Novæ**, or New stars, also called 'Temporary Stars,' suddenly blaze out where no star of that magnitude has been known before, but soon fade away to a small fraction of their maximum brightness; may be visual, telescopic, or photographic, and generally identifiable with some previously-known very faint star. Characteristic spectrum, with maximum intensity far in the ultra-violet—sometimes having broad, bright, and dark bands side by side, which soon changes, following, on the whole, but with individual peculiarities, the sequence detailed on page 42, and finally becoming identical with that of a Wolf-Rayet star (p. 19). (See List of Novæ on p. viii, and note on Nomenclature, p. ix).

It is probably significant that most Novæ yet discovered (except those in nebulæ), are either in, or near, the Milky Way, and that they greatly preponderate in one direction, 14 Novæ (modern) having appeared from 0° to 90° Galactic longitude; 8 Novæ from 90° to 180°; 4 Novæ from 180° to 270°; and 16 Novæ from 270° to 360°. Novæ appear in Spiral nebulæ, apparently of two types—ordinary Novæ, of absolute mag. about −5, and *Supernovæ*, about −15.

II. **Long-Period Variables.** Periods, 70-700 days, mostly about 275 days: red stars (Giants), of M Types or N, sometimes S, K, or R. Range of variation usually several magnitudes; periods, and maximum magnitude attained, are usually irregular; rise of magnitude usually faster than the decrease. Typical star, ο Ceti (*Mira*): see Notes on Map 6.

III. **Irregular Variables.** Stars of all types from B to N, sometimes associated with nebular matter; no regular period; most vary only a magnitude or two. Many varieties, but five chief divisions:—

a. Red stars with slight variations, like μ Cephei. Also some semi-regular variables.

b. *RV Tauri* Type. Variation averaging 2 magnitudes. Bright and faint maxima somewhat like the *β Lyræ* Type. Typical stars, RV Tauri, R Scuti.

c. *U Geminorum* Type. Constant minimum for many weeks or months, then a sudden blaze-up of several magnitudes in often alternate long and short maxima, with slower fall to a constant minimum.

d. *R Coronæ Borealis* Type. Normal for months or years, then decreases many magnitudes, and after an irregular interval returns to normal. Rises less quickly than it falls. See Notes, Maps 11-12.

e. *Nova-like Stars*; quick rises like the Novæ. Most notable star, η Carinæ, see Notes on Maps 9 and 10.

IV. **Cepheid Variables,** with periods mostly less than 50 days.

Classical Cepheids. Giants with a rather sudden rise of light, followed by a more gradual fall to minimum; periods from a few hours to a month or two, but mostly about 4½ days; range of variation usually less than one magnitude; spectrum at minimum may be a whole Type lower than at maximum. Typical star, δ Cephei; see Notes, Maps 3 and 4. Cepheids are of great importance for finding stellar distances, as those of the same period have the same absolute magnitude.

Cluster-type Cepheids are those with less than 24-hr. periods, being found in great numbers in the globular clusters.

V. **Eclipsing Variables,** so called because the decrease in brightness is due to eclipse, at regular intervals, by a companion which may be fainter or dark.

Algol Type. A single well-marked minimum, sometimes a slight secondary one. Typical star, *Algol* (Notes Map 5).

β Lyræ Type. Two equal maxima, with a small intervening minimum between them, followed by a large minimum: also called *ellipsoidal* on account of the shape of their components. Typical star, β Lyræ; see Notes on Maps 13 and 14.

VI. **Secular Variables**—stars which, in the course of centuries, have imperceptibly faded or increased in brightness, of which there is some evidence. Thus the Greek legend of the fading away of *Sterope*, one of the Pleiades, is probably based on an astronomical fact. β Libræ, and *Castor* are other supposed examples.

TABLE.

The rough distribution in percentage by main types of some 9000 Variables shown in Kukarkin and Parenago's Catalogue (1948) is as follows:—

Type	%	Type	%	Type	%
Cluster Type Cepheids	18	Semi-regular Variables	6	Eclipsing variables	20
Classical Cepheids	5	Irregular Variables	10	All other types	3
Long-Period Variables	36	Novæ and associated types	2		

Nebulæ are small, faint, misty, patches of light; only a very few are visible to the naked eye, such as the Great Andromeda and Orion Nebulæ, representative of two different types. They are usually more or less regular in form—spirals, spindles, ovals, and spheroids—but some are irregular or indefinite in outline; some are resolvable into patches of very faint stars; others are masses of gas of extreme tenuity, estimated as a thousand millionth of the density of air. There are various types:—

I. **Galactic, Gaseous, or Green Nebulæ** (belonging to our System). Classes (*a*) and (*b*) of these tend to cluster in the plane of the Milky Way—unlike the extra-galactic or 'White' Nebulæ, chiefly found towards its north pole. There are several sub-divisions; (*a*) and (*b*) have bright-line spectra; but shine not by their own light, but by absorption and re-emission of radiation from high-temperature stars within them.

a. Irregular Nebulæ. Preponderate towards the Milky Way; irregular or indefinite in form, distinguished telescopically by their greenish or bluish colour; small radial velocities. Chiefly composed of 'nebulium' (λλ5007, 3727), *i.e.*, ionised oxygen, OIII, OII, with hydrogen and helium; may be connected with earlier stages of star formation, usually but not always, having stars shining in them, evidently intimately connected. The Great Orion Nebula (M42, N.G.C. 1976) is of this Type; distance may be about 1900 light years. Much fainter, and shown best by photography, are the nebulosities round, or joining, some stars (as in the Pleiades), also obviously connected with the stars.

b. Planetary Nebulæ. More or less circular in form, and so-called because in a small telescope they somewhat resemble the faint disc of a planet; only a few have a brighter central condensation. All have a central star of small mass and high temperature (White Dwarf) within them—occasionally not distinguishable—to which the visibility of the nebula is due. Tend to condense towards the Milky Way: related to Wolf-Rayet stars (p. 42), which have similar spectra but smaller masses and velocities; also to Novæ, which towards the end of their outburst first become planetary nebulæ, then pass into their final stage, showing spectra identical with those of Wolf-Rayet stars. Mean velocity 25·3 km. (15·7 miles) per second: masses up to 150 times the Sun's.

c. Invisible Nebulæ or interstellar matter—unseen either by eye or camera—non-luminous, fairly evenly-distributed, excessively tenuous clouds of calcium, hydrogen, and sodium, inferred to exist as the simplest means of accounting for stationary lines of these elements in the spectra of Novæ, and of very distant O and B binary stars. The star-light, traversing an enormous length of the interstellar matter, suffers another absorption, and as the matter rotates with the Galaxy, its absorption lines do not move to and fro as those of the moving components do (see page 23).

Note.—The temperatures of gaseous nebulæ and of interstellar matter are given as being of the order of 100,000° and 15,000°K., respect tively. This means that their atoms are moving with the velocity corresponding to those of a dense gas at these temperatures

II. **Dark Nebulæ**. Supposed to cause the dark gaps, and the great irregularity of width and outline, in the Milky Way, and dark patches elsewhere: revealed by photography and star counts. Great irregular clouds of non-luminous opaque matter, most probably dust, which, being nearer to us than the Galaxy, shut out the light from the celestial objects beyond them. Largely in the neighbourhood of the Galaxy; some are probably only a few hundred light-years away. Herschel believed these to be empty lanes between the stars; his 'Hole in the Heavens' is almost certainly No. 86 in Barnard's Catalogue (p. vi).

III. **Extra-galactic or 'White' Nebulæ**.—'Island Universes,' similar to our own Galaxy. Appear about galactic lat. 10° N. & S.; rapid increase to 30°, slower to 70°. Faint continuous spectra, more or less resembling that of a star; may be composed of myriads of faint stars; by far the most numerous type. Probably evenly distributed through space, those in lower galactic latitudes being veiled by absorbing matter.

a. Irregular Nebulæ. Irregular outline; the Magellanic Clouds are of this type.

b. Spiral Nebulæ, mostly found by photography. Outline regular—elliptical, spindle-shaped, spiral, and barred—with a definite nucleus. The Spiral Nebulæ are the most common; not found in the Milky Way, but tend to cluster about the Galactic Poles, especially the Northern one; thickest in the region opposite that in which the Globular clusters are most numerous. Distances of the order of millions of light-years; mostly receding from us at high velocities—300-40,000 km. (200-25,000 miles) per second—approximately proportional to their distance, about 250 km. (150 miles) per megaparsec. Some seen as 'spindles' or ellipses, are obviously spirals viewed edge-on. Spiral nebulæ frequently occur in groups, the more noteworthy being those in Ursa Major, Virgo, Canes Venatici, and Leo.

The Great Andromeda Nebula (M31, N.G.C.224, visible to the naked eye), is of this type; the distance is between 1,500,000 and 2,000,000 light-years. Apparently approaching, as the result of the Galactic rotation, but actually receding.

The Magellanic Clouds or *Nubecula Major* (the Greater Little Cloud), and *Nubecula Minor* (the Lesser Little Cloud) are now recognised as extra-galactic objects—island universes, the nearest neighbours to our System, and typical 'Irregular' Nebulæ (extra-galactic). They are invisible from the latitude of Europe and the United States, their respective Declinations being 70° and 73°S.; their R.A.s 5h.30m. and 0h.50m.

To the naked eye they appear like detached portions of the Milky Way, from which they are some 30° to 40° distant; in the telescope they are seen as a marvellous combination of stars, clusters, and nebulæ. Their distances are of the order of 200,000 light-years.

Radio-Astronomy.—This subject is at present almost completely divorced from those mentioned elsewhere in this atlas. The objects which it examines can seldom be identified with those which can be seen or photographed, and the methods it uses, due largely to radio engineers rather than to astronomers, have little in common with those of other lines of astronomical research. Its "telescopes" may resemble reflecting telescopes or optical interferometers, but are of much larger dimensions.

Not merely can the subject be pursued irrespective of terrestrial clouds, but, even more important, also of the obscuring matter of our Galaxy by which its more remote parts are made inaccessible to optical telescopes. An immediate result is that the suspected spiral structure of our Galaxy has been verified.

The only star from which appreciable radio emission has been detected is our sun. What have been called "radio stars" are sources whose dimensions are probably large in comparison with a super-giant star. Among those few which correspond to telescopic objects are colliding extra-galactic nebulae and certain galactic nebulae such as the Crab nebula, which occupies the position of the super nova of 1054. One of the invisible sources coincides with the position of the super-nova of 1572.

The period of rotation of the planet Venus given on pp. 32 and 33 was found by radio observations.

Parallax is the angular difference in direction of an object when viewed from two different standpoints, expressed by the number of seconds or minutes of arc subtended by the line joining the two standpoints, *as seen from the object.* The parallax of a star is reckoned on a different basis from that of the Sun or of a planet.

In *Diurnal Parallax*, used for members of the Solar System only, the two standpoints are the Earth's centre and the observer, separated by the radius of the Earth's diurnal or *daily* circuit; it is greatest when the object is on the observer's horizon—the *Horizontal Parallax*—and decreases to zero at the zenith, when object, observer, and Earth's centre are in the same line; as ordinarily stated it is the *Equatorial* horizontal parallax, for the Equator, where the Earth's radius is greatest. When the object is not on the horizon it has *Parallax in Altitude*, which decreases to 0″ at the zenith. The Moon has the greatest diurnal parallax, max. 1° 28′, mean 57′.*

Annual Parallax—used for stars and nebulæ only, their diurnal parallax being unmeasurably small—is the angle subtended by the mean radius of the Earth's orbit—the *yearly* circuit, as seen from the star. Except for the very nearest stars, the very minute angles involved make the results somewhat uncertain; photographs taken six months apart have replaced, with far greater convenience, direct angular measurement, angles with a probable error as small as 0″·01 (1/360,000 degree) being measurable. The greatest parallax known (0″·765) is that of *Proxima Centauri*, though very faint the nearest star: it is physically connected with α Centauri, 2° away, which has parallax 0″·758.*

A *Negative Parallax* (annual), stated in figures prefixed by *minus*, indicates an unsuccessful attempt at measurement, the distance of the star being made greater than that of the (assumed) much more distant comparison stars: the errors of observation may have exceeded the amount of the parallax, or the comparison stars been more displaced.

Stellar Parallax.—When stating a parallax it is usual to give the basis of measurement, so that the 'weight,' or degree of reliability, may be estimated, some of the many methods now available giving better results than others.

Trigonometrical Parallax, the foundation for the others, is that measured by angular observations, direct or photographic. When measured with reference to some other stars, assumed to be much more remote on account of their faintness and small proper motion, the parallax is called the *Relative Parallax*; if the average parallax of these reference stars can be estimated by some means, the relative parallax so corrected is called the *Absolute Parallax.*

Absolute Magnitude Parallaxes are calculated from the absolute magnitudes deduced from various phenomena; comparison with known trigonometrical parallaxes shows that each method gives results more or less in fair agreement:—*Cepheid* parallax, derived from variation-periods of 'Cepheid' variables (p. 12), is probably very accurate on the whole, subject to some uncertainty as to zero-point; it is specially valuable for extremely remote objects.

Spectroscopic Parallax is found from the intensity of certain lines in some types of spectra: *Spectral* parallax, from spectral Type and Giant or Dwarf classification (p. 20), where there is *no* marked separation into Giants and Dwarfs.

Dynamic or *Hypothetical* parallax is a probable parallax calculated from the period and angular dimensions of the orbit of a binary star, the mass of the system having to be guessed. As, however, the average star mass appears to be about that of the Sun (p. 20), this unknown factor can be estimated on that basis with little likelihood of introducing much error, as, fortunately, a very considerable change in the mass value makes only a small change in the parallax.

Interstellar-line parallax, based on a definite relation between the intensities of these lines (see p. 23) and the rotational term of the Galaxy, "should give more reliable parallaxes and absolute magnitudes than any other available," for the distant O and B stars. (*See Pub. D.A.O., Vol. 5, p, 94, 1933*).

Mean Parallax, though not applicable to single stars, is valuable in statistical work for groups or classes of stars; it is based on relationships of their proper motions to the velocity of the Sun's own motion in space, and the stars' angular distance from the Solar Antapex (see p. 27). It becomes increasingly important as the lapse of time enables proper motions to be known more and more accurately.

Secular Parallax, also for groups of stars only, is deduced from their 'parallactic motions' (p. 15), valued at 90° from the Solar Apex (p. 27). *Secular Variation* of parallax results from the radial motion of a star towards or away from the Sun, which will, sooner or later, sensibly change its annual parallax.

Group or *Statistical* parallax is based on the reasonable assumption that in a fair-sized group of stars, those of the same magnitude are at the same average distance, the visual magnitude being thus an index of their distance. It requires, however, a starting point based on some other parallax, such as Secular parallax.

Mass-luminosity parallax, found from mass-luminosity (p. 20), is perhaps not so reliable for the hottest stars.

Astronomical Unit (A.U.).—The unit for Solar System measurements, and the base-line for stellar parallax, is the Earth's mean distance from the Sun, 92,897,400 miles, or 149,504,200 kilometres (last four or five figures not significant), the distance corresponding to the mean equatorial parallax 8″·80. This parallax, adopted in 1896 as the international basis for ephemerides, is expected to be near enough to the true value to require no alteration later.*

Unit Distance. The angular diameter of a planet 'at unit distance,' used when comparing the diameters of planets, is that which the planet would have, as seen from the Sun's centre, if it were placed at a distance of 1 astronomical unit. A million astronomical units has been called a *Siriometer*, a term first used by Sir W. Herschel in another sense—the distance (then unknown) of an average first magnitude star, assuming brightness as an index to the nearest stars.

* See pages viii and 53 for Tables of Parallaxes.

Parsec: Light-year.—A *Parsec* is the distance of a star having a parallax of 1″; a *Light-Year*, the distance that light, travelling 186,300 miles (299,800 km.) per second, traverses in a year—a convenient popular unit.

10 parsecs (a *dekaparsec*, in Metric notation) is the distance at which absolute magnitude (p.17) is computed;* a *Kiloparsec* is 1000 parsecs. A *Megaparsec*, for remote nebulæ, is a million parsecs, or 3¼ million light-years.

Distance-Unit	=Parsecs	=a Parallax of	=Astronomical Units	=Light-Years	=Billions of Miles		Billions of Kilometres	
					British (10^{12})	U.S. (10^{9})	British (10^{12})	U.S. (10^{9})
Light-year	0·3069	3″·259	63,290	1	5·88	5880	9·463	9463
Parsec ...	1	1″·000	206,265	3·259	19·16	19,160	30·840	30,840
Dekaparsec	10	0″·100	2,062,650	32·590	191·60	191,600	308·400	308,400

Radial Motion.—The Radial motion of a star is its apparent motion in the line of sight, either towards us or away from us: it is not the star's own real space motion (see below). *The Radial Velocity* is the radial motion expressed in miles or kilometres per second, which is found by the spectroscope to within ¼ mile per second under favourable circumstances: + is used to indicate recession from us, and − to indicate approach to us.

Proper Motion, or *Tangential Motion*, is a star's apparent angular motion (if any) on the star sphere at right angles to the line of sight, expressed in seconds of arc per year or per century; it is found by comparing the star's present position with that which it occupied at the time of the earliest reliable observation—precession, nutation, parallax, and aberration, being allowed for. As this angular motion is continuous, though in general very minute, it has to be taken into account when preparing a star catalogue for a given epoch (see note p. vi as to + and −). The following are some of the greatest proper motions known: a long list is given *Astrophys. Journal*, vol. 41, 1914.

Ursa Major. Groombridge 1830 (mag. 6), Proper motion 7″. annually ... ...
Pictor. ... C.Z. 5 h. 243 (mag. 9), „ „ 9″. „ ... ...
Ophiuchus. Munich 15,040 (Barnard's star, mag. 9·4) 10″, found 1916, the greatest yet discovered ... ...

The observed proper motion is not a star's real tangential motion in space, but an 'apparent' motion, being affected by the Sun's own motion through space towards the Solar Apex (page 27). Some stars have practically no proper motion—a result due in general to their very great distance. The *Tangential Velocity* is the Tangential motion expressed in kilometres or miles per second: the star's distance must be known.

Linear Motion.—A star's linear motion is the resultant of *(a)* the radial motion, and *(b)* the proper motion, expressed in *lineal*, not angular, measure, and requires a knowledge of the parallax. The *linear velocity* is the linear motion expressed in kilometres or miles per second: to obtain that with reference to the Sun, at right angles to the line of sight, divide the annual proper motion by the parallax, and multiply by 4·74 for kilometres, or 2·95 for miles.

Space or Peculiar Motion.—A star's space or peculiar motion (also known as Absolute, or Real motion), with reference to the surrounding stellar system, is the resultant of its Radial motion, and its motion at right angles to the line of sight, corrected for the Solar System's motion (p. 27): the corresponding velocity is its *Space-velocity.*

The K-term. If the space-motions of the stars were at random, there should be as many stars with recessional (+) velocities, as there are with approaching (−) velocities. Statistics, however, show a surplus of recessional (+) velocities; this excess over the − velocities is the K-term. Improved data have reduced the original amount.

Cross Motion.—This term denotes a star's angular motion at right angles to the great circle joining the star with the Solar Apex or Antapex: the *Cross Velocity* is the Cross motion expressed in miles or kilometres per second.

Parallactic Motion, also known as 'Secular parallax,' is the apparent displacement of a star caused by the Sun's motion—which displacement is known with ever-increasing accuracy as the years go on. The average distance of any class of stars can be found from their Parallactic motions, but the method is not applicable to individual stars.

Star Drift; Star Streaming.—Sometimes the members of large groups of stars are found to have proper motions similar in direction and amount; Proctor called this *Star Drift.* 'Drift' may also denote the motion of a group of stars relatively to the Sun. *Star Streaming* is Star Drift on a large scale. In 1904, Kapteyn found that the stars, in general, are moving in two favoured directions, which, when corrected for the Sun's motion, are diametrically opposite on the star sphere, and both exactly in the plane of the Milky Way. 60% of the stars belong to Stream I, and are moving towards R.A., 6 hrs. 20 min., Dec. 12° N.; the other 40%—Stream II, which has about half the velocity of the first—move towards R.A., 18 hrs., Dec. 12° S. These points are known as the *Vertices of Star Streaming.* The centre of mass (or rather, of mean position) of the stars in a streaming star group is called the *Centroid.*

A third stream, known as 'Stream O,' practically stationary, consists of the majority of the B-Type stars, which seem to belong to the 'Local Cluster' (p. 11).

Gould's Belt of Bright Stars, the nearer or brighter stars of the Local Cluster (which includes the Sun), is a great-circle belt of bright stars which is inclined some 20° to the Galactic Plane: its equator is (roughly) a line drawn from γ Cassiopeiæ between ε and β Orionis, δ Velorum and ε Carinæ, α and β Centauri, α and ε Scorpii, back to the start, passing some 9° S. of α Ophiuchi and *Vega*, and close to δ Cygni.

---

* The distance of *Pollux*, very nearly.

Star Magnitudes.—The brightest stars are said to be 1st magnitude; those less bright, 2nd magnitude; those still less bright, 3rd magnitude, and so on. Each magnitude is 2·512 (about 2½) times as bright as the one below it, a standard 1st magnitude star (*e.g, Aldebaran, Altair*) being 100 times as bright as a standard 6th magnitude star, which is about the faintest 'lucid' star, *i.e.*, visible to the naked eye. As, however, several 1st magnitude stars are much brighter than *Aldebaran*, the range of magnitudes also runs in the other direction, a star of magnitude '0' being about 2½ times as bright as one of magnitude 1, and a star of magnitude *minus* 1, about 2½ times brighter than one of magnitude 0, and so on. After magnitude 6, the magnitudes run on, 7th, 8th, &c., for the telescopic stars, the 11th magnitude being about the faintest visible in a three-inch telescope, and the 18th, in the most powerful telescopes yet constructed; stars several magnitudes fainter are obtained by photography. (See Table of relative brightness, p. x).

Intermediate magnitudes are denoted in tenths or even hundredths, thus magnitude 3·00 is slightly brighter than 3·01, but less bright than 2·99, the magnitude increasing as the brightness decreases. On the *minus* side of 0·0, however, this is reversed, the magnitude figure increasing with the brightness. Thus magnitude −0·1 is brighter than 0·0; −1·0 is brighter than −0·9; and −1·9 is brighter than −1·8, and so on. Where there is no sign, magnitudes are always understood to be +, but + is usually given in the case of 'absolute magnitudes' (see p. 17). In the general sense, '1st mag.' usually means all stars brighter than mag. 1·5; '2nd mag.' those between 1·5 and 2·5. The magnitudes in modern catalogues are *always calculated for the zenith*: at lower altitudes atmospheric absorption diminishes the brightness, and has to be allowed for when comparing stars at different altitudes: see Table, page 42,

Numerical Ratios of Magnitude.—On the 2·512 times basis of reckoning each magnitude, every difference of 5 magnitudes means a multiplication or division by 100 of the starting magnitude, thus 1st magnitude is 100 times brighter than the 6th; 10,000 times brighter than the 11th, and a million times brighter than the 16th, while magnitude 0·0 is 100 times brighter than magnitude 5. This "stellar magnitude" method of comparison is now used for other comparisons than its original one of visual brightness—as for stellar heat-radiation, and even for temperatures.

If the stars were uniformly scattered through space, there would be 3·98 times as many stars of a given magnitude as in the one just above it; departure from this number (called the *star ratio*) indicates crowding, or, thinning out.

The 2·512 scale, now the standard, was introduced by Pogson in 1850, 2·512 being the 5th root of 100, or the logarithm 0·4. Boss's *P.G.C.*, 1910, employs an older system with a light-ratio 2·291 (log. = 0·36), approximately that of Argelander's *Uranometria Nova*, 1843. Boss and Pogson magnitudes are the same about mag. 3·8; below* 3·8 Boss is fainter, mag. 6·0 Pogson being about 6·2 Boss. Above* mag. 3·8, Boss is brighter, *Vega* being 0·0, *Sirius* −2·0, Boss; against 0·14 and −1·58 Pogson.

International Magnitude Scale.—Though based on the same light-ratio, the magnitudes found at Harvard, Mount Wilson, Potsdam, &c., show small systematic discrepancies, due to the instruments, atmosphere, &c. Thus for accurate comparisons, each must be 'reduced' to the scale with which it is to be compared, by means of Tables prepared by laborious analysis (see Harvard Annals, Vol. 14, and Astrophysical Journal, Vol. 61). The Harvard (photometric), and Mt. Wilson (photovisual) Scales are most generally used, and the former was adopted (1922) as the basis of *International Magnitudes*—a photographic Scale. Taking the stars of Type A0 between mags. 5·5 and 6·5, in the Harvard *North Polar Sequence* (a list of carefully-measured stars near the N. Pole arranged in order of photographic magnitude), the mean International magnitude of these stars is defined as being the same as the mean magnitude of these stars on the Harvard visual (photometric) scale—which, for Type A0, is identical with the Harvard photographic scale.

Visual or Apparent Magnitude is the brightness as directly estimated by the eye; when the brightness is measured instrumentally by the photometer, it is called the *Photometric* magnitude.

Photovisual Magnitudes are obtained photographically, using a colour screen and isochromatic plates adjusted approximately to the light-sensitiveness of the eye; they tend to be rather brighter than the visual or photometric magnitudes, and are becoming of great importance as they give more uniform results. They minimise both the instrumental and the brightness 'colour equation' difficulties (see p. 17), and the photographic plate and colour screen used seem to make no great difference in the results. (Red and photo-electric magnitudes, see p. 17).

Photographic Magnitudes are those obtained by measuring the diameters of the images on a stellar photograph. For one-half of the stars the results are accordant with the visual magnitudes, but in the other half, owing to the bluer stars being more actinic, and the redder stars less actinic, the blue stars photograph brighter than they are visually, and the red stars fainter, by an amount depending on the spectral Type of the star (p. 18).

Colour Index (contracted, c/i) is the difference, in stellar magnitudes, between the photographic magnitude and the photometric (or photovisual) one, the photovisual index tending to be the greater; on the Harvard colour index scale, Type A0 has c/i 0·00, its visual and photographic magnitudes being the same. Colour indices greater than 2·0 are probably very rare; S Cephei, Type Nc, has the very great colour index +5·5. Colour Index Table on p. viii.

Photographic Magnitude minus the c/i = photometric magnitude. **Photometric Magnitude plus the c/i** = photographic mag.

Colour Index = photographic mag. *minus* the photometric mag. ‖ Thus ε Orionis, Type B0, visual mag. 1·75, *plus* c/i −0·31 = photographic mag. 1·44.
Betelgeuse, „ M0, „ 0·92 „ +1·68 = „ „ 2·60.

The − indicates that ε Orionis is brighter, the + that *Betelgeuse* is fainter, than A0—photographically.

* Used in connection with magnitude, 'above' means brighter than; 'below,' fainter than.

Absolute Magnitude.—Visual magnitude is no criterion of intrinsic luminosity, as many distant stars appear far brighter than some very near stars. Absolute magnitude is the brightness a star would have if all the stars were at the same distance from us: it is found by calculating what the observed visual magnitude of each star would be if each were placed at a distance of 10 parsecs—that equivalent to a parallax of 0″·1, or about 33 light-years*—which of course requires a knowledge of the star's distance. Conversely, if the absolute magnitude can be found by some other means, the star's distance can be calculated. Absolute magnitude is therefore of great importance in stellar research, as it enables luminosities to be compared, and gives many unmeasurable parallaxes. In absolute magnitude, as in visual, the 'greater' (numerically) the magnitude the less luminous is the star, if +; the more luminous, if −. The *Integrated* absolute or visual magnitude, of a nebula or star cluster, is that of the total light received from the object.

The Sun's absolute visual magnitude is +4·9, roughly +5·0. A 1-parsec standard distance was in use till the international adoption of the 10-parsec standard (1922); it had the advantage of having the Sun's absolute magnitude 0·0.

The absolute magnitudes of Giant stars vary only one or two magnitudes (from about +1·0 to −1·0) in their progression from Types M to B. Those of the Dwarfs fall off a magnitude or two as each successive Type below is reached, until about +15½, in *Proxima Centauri*, a red star perhaps nearing extinction, and in *Procyon B*, almost the faintest absolute magnitudes known. *Rigel* and *Canopus*, on the other hand, attain about −6·0; Supernovæ in Spirals, −15.

The most luminous star known is S Doradûs, a variable star in the larger Magellanic Cloud, some 14 magnitudes, or 300,000-500,000 times brighter than the Sun: photogr. abs. mag. at brightest, −8·9. The least luminous is Wolf 359, a near-by star of mag. 13·5 visual, 16·5 absolute: its luminosity is only 1/50,000th that of the Sun.

To find Absolute Magnitude:—Abs. Mag. = visual mag. + 5, plus 5 times the logarithm of the parallax. $M = m + 5 + 5 \log \pi$.

Red Magnitude and Colour Index (Harvard photo-red, *H.A.*, vol. 89, p. 92; effective wave-length λ6300).—On this system—the effective wave-length of which is halfway between the C and D lines, and about the wave-length at the average intensity of the *visible* solar spectrum—red colour index is about 30% greater than *yellow* c/i (Internat. photographic [I] *minus* photovisual [m_{pv}] mag.): *blue-red* and *yellow-red* c/i = $I - m_{pr}$, and $m_{pv} - m_{pr}$.

Photo-electric Magnitudes are measured by a photo-electric cell (different from the thermo-couple used in the bolometer); it gives great accuracy for differences between stars of the same spectral type. There is no photo-electric magnitude scale, as cells vary in sensitivity to different colours: (the bolometer integrates all the radiation).

Radiometric or Bolometric Magnitude gives the *total* radiation emitted by a star—the light, heat, actinic rays, etc.—using a thermo-couple or bolometer, instead of the eye. The variable stars *Mira* and χ Cygni, at maximum, emit nearly twice as much radiation as at minimum, but their light increases some 1000-2000 times.

Radiometric Magnitude is expressed on the same system as visual magnitude, and the difference between the radiometric and visual magnitude is called the *Heat Index* (corresponding to the photographic Colour Index), the two being assumed to coincide for Type A0. (See Mt. Wilson Annual Report, 1925).

Bolometric Magnitude, on the other hand, agrees with visual magnitude for that Type of star whose radiation has maximum luminous efficiency, so that visual *minus* bolometric magnitude is always positive (+), or zero. The Type for which the visual and bolometric magnitude agree is very nearly that of the Sun (Type G0). The Sun's absolute magnitude is about 4·6 visual, 4·6 bolometric; radiometric, 4·9. (See *M.N.*, vol. 77, pp. 29 and 604).

Combined Magnitude is the resultant magnitude of two or more stars, so close together as to appear to the eye (or be treated) as a single star. It is the magnitude corresponding to the sum of each star's individual brightness, referred to that of mag. 0·00 taken as 1, and is found as follows (adding the two magnitudes would give a fainter one),

A star's magnitude multiplied by −0·4 gives the logarithm of its brightness relative to mag. 0·00.
The logarithm of a star's brightness relative to mag. 0·00 when divided by −0·4 gives the magnitude.

Colour Magnitude is the magnitude of a star measured for each of the wave-lengths (referred to B0 as standard), and reduced to standard A0 by theoretical black-body radiation (see *H.B.* 848).

Opposition Magnitude is the magnitude of a superior planet when in opposition (p. 5); the planet is then nearest the Earth and brightest, and (in theory) is only then seen with its disc fully illuminated. Ordinarily the term denotes the opposition brightness at *mean* distance, as a planet's distance and brightness vary at different oppositions. The following Table gives the approximate range of planetary variation in magnitude (see also diagram page 41).

Planet	Max. mag.	Mean oppos.	Min. mag.	Planet	Max.	Mean oppos.	Min.	Planet	Max.	Mean oppos.	Min.
Mars	−2·8	−1·85	−1·1	Saturn	−0·4	−0·16 to +0·89	0·9	Neptune	7·62	7·65	7·84
Jupiter	−2·5	−2·23	−2·1	Uranus	5·65	5·74	6·07	Pluto	12·8	14	15·2

Limiting Magnitude.—The *Limiting Magnitude* of a star catalogue—the index of its completeness, as omissions become inevitable at a certain stage—is that magnitude on the brighter side of which stars *omitted* from the catalogue about equal in number the stars on the fainter side *included* in the catalogue.

Colour Equation: Magnitude Equation.—The first is a small correction on the magnitudes in different catalogues to eliminate (*a*) the colour-selectivity of the instruments, atmosphere, &c., of the observatories responsible for them, which affects the results, especially in photographs; (*b*) the uncertain brightness-colour error, due to the eye, known as the *Purkinje Effect* (p. 42). The *Magnitude Equation* is a similar small correction, to remedy the error caused by transits of faint stars being ordinarily registered later than those of bright stars in the same position.

* Approximately that of *Pollux* π = 0″·101.

Luminosity: Surface Brightness.—The luminosity of a star differs from its magnitude in being the *actual* amount of light emitted by the star, instead of the apparent amount, judged by its brightness to the eye. It depends on the star's diameter and temperature, being the star's area (actual, not angular) multiplied by the amount of light it emits per square centimetre, or other unit—*i.e.*, by its *Surface Brightness*. The Sun's surface brightness is taken as mag. 0, and a star's relative surface brightness, + or −, is expressed in magnitudes (Table, p.viii)—symbolised by *J*. The luminosity relatively to other stars is given by the absolute magnitude, or brightness at 10 parsecs distance.

The higher the temperature, the greater the surface brilliancy; thus stars of the same absolute magnitude may differ greatly in size and surface brightness, for a low-temperature 'Giant' (p.20) must have a larger diameter than a high-temperature B-star, to be of the same absolute magnitude. From this relationship the diameter of stars can be calculated, independently of their distance, from the visual magnitudes, the surface brightness being obtained from the Type. The diameters that had been predicted on this basis were found to agree closely with the observed values.

Star-classification by their spectra.—Secchi in 1863-67 found that when the light emitted by different stars was analysed by the spectroscope, their spectra fell into four well-marked groups which graded into one another. In 1874, Vogel modified Secchi's scheme by adding two subordinate classes to Class I; another (Wolf-Rayet stars), to Class II; and including his third and fourth types as sub-divisions of the same order. Secchi's Types are now little used, except historically, but for very uncertain cases the I.A.U. defines them as follows (O5 was formerly Oe):—

TYPE I. O5-F5, predominant hydrogen lines.
„ II. F8-K5, prominent metallic lines.
TYPE III. M, titanium oxide bands.
„ IV. N and R, carbon bands.
TYPE V. Oa-Od, bright Wolf-Rayet lines.

About 1890, Pickering introduced the 'Harvard' classification, now universally adopted, lettering Secchi's original groups, with others, as in the table opposite, the various sections being spoken of as Type O, Type B, &c. Gradations or intermediates are indicated by combinations of the letters with figures denoting tenth parts. Thus B2 (a convenient abridgment for B2A) denotes a spectrum nearly like that of Class B, but estimated to be two-tenths of the way from B to the following Class A: and O5 (= O5B) means five-tenths of the way from O5 to the next Class, which is B, as Types W, O, are first in sequence—the original order was A, B, C, &c., but from later information it was altered, and some unneccessary letters dropped. Secchi's classes were based on visual, the Harvard on photographic, spectra, but on the whole they are fairly accordant. Type R was added 1908; S, 1922; W, 1935 (I.A.U., recommended).

B0 is the highest of Class B (the '0' is a starting cypher, not a letter), and the sequence is O8, O9, B0, B1, B2, B3, . . . B9, A0, A1, A2, &c.; the scale is thus a descending one. Sub-divisions a, b, c, &c., are used where there is uncertainty as to the details, but numbers are substituted when the necessary information is obtained: 'c' and 'n' stars, however, are not subdivisions, but stars having 'c' or 'n' characteristics (p.19). Variable stars are now classed at maximum (1922). For the sub-divisions included in a 'Type' when used in the average sense, or in statistical work, see next page. For details of Types O to N, see *H.A.*, Vol. 28; *H.C.* 145; and *Draper Catalogue*, 1924 (*H.A.*, vols., 90-99).

Early and *Late Type* stars denote Types B-A, and K-M, respectively, somewhat inconvenient survivals, in certain respects, of Vogel's assumption that Type I stars were the youngest, and Types III and IV the oldest, before the Giant and Dwarf divisions (p.20) were known. For the same reason, the *Main Sequence* is the downward progression of increasing redness, O, B, A, F, G, K, M—Types R, N, branching off at G; and S, perhaps, at K5 or M0. Type W may be the last stage of another sequence from Nova through planetary nebula to join Type O at the other end.

Russell Diagram:—This shows very effectively the Giant and Dwarf relationship and the Main sequence, the stars being plotted according to Type (temperature), and absolute magnitude (luminosity). By adding curves representing masses, the Diagram has been extended to exhibit the mass-luminosity relationship as well.

Star Colours.—Colour is an index to physical condition and temperature (p.21). A list of the mean colour of each Type, and sub-division, is given in Monthly Notices Royal Astron. Society, Vol. 84, p.22. Oa to Oc are given as greenish yellow; B2, B3, white; A0, pure yellow; A5, yellow; K2, orange yellow; M0, orange; R, orange red; Nc, deep orange red: intermediate types merge into the next colour. Colour also affects twinkling, as explained on page 38. The components of many double stars exhibit the curious phenomenon—sometimes merely optical—of being complementary in colour—orange and blue, or crimson and green, &c: for examples, see Notes Star Charts.

Relative Numbers of different Types (Shapley)—Of the 225,000 stars, to about mag. 10, in the Draper Catalogue, only some 2000 are of other types than B, A, F, G, K, M. Nearly 60,000 are brighter than about mag. 8½: 20,000 are essentially identical with the Sun, and 95 per cent are probably within 3000 light-years of us. A and K are most common in the Milky Way.

Type ...	O	B	A	F	G	K	M	N	R	S
Types included	...	*(B0-B5)*	*(B8-A3)*	*(A5-F2)*	*(F5, G0)*	*(G5-K2)*	*(K5-M8)*	...	...	...
No. of Stars ...	...	3,567	64,259	21,120	46,552	73,208	13,864			
Percentage; to Mag. 6¼	...	10·9	30·5	10·4	9·9	30·1	8·1	...	...	...
„ „ „ 8¼	...	2·5	26·7	11·0	16·7	35·4	7·6			

The Harvard (Draper) Spectral Classes.—The Table below gives the salient features*: the Roman numerals indicate Secchi's Classes (p. 18). The temperatures are those for a 'black body' (p. 21), and are more or less approximate, those below Type G (Sun = G0) being probably rather low. For the Radial velocity of each Type see page 21. Be, Me, Se, Oe, &c., stars denote B, M, S, O, &c. stars having bright emission lines (see p. 23).

'Type B,' 'Type A,' &c., when used in the general sense, or in statistical work, does not usually mean the series B0 to B9, or A0 to A9, but an *average* Type, in which A0, B0, &c., are approximately central, including the latter half of those lettered in the Type earlier, just as '2nd. magnitude' is not 2·0 to 2·9, but 1·5 to 2·5, or 1·6 to 2·5. Shapley's Table, opposite, indicates an (approximate) usual basis, but there is no definite rule: some begin Type B with O5.

VI. TYPE W. WOLF-RAYET STARS (at present in Type O). Continuous spectrum with many strong emission bands due to atoms of high ionisation potential: most important *He.* I, II, associated in a nitrogen sequence with *N* III, IV, V (Type W); or in a carbon one with *C* II, III, IV (Type W′) *O* II, III, IV, V: typical stars, W5, H.D. 187,282, W6, 16,523. (See *Trans., I.A.U.* 1938.)

V. TYPE O. WOLF-RAYET STARS (Greenish-white). Very high temperatures, large masses and velocities: bright bands in their spectra indicate connection with planetary nebulæ and final stage of Novæ. All in Milky Way, or Magellanic Clouds. Subdivisions Oa, Ob, Oc, Od (Wolf-Rayet stars proper); and Oe, abolished 1928, O5-O9 being substituted, with Wolf-Rayet bands described by affixing a, b, c, d, as Oeb. (35,000° K., 62,000° F.). *γ Velorum.*

I. TYPE B. ORION or HELIUM STARS (Bluish). Helium lines prominent: very brilliant and hot: large masses; mean density 1/10th Sun's. Very distant: small proper motions and mean velocities: strong Galactic concentration; brightest mostly belong to Local Cluster; great globes of glowing gas. (25,000° K., 44,000° F.). *ε* (B0), *δ, ζ Orionis*; *β Crucis.*

Type A. SIRIAN or HYDROGEN STARS (White). Balmer Hydrogen lines very intense, Helium absent. Most numerous Type after K. Predominate in low galactic latitudes. Greater proper motions than B. (11,000° K., 20,000° F.). *Sirius* (A0), *α Andromedæ, β Carinæ.*

TYPE F. SIRIAN-SOLAR or CALCIUM STARS (Yellow-white). Calcium H and K lines very prominent: Hydrogen lines much less intense, metallic lines increase. Much less numerous than A, but includes majority of known binaries, and large-proper-motion stars; little Galactic concentration. (7500° K., 12,200° F.). *Canopus* (F0), *γ Bootis, α Hydri.*

II. TYPE G. SOLAR STARS (Yellow). Hydrogen lines narrower and still less intense; H and K calcium lines prominent, and many fine, dark lines in spectra. Density of Dwarfs about 1½ times that of water. Move more rapidly than preceding types. Little Galactic concentration. (6000° K., 10,000° F.). *Sun, Capella,* (G0); *α¹ Centauri, β Hydri.*

TYPE K. ARCTURIAN or RED-SOLAR STARS (Orange-yellow). Hydrogen lines fainter, hydrocarbon bands appear; density of Giants about 1/10,000th Sun's: most numerous type, predominate on the whole in low galactic latitudes. (4200° K., 7000° F.). *Arcturus* (K0), *α Ursæ Maj.*; *α, β, Indi.*

III. TYPE M. ANTARIAN STARS (Orange). Spectra like that of the Sun, but with broad titanium oxide and calcium bands or flutings. Density of Giants less than 1/20,000th of Sun's; of Dwarfs, greater than Sun's. Very distant: higher mean velocities than B to K, in all directions; widely scattered. Fainter stars show a preference for the galactic centre (Sagittarius region). Sub-classes were Ma, Mb, Mc, Md (bright lines): Md was abolished 1922 (the 'emission' sign 'e' suffices), the others were made M0, M3, M8. (3000° K., 4900° F.). *Betelgeuse* (M0), *Antares, Mira.*

IV. TYPE N. CARBON STARS (Deep orange-red). Peculiar band spectra like those of comets and candle-flames, due to carbon compounds; two-thirds in or near Milky Way. Probably in a branch sequence, G, R, N. Sub-classes Na, Nb, (made N0 and N3, 1922), and Nc, the deepest red of all the stars (as *S Cephei*). (2600° K., 4200° F.) *Y Canum Ven.,* [*U Hydræ, 19 Piscium.*

TYPE P. Used for gaseous nebulae. *(For details see H.A., vol. 28).*

TYPE Q. Used for Novae. Divided meanwhile (1928) into Qa, Qb, Qc, Qd, Qu, Qx, Qy, Qz; the last has weak Wolf-Rayet bands, but, unlike those before it, no bright hydrogen lines. (See page 42; and *Trans. I.A.U.*, 1922, 1928).

TYPE R. (Orange-red). Carbon bands; visually resembles N, but photographically different, blue and violet being brighter; not so red as M or N: brightest, mag. 7. Probably joins main sequence at G, the branch sequence being G, R, N. Added 1908 (*H.C.* 145); mostly in N previously. (2300° C., 4500° F.). *B.D. −10° 5057* (R0), *C.D. −24° 12084.*

TYPE S. Red stars. Mostly long-period variables; very complicated spectra, bright hydrogen lines, absorption and emission lines, and some zirconium oxide absorption bands; perhaps a branch from K5 or M0. Added 1922; mostly in N previously. (See a list *Mt. W. Contr.* 252). ... ... *π¹ Gruis, R Andromedæ, R Cygni*

Notation for Peculiarities.—There are two sets of notations, one prefixed, the other affixed to the Type; 'earlier' means in the Type B direction'; 'later', in the M direction. (The letters may be combined, as O6k.)

Prefixed. (See full list and details *Tr. I.A.U.*, 1922, 1928).

- c All lines normally narrow and sharp (p.25); later than B0, hydrogen lines and enhanced lines abnormally strong.
- g Giant Stars. Enhanced lines fairly strong; low-temperature lines relatively weak; hydrogen lines strong.
- d Dwarf Stars. Enhanced lines weak, some calcium & titanium [lines strong.

('c' Not used earlier than B0; 'g' and 'd' than F0.)

Affixed.

- e Bright emission lines, except in P, Q: remarkable, e!
- eq *do.* ; with absorption line on the violet side.
- er *do.* ; bright lines conspic'sly 'reversed', dark centre.
- em Bright hydrogen & fairly conspicuous bright metallic lines.

Affixed—*contd.*

- ew Wolf-Rayet emission lines or bands: conspicuous, ew!
- k Stationary hydrogen and calcium lines.
- n Lines unusually wide or diffuse.
- p Peculiarities: symbol of the element most affected in
- ! Remarkable. [parenthesis: unidentified lines 'Un.').
- q Absorption line on the violet side (with e).
- s Lines sharp, but 'c' characteristic not present.
- v Indicates a variable spectrum.
- [ ] Forbidden lines; symbol of element in square brackets.

* Types C, D, E, &c., of the original scheme were found redundant.

Giant and Dwarf Stars.—Spectral type indicates the temperature; temperature regulates the surface brightness; and the surface brightness of a star multiplied by its area gives the luminosity or total amount of light emitted. This, again, regulates the absolute magnitude. Hence, when two stars of similar Type have different absolute magnitudes, they must have different light-emitting areas, and diameters. This is well shown on a *Russell Diagram (p.18)*.

Analysis of absolute magnitudes shows that on the one hand there is a continuous series of stars from Types M to B, with increasing temperatures, which have great and fairly constant absolute magnitudes, ranging from about +1·0 to −2·0, or about three magnitudes. On the other hand there is a reversed series from A to M, with decreasing temperatures, and absolute magnitudes falling off a magnitude or two as each successive Type below is reached.

Stars of the increasing-temperature series are known as *Giants*, those of the decreasing-temperature one as *Dwarfs*, because the Giant M-stars must have enormous diameters to appear as bright as they are with their low temperatures, while the Dwarf M-stars must be small in diameter to appear as faint as they are, with similar temperatures. These names, however, only apply literally to the M or late K stars of the two branches, as the difference in diameter between each branch continually lessens with each step forwards or backwards towards A and B, until, in these Types, the members of each series cannot be distinguished: from F0, however, Giant and Dwarf stars are known by their 'enhanced' and 'low temperature' lines (p. 25), the Giants having a lower temperature than the corresponding Dwarfs, which are bluer. The Dwarfs greatly out-number the Giants; the cooling stage probably lasts much longer.

Super-giants are about 1000 times brighter than the Sun, with absolute magnitudes greater than about −2·0, like *Betelgeuse*; mean *M* (abs. mag.) about −2·7. *Sub-giants*, a well-marked group, average about 10 times the Sun's brightness, with mean *M* = +2·3.

The *White Dwarfs*—exceptional stars like the companion of *Sirius (Sirius B)*—are stars of high temperature, yet so very faint, in proportion to their distances, that their diameters must be of planetary size, and their average density almost incredible—some of them millions of times that of water, their largely electron-stripped atoms being packed enormously closer than in the matter we know (see below). Being so faint, only the nearer ones can be seen.

Stellar Evolution.—These facts suggested the Hertzprung-Russell theory, that a star begins its visible life as a diffuse low-temperature M-giant. In accordance with 'Lane's Law'—that a gaseous body radiating heat, and contracting under its own gravity, must get hotter as long as it behaves as a perfect gas—the star gradually rises in temperature, and so passes into successive higher Types. At last a Type is attained—determined by its mass (see below). —at which radiation balances the energy supplied by contraction, and the star therefore begins to cool, and, entering the ranks of the Dwarfs, passes downwards through the same Types again to invisibiliy.

This theory, while it offers a very simple explanation of the Type-gradations, by no means explains all the facts, and from the phenomena of Novæ and White Dwarfs, it is now suspected that change of Type may be of a catastrophic nature, due to the collapse of a star.

Mass-Luminosity Law.—If stars are plotted according to mass and absolute magnitude (luminosity) they lie along a smooth curve on the whole, mass ÷ luminosity being practically a constant (except White Dwarfs). This *mass-luminosity* relationship enables star masses to be approximately calculated from the apparent magnitude and luminosity. A star's mass seems to determine its temperature, for only those of great mass attain Type B, and those of very great mass Type O. It now seems certain that as a star grows older its mass decreases, mass being converted into energy.

Period-Luminosity Curve.—Many stars vary in brightness, some irregularly, others in more or regular periods A certain type of these, known as Cepheids (p. 12), have the peculiarity that those of a given period have practically the same absolute magnitude (luminosity); the longer the period, the greater the absolute magnitude. The visual magnitude of a Cepheid star, of known period, will therefore give its distance. This property of Cepheids is of great importance in measuring the distance of extra-galactic objects, but the reason for it is not yet known.

Star Masses are only known directly in the case of binaries, the average binary system having about 1·8 times the Sun's mass (contracted, 1·8 ⊙); halving this, gives the average individual star mass as 0·9, or nearly that of the Sun The mass of non-binary stars is roughly calculable from mass and luminosity, see above.

Masses five or six times that of the Sun are not common, and no mass less than that of Kruger 60B, 1/6th of the Sun's, is known. The greatest known masses are the components of a mag. 6 O8 binary, *Plaskett's Star (H.D.* 47,129, combined absolute mag. −6·3), at least 158 and 113 times the mass of the Sun.

Star Densities.—Those of Giant M-stars are very small, less than that of air, being only some 1/10,000th to 1/20,000th of that of the Dwarf Sun, which is 1·42 times that of water; *Antares* has no greater average density than the vacuum in an electric bulb. To make up, their diameters are of the order of 100 to 500 million miles (see p. 21).

The White Dwarfs are at the other extreme; *Van Maanen's Star*, absolute mag. (visual) 14·4, is found to be about the size of the Earth, and some 300,000 times as dense as water—20 tons per cubic inch. A.C. + 70° 8247, a 13th mag. O0 star, is half the size of the Earth, and 36 million times denser than water = 620 tons per cubic inch!

Star Temperatures.—Spectral Type is chiefly a temperature phenomenon, and stellar temperatures can be measured by analysis of the 'energy distribution' in their spectra—that is, by ascertaining the point at which the intensity is greatest: the further the maximum intensity is towards the violet end, the higher is the temperature.

A star temperature so found, however, is not that of the interior (which in the Main Sequence is of the order of 30 million degrees K.), or of the surface, but is what is called the *Black Body* or *Effective Temperature*, which may be defined as the temperature of a 'perfect radiator' (say that of a sheet of lampblack, the nearest approach to it) which sends out the same amount of radiation per unit of area as that emitted by an equal area of the star. This is based on 'Stefan's Law'—viz., that the total radiation is proportional to the 4th power of the absolute temperature (see below), multiplied by a constant depending on the nature of the radiating surface. For the approximate effective temperatures of each Type, see p. 19. The White Dwarfs have central temperatures of the order of 15 million degrees K; the M Giants, only a few million degrees K. The lowest effective temperature known is about 2000°K.

The Colour Temperature of a star is determined from the *distribution* of intensity in the continuous background between the lines of its spectrum: it is always higher than the effective temperature based on the total radiation; the difference increases with the temperature. The average Colour temperature of the A0 stars (18,000°K.) is the zero.

The Absolute Temperature is the temperature above *Absolute Zero*, the temperature of a gas containing no heat, −273°C. (−460°F.), usually stated in degrees 'K' (Kelvin), which is the ordinary Centigrade temperature *plus* 273° C.

To convert K° into Centigrade degrees, subtract 273°; into Fahrenheit,* multiply by 9, divide by 5, and subtract 460°.

Opacity and Radiation Pressure are factors of great importance in the theory of stellar interiors. The first is the resistance of the gaseous material to the outward flow of radiation—hydrogen, the lightest element, offering least resistance; the opacity of the highly-ionised atoms in stellar interiors is very great. *Radiation Pressure*, the momentum of radiant energy, and proportional to the 4th power of the absolute temperature, is very great inside a star, and largely contributes to the support of the super-incumbent matter. It also seems responsible for comets' tails; as the weight of spheres diminishes as the cube, and their projected areas as the square, of the diameter, for exceedingly small particles in the comet, when near enough to the Sun, a point is reached at which radiation pressure exceeds the gravitational pull, and these particles will be repelled from the Sun.

Star Diameters.—The angular diameters of the stars are far below the limit of direct angular measurement, but, in 1921, interferometer measures showed that *Betelgeuse*, *Antares*, *Arcturus*, and later, *Mira*, have angular diameters of ·047″, ·041″, ·022″, and ·056″, corresponding to 217-, 400-, 210-, and 125 million miles respectively, less or more, according to the parallax adopted. (The mileage for any parallax may be found by the simple rule given below). *Betelgeuse*, however, apparently pulsates, varying from 0″·034 to 0″·047. Stellar diameters can also be calculated on the basis of surface brightness and visual magnitude (see 'Luminosity').

The diameters of White Dwarfs are of planetary size, *Sirius B* being rather smaller than Neptune; and A.C. + 70° 8247, roughly half the size of the Earth.

Diameter in Miles.—Multiply the angular diameter in seconds of arc by 93,000,000, and divide answer by the annual parallax.
„ **Kilometres.**— „ „ „ „ „ 150,000,000, „ „ „ „ „

Stellar Rotation.—In some spectra all the lines are equally wide, mostly faint, and fairly sharp-edged; the metallic lines being wide, the Stark effect cannot be responsible. The wide lines are interpreted as being due to the star's rapid rotation, the widening being the effect of the lines produced by each limb, which are displaced in opposite directions. The most rapid rotation yet found is that of *Altair*, 260 km./sec. (160 m./sec.), which rotates in about 7 hrs., although its diameter is about 1½ times that of the Sun. Smallest velocity detectable, about 30 km./sec.

Star Velocities are best known from the radial velocities, found by the spectroscope with considerable accuracy: it gives the minimum-possible value for the 'space' or real velocity, which, in general, is greater, but is known less accurately, its other factors of parallax, proper motion, and solar motion, being more or less uncertain. The space-velocities cannot, however, differ greatly from the radial ones, unless the cross velocity is relatively great. As cross velocities, on the average, apparently do not differ greatly from the radial ones, the average space-velocity may therefore be taken to be of the order of 1½ times the radial velocity, *i.e.* the approximate resultant of two equal velocities at right angles. Velocities are expressed in kilometres or miles per second (contracted, 'km./sec.', m./sec.).

The majority of star velocities are under 30 kilometres (19 miles) per second, those of 50 km. (31 miles) are not common; but there are notable exceptions, RZ Cephei having the enormous velocity of 1100 km. (680 miles) per second. This is far surpassed by the spiral nebulæ, which seemingly speed through space with velocities approximately proportional to their distance (about 500-550 km./secs. or 310-340 m./secs. per megaparsec), up to 200 million light-years. or more, for which the corresponding speed is some 2650 million kilometres (1650 million miles) per day (Table p. xi).

On the average, velocities tend to increase with advancing Type, as shown by the Table of approximate average radial velocities *(Campbell, &c.)* below: the velocity also increases as the absolute magnitude increases. The velocities of the few R stars known, fall into three groups; under 10 km./sec., about 40 km./sec., and high velocity 250-380 km./sec.

Radial Velocity:— *Type*	O	B	A	F	G	K	M	Me	N	R	Se	P
Km. per sec. ...	25½ km.	6½ km.	11 km.	14½ km.	15 km.	16¾ km.	17 km.	35 km.	18 km.	21 km.	24 km.	30 km.
Miles per sec. ...	16 miles	4 m.	7 m.	9 m.	9 m.	11 m.	11m.	22 m.	11 m.	13 m.	15 m.	18½ m.
Mean abs. mag. (Dwarfs)	−4·5	−2·4	+0·6	+2·6	+4·4	+6·2	+9·8	...	...	...	...	(gaseous nebulæ)
„ „ (Giants)				−0·6	+0·3	+0·6	0·0	−0·5	(−1·5)	(−1·5)	(+0·4)	

* Approximately, within 32°.

Stellar Equipartition of Energy.—While there are considerable differences in the velocities of individual stars in each Type, stars of low velocity, *on the average*, have large masses, and those of high velocity small masses, The kinetic energy of each star—the velocity squared multiplied by half the mass—is also, on the average, approximately a constant quantity. This has been shown to result from the inter-action of the stars on one another over enormous periods. The B stars, however, do not conform to the rule.

Light-Absorption in Space seems to be almost negligible, as the distances derived from the brightness and diameter of the remotest spiral nebulæ are fairly accordant. Within our System, however, especially near the Galactic plane, evidence favours a slight absorption, which *reddens* the stars—*i.e.*, lessens their maximum intensity, displacing it nearer the red than the normal for their Type—making absolute magnitudes more than they should be, and distances derived from them too great. For 0·7 mag. absorption per 1000 parsecs, at 500 parsecs the real distance would be 14% less than the apparent; at 1000 parsecs, 24% less; at 5000 parsecs, 56% less; but later evidence favours a smaller absorption, 0·40 mag. per 1000 parsecs being the most probable for uniform interstellar absorption in the Galactic system.

Colour Excess is the greater redness of a star (or external galaxy) over a normal star of the same spectral Type; it implies some special factor, such as giant and dwarf difference (p. 20), or space reddening.

IV. SPECTROSCOPY.

Spectroscopy has now become of such far-reaching importance in astronomical research that some knowledge of its salient facts and terminology has become a *sine qua non* for understanding the differences between the various Types of stars, and the references in current astronomical literature. A similar knowledge of the atomic changes giving rise to the various spectra is also useful: the following brief outline may help those unfamiliar with the subject

Light is supposed to be due to undulations or waves in a (hypothetical) light-transmitting medium known as the ether; these light-waves are of infinite variety in their crest-to-crest or 'wave-length' distances, some being exceedingly short, others comparatively long, but the eye only perceives those within narrow limits. The shortest wave-lengths visible produce the sensation of violet in the eye; those about twice as long, the sensation of red; those of intermediate wave-length give the sensation of blue, green, yellow, orange, &c. The light from an object is analysed by passing it through a slit in the spectroscope 1/500th to 1/1000th inch wide, then either (*a*) through a prism or prisms; or (*b*) letting it fall obliquely on a finely-ruled 'grating': in both cases the narrow beam of light is spread out, or 'dispersed,' either into a long coloured band, or, for some kinds of light, into a series of separate hair-like coloured lines. (*a*) forms what is known as a *prismatic* spectrum, in which the wave-lengths at the red end are much less spread out than those at the violet end; (*b*), a *normal* or *diffraction* spectrum, in which the dispersion is uniform throughout, and spreads out the red end to better advantage than a prism does; the loss of light in gratings, however, is so considerable, that they cannot be used for faint spectra. The narrower the slit, the purer, but fainter, the band spectrum.

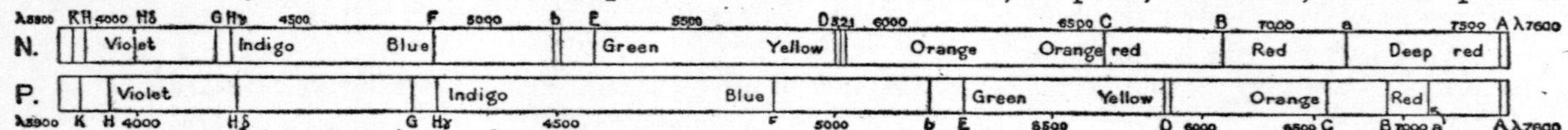

N. 'Normal' or 'Diffraction' spectrum; dispersion uniform. P. 'Prismatic' spectrum, same length: small dispersion red end, large at violet end

*A λ7594, *Telluric*	C λ6563, *Hydrogen, Hα*	D_2 λ5890, *Sodium*	E λ5270, *Iron & Ca.*	F λ4861, *Hydrogen, Hβ*	H λ3968, *Calcium*
B 6867, ,,	D_1 5896, *Sodium.*	D_3 5876, *Helium*	b_1 5184, *Magnesi'm*	G 4308, *Iron (& Calc'm)*	K 3934, ,,

Angstrom Units.—The crest-to-crest distances, though very minute, can be measured with great accuracy, and are expressed in *Angstrom Units* (contracted, A.U., or angstroms)—each 1/ten-millionth (10^{-7}) of a millimetre, or a 'tenth-metre'—symbolised by the Greek letter λ (denoting Ang. wave-length), followed by the number of ten-millionths from crest to crest.†

The International Primary Standard wave-length to which other lines are referred, is λ6438·4696, the wave-length of a red line emitted by gaseous cadmium, and units on this basis are designated 'I.A.' (International angstrom), as the original A.U. was slightly over-valued. There are 'Secondary' and 'Tertiary' standards, using the lines of other elements. (See *Tr. I.A.U.* 1922-28).

The Greek letter μ is sometimes used instead of λ, especially for the longer wave-lengths, indicating that the figures are in thousandths of a millimetre (microns) instead of ten-millionths; μμ, or millionths of a millimetre, are also sometimes used. Thus μ 0·64384696 = μμ 643 84696 = λ6438·4696. λλ is used as the plural of λ. (λ = μ × 10,000 ; μ = λ ÷ 10,000).

The Visible Spectrum ranges from about λ3900 in the extreme violet, to λ7600 in the extreme red, but it has no definite limits, as eyes vary in sensitivity. Unseen, beyond the violet, is the *ultra-violet* spectrum, of ever-shortening wave-lengths, recorded by ordinary photographic plates up to about λ2000, and by special apparatus to λ150. Beyond the red, also unseen, is the *infra-red*, of ever-lengthening wave-lengths, sometimes called the 'heat spectrum'; it is traceable to λ12,000 by special photographic plates, thereafter by other means, to the limit of the solar spectrum, about λ50,000—but there are wave-lengths far longer and shorter than these limits. Oxygen in our atmosphere, and an ozone layer high up, absorbs all radiation from outside shorter than λ2900, except Cosmic; in the infra-red, less than 1% of the solar radiation is of greater wave-length than λ40,000 (4μ).

Conventional Divisions of Wave-length (boundaries indefinite, each kind gradually merges into the next: λ = angstroms).

γ-rays (Invisible)		X-rays (Invisible)		Ultra-violet	Violet light	Red light	Infra-red	Hertzian
Hard, to:	Soft, to:	Hard, to:	Soft, to:	(Invisible), from:	(Visible) from:	(Visible) to:	(Invisible)	(Radio)
·000,000,000,5 cm.	0·000,000,04	0·000,000,001 cm.	0·000,000,25	0·000,001,4 cm.	0·000,039 cm.	0·000,076 cm.	from λ7600	0·1 metres
λ0·05	λ4·0	λ0·1	λ25	λ140	λ3900, or	λ7600, or	to ·003 cm.	to 25,000 ,,
					0·39μ	0·76μ	to 30μ	

Cosmic (invisible), 0·000,000,000,004 cm. (λ0·0004, see p. 25).

The Effective Wave-length of a radiating body may be stated generally as the wave-length at its average intensity, *for defined conditions*—visually, photographically, &c.—the wave-length at which the amount of such radiation is equal on each side.

* Fraunhofer's letters run from red to violet; violet to red is now preferred—wave-length order. † *Frequency* is also used—the number of undulations per second.

Emission and Absorption Spectra.—An incandescent solid, liquid, or gas under *high* pressure, gives what is called a *continuous spectrum*, when the light it emits is passed through the prisms of the spectroscope. In other words, it emits light of all wave-lengths between the deepest red and the deepest violet. Under ordinary pressures, however, each elementary substance in the gaseous state emits, when excited, only certain definite wave-lengths peculiar to itself, the rest of the spectrum being missing; in the spectroscope these appear, when a narrow slit is used, as a series of isolated hair-like bright coloured lines, forming an 'emission' or bright-line spectrum, and the appearance of these particular lines always indicates the presence of that element.

On the other hand, each element in the gaseous state cuts out or absorbs, from continuous-spectrum light traversing it, the *identical wave-lengths that it emits when excited*, so that in the spectroscope, the light seen after the absorption is no longer continuous, but broken up by a series of hair-like dark lines (the image of the slit) where the absorbed wave-lengths are missing. These dark lines occupy the same positions as the bright lines of the emission spectrum, and are called *absorption lines*; they not only indicate the presence of the element, but also tell that it is at a lower temperature than the light-source behind it, as absorption only takes place if the emission of the absorbing substance is less than that of the emitting substance behind. Absorption lines are also found in the ultra-violet and infra-red. Many elements are represented by hundreds of lines—sometimes thousands, as iron.

Fraunhofer Lines.—The dark lines of the solar spectrum are called after Fraunhofer, who re-discovered them in 1814, and lettered the most prominent ones as in the Table above, which also gives the corresponding element and wave-length: (L), (M), &c., in the ultra-violet, were added later, and the original (H^1) and (H^2) re-lettered (H) and (K). But as the same letters are also used for star Types, and as chemical symbols for elements, to prevent confusion the I.A.U. recommended as follows, in 1922:—

Letters denoting Fraunhofer lines in astronomical works: should be printed in ordinary Roman capitals, in parentheses.
„ „ **Chemical Symbols** „ „ „ „ „ *italic* capitals.

The (H) Fraunhofer line (calcium), must not be confused with $H\alpha$, $H\beta$, $H\gamma$, $H\delta$, &c., lines—so lettered by Vogel—which denote the 'Balmer' series of hydrogen lines belonging to the normal hydrogen spectrum (only four appear in the ordinary solar spectrum); other 'series' of hydrogen lines appear under different conditions. $H\gamma$ is λ 4340; $H\delta$, λ 4102. b_2 (λ 5173) is magnesium.

Telluric or atmospheric lines in the spectrum as (A), (B), oxygen; and (a) water vapour (λ 7185), result from absorption by the oxygen and water vapour in our atmosphere, and have no place, or only a very faint place, in spectra before they reach the Earth.

Bands, groups of very close lines—one side sharp, the 'head'—in low-temperature spectra indicate a *molecular spectrum*, i.e., one produced by molecules, atoms of two elements chemically combined; the ordinary spectrum is that of the normal or neutral atom (see below). A *fluted* spectrum is one that has recurring groups of lines or narrow bands, giving it a fluted appearance.

Flame, Arc, and Spark Spectra.—The lines produced by each element are not the same under all circumstances, being changed or modified under different conditions of temperature, pressure, &c., especially the former. The *Flame*, *Furnace*, or low-temperature spectrum given in a Bunsen burner (some 2000° C.) has comparatively few lines, and differs in some respects from that of the *Arc* spectrum obtained in the electric arc at a temperature of some 3600° C., in which new lines may appear. The *Spark* spectrum, again, produced by high tension discharges, has different characteristics from that of the arc one, some 'low-temperature' lines, that have been fading as the temperature rose, disappearing altogether, while other lines are '*enhanced*' (p. 25), that is, have grown more intense. Spectra can be studied up to temperatures of some 20,000° C., by electrically-exploded wires.

Doppler Effect, or the displacement of the lines as the result of motion of the light-source in the line of sight, is of great importance, as it enables radial velocities and rotation periods to be found, and spectroscopic binaries to be discovered. If a source of light is approaching the observer, any lines seen in its spectrum will not be in their normal positions, but some distance nearer the violet end of the spectrum, or if the light-source is receding, nearer the red end of the spectrum. As the displacement is proportional to the velocity, the radial velocity can be calculated by identifying a series of lines and measuring the amount of shift.

In the case of a binary star, each star produces its own set of lines; when both stars are in the line of sight, the two sets are super-imposed and appear as a single set, there being no orbital radial motion towards us, as their motions are at right angles to the line of sight. But when the stars open out again, one star is moving towards, and the other away from us, so that the two sets of lines separate in opposite directions, and reveal the duplicity, and the respective orbital radial speeds; the same principle applies to the opposite limbs of the Sun, of a rotating planet, or of a star (p. 21), one of which is moving towards, the other from us.

Interstellar Lines.—Sometimes in Novæ, and in O- and B-type binaries, which are very distant, a third set of practically stationary lines of calcium and sodium appears. These lines are now known to result from the presence of interstellar matter, uniformly distributed, in general, through our System, and which rotates practically with the Galaxy: in stars nearer than say 1000 parsecs, it does not reveal its presence, because their light does not traverse a sufficient length of the absorbing medium to produce a perceptible effect. The more distant the star, the stronger the lines, which property can be used to find the star's distance (p. 14).

Zeeman Effect.—If a magnetic field is present, lines normally single may split up into two or more lines—from which the polarity of sunspots, and the position of the Sun's magnetic axis are found.

Stark Effect.—The splitting up of lines by an electric field; those of helium and hydrogen are greatly affected, those of the metals but little; thus it can be distinguished from the Zeeman effect. The hazier the helium and hydrogen lines, the stronger is the electric field, and the more prominent the forbidden lines; also the denser the stellar atmosphere must be, to give the electric field required to allow the forbidden lines to be produced in quantity. (See also Stellar Rotation, p. 21).

The Atom and its Properties.—The varied stellar spectra, and most of the above 'effects', are due to internal changes in the atoms of the elements in the stellar atmospheres, under different temperature and pressure conditions; the following main facts underlie the various phenomena, on the Rutherford-Bohr theory, which explains them well, though not completely.

The atoms of an element are the smallest particles distinguishable by chemical means; those of each element differ in weight and properties, but all are built up of the same fundamentals—*protons*, *electrons*, and energy. Each proton (*i.e.* hydrogen nucleus, see p. 24) has a constant positive charge of electricity; and each electron (mass only 1/1847th that of the nucleus), an equal negative charge. In the normal atom, these charges balance, and there being no electric field, in this condition it is called a *neutral atom*.

The Structure of the Atom.—Atoms are pictured as miniature sun-and-planet systems, the atom of each element being supposed to consist of a nucleus (extremely small, even compared with the tiny atom, and itself composed of protons and neutrons, see below), positively charged, and surrounded by one or more 'shells' (orbits) of electrons: each electron carries a single negative electric charge, each orbit only one electron.

In its normal (non-ionised) state, an atom is not charged with electricity, hence the number of unit positive charges (protons) in its nucleus is equal to the number of electrons which surround it; this number is called the *atomic number* (different from the *atomic weight* or mass of the element), and determines its chemical properties. Elements range in atomic number from 1 (hydrogen, the simplest, with one electron) to 92 (uranium, with 92 electrons revolving round the nucleus).

The K-ring, &c.—The electron-orbits are spaced in groups, each member of which has about the same energy and diameter, but may differ in eccentricity. These groups are known as *Rings*—usually, more appropriately, as *shells*, because the members of each group presumably move in different planes, their diameters being about the same.

The group nearest the nucleus consists of two orbits of equal energy known as the *K-ring*, which has the lowest energy of all the rings; next comes the *L-ring*, with eight orbits; then the *M-ring*, with 18 orbits, and so on; the outer ring of an element's electrons may contain only one electron. The chemical and spectroscopic quantities of an element are largely determined by the number of electrons in its outermost layer; these are also the most easily 'excited' or 'ionised' (knocked off, see below).

Collisions.—The atoms of a gas, under the action of the heat which it contains, rush about at very high speeds—to which gas pressure is due—and are incessantly colliding; the higher the absolute temperature (p. 21), the greater their speed, and the more violent the collisions. In a rarefied gas—*i.e.*, one at a very low pressure—the journey without any collision, or *free path*, of the atom is long, the distance between the atoms being relatively great; collisions are therefore less frequent than in a dense gas.

Molecules.—At ordinary terrestrial temperatures, gases do not exist as single atoms but as *molecules*, composed of a pair (or more) of atoms in combination, either of the same or a different element; when the temperature rises sufficiently, however, molecules are *dissociated*—*i.e.*, resolved into single atoms—few exist even at the lowest stellar temperatures. The speed of the molecules composing a gas is proportional to the square roots of:—*(a)* their molecular weight, inversely, *(b)* the absolute temperature, directly; the lighter the gas, and the higher the temperature, the greater the velocity of the molecules—each gas having its own velocity for a given temperature. Left to themselves, the molecules would dissipate into space, but on a sufficiently massive body, the gravitational force retains them with a force depending on the body's mass and radius—an important factor in planetary atmospheres.

The Velocity of Escape is the velocity at which a planet's mass ceases to be able to retain a gas (p. 35). Hydrogen, the lightest element, is lost first, then helium, water vapour, oxygen, nitrogen; carbonic acid last, but at velocities no greater than a quarter of the velocity of escape, gases dissipate into space rather rapidly. For the velocities of escape, see p. viii.

Quanta.—The energy component of an ('excited,' see below) atom is stored up in (popularly) 'energy-atoms,' which cannot be sub-divided. Each of these is known as a *Quantum* (plural, quanta), and represents energy equivalent to that of radiation of some particular wave-length, quanta of long wave-length having small, those of short wave-length great, energy. (*Short* and *long* wave-length, as general terms, denote those at and beyond the blue and red ends of the spectrum, respectively).

There are quanta corresponding to all wave-lengths, each element having its own particular quanta of energy, corresponding to those wave-lengths of radiation which its atoms emit or absorb under different conditions: only quanta with nearly these wave-lengths can effect 'transitions' in that kind of atom, but those of shorter wave-length may 'ionise' the atom—*i.e.*, knock off one or more of its electrons (see below). The amount of short wave-length energy in a gas depends on its absolute temperature; thus, at high temperatures, short wave-length quanta are more plentiful than long ones. To sum up; in a stellar atmosphere:—

Temperature is an index of (*a*) the number of atomic collisions per second, for a given pressure; (*b*) the speed of the atoms; (*c*) the violence of the collisions; (*d*) the proportion of short wave-length energy.

Pressure only affects the frequency of the collisions, by increasing or decreasing the distance between the atoms.

Transitions.—When all the electrons of a neutral atom are revolving in the orbits nearest the nucleus, the atom is said to be in its *lowest energy* or *ground* (normal) state. But (*a*) by a sufficiently violent collision with an electron or another atom, or (*b*) by encounter with, and absorption of, a quantum of energy of wave-length the same as one of its own fundamental quanta, an atom may undergo *transition*, being 'raised' or lifted to a 'higher level'—*i.e.*, of energy, and from that, it may be, to still higher and higher levels, the electron being forced out into an orbit of larger diameter, in accordance with certain laws. *Forbidden transitions* are those forbidden by these laws, though they may occur in certain unusual sequences or steps.

Excitation.—At every transition of an electron to a larger orbit, a quantum of definite wave-length is absorbed by the atom, which is then said to be *excited*: it thus becomes a greater and greater reservoir of energy as the excitation increases; whatever the amount of excitation, however, it still remains a 'neutral' atom.

If left undisturbed, an excited atom 'falls' back to its lowest energy state in a hundred-millionth of a second, emitting in the process as many quanta of the same wave-lengths as it has absorbed; the process may be accomplished in stages. Certain transitions, however, are *metastable*—that is, if left to themselves, excited atoms in that state may continue in it for hundreds of thousands of times longer than ordinary excited atoms are able to do, sometimes even for seconds.

Ionisation.—An electron of a neutral atom may not only be raised to a larger orbit, but may also be completely knocked off, and left to travel on its own account; the atom is then *ionised*, and is no longer neutral, but positively charged, the negative electron being lost. Ionisation may be caused (*a*) by a sufficiently violent collision; (*b*) by encounter with a quantum of short wave-length, with more than sufficient energy to lift an electron to the outermost level. Ionised atoms may also be excited.

Atoms may be singly, doubly, trebly, &c., ionised. The neutral atom is indicated by the chemical symbol of the element with the Roman numeral I affixed, as *O*I*, neutral oxygen; for singly and doubly ionised, II, III, are added, and so on, as *O*II, *O*III.

An older system affixed a small + for single ionisation, ++ for double, and so on, instead of Roman numerals, as O^{+}, O^{++}; still further back, the atoms causing enhanced lines were known as protocalcium, protomagnesium, &c.

Atoms vary in the amount of energy required to excite and ionise them, and the amount of energy denoted by 1 (electron-) volt† is taken as the unit of measurement. The number of (electron-) volts required to excite, or to ionise, the atom of each element, is called its *Excitation* and *Ionisation Potentials*, the latter, of course, being greater than the former (see Table, p. xi).

* Large capitals are also used, but the small capitals are much clearer.

† Somewhat different meaning from the ordinary volt.

The Mass of the Atom, or *atomic weight*, consists almost entirely of the mass of the nucleus, and ranges from that of the hydrogen atom (approx. unity, 1·007), to the 238 of the uranium atom (the standard is oxygen, 16). Generally, but not always. the weight of the atom increases as the atomic number. Several elements may exist having identical atomic numbers, but differing in mass (atomic weight). Such elements, which are chemically identical, are called *isotopes.* Thus, in ordinary common salt, the chlorine (atomic *number*, 17) consists of a mixture of two isotopes of masses (or atomic *weights*) 35 and 37, while hydrogen as normally found contains traces of an isotope of mass 2 (deuterium or heavy hydrogen, symbol *D*).

Rays.—The heaviest elements and their isotopes, and some of the isotopes of the lighter elements, are *radio-active*, that is to say, their nuclei break up spontaneously, into other nuclei and particles, some of which (electrons or β rays, helium nuclei or α rays) may be ejected at very high speeds—when fastest, and most penetrating, being known as *hard* rays; when slower, *soft* rays. They also give out electro-magnetic radiations, called γ rays, which resemble X-rays, but are of harder (*i.e.*, shorter) wave-length.

When an α ray (a rapidly-moving helium nucleus) strikes another nucleus it may cause it to break up into lighter nuclei. In these changes, uncharged nuclei of mass 1 (*neutrons*), and particles of extremely small mass (*neutrinos*), are sometimes emitted. They can be detected only when moving at high speeds, and being small and uncharged have great penetrating power.

Cosmic radiation, arriving from unknown sources in space, may consist either of very high speed 'cathode' or β rays (moving electrons) or of electro-magnetic radiation of even shorter wave-length than γ rays. This radiation, striking atoms, may give rise to rapidly-moving *positrons*, similar to electrons but carrying a positive instead of a negative charge of electricity.

The following Table shows the relationship of some of the lighter charged particles and atoms (the mass rises with the speed, increasing enormously as the speed approaches that of light). The third column gives an idea of the bulk of the particle—for the more the atom is ionised (p. 24), the less is its bulk, especially when completely ionised.

Name	Total charge	Approx. Mass	No. of electrons
Neutrino ...	0	0	0
Positron ...	+1	0	0
Electron (β Ray)	−1	0	0
Neutron ...	0	1	0

Name	Total charge	Approx. Mass	No. of electrons
Proton (Ionised *H*)	+1	1	0
Hydrogen atom (*H*)	0	1	1
Deuteron (Ionised *D*)	+1	2	0
Deuterium atom (*D*)	0	2	1

Name	Charge	Mass	electrons
α Particle (dbly ionised *He*)	+2	4	0
Singly ionised (*He*) ...	+1	4	1
Helium atom (*He*) ...	0	4	2
... ...	...	...	...
... ...	...	...	...

Sets of Lines.—Each state of the atom gives rise to a different set of lines in the spectrum, the neutral atom causing one set, excited atoms other sets, and variously-ionised atoms others still; pressure also affects the appearance of the lines. And in stellar atmospheres of similar composition, for a given temperature and pressure there is always definite proportion of atoms in each state.

The strength of a line is proportional to the number of atoms producing it; strong lines indicate plentiful atoms in that condition, faint lines relative scarcity. Strong lines usually have *Wings—i.e.*, shading on both sides of the *Core*, or line itself.

Contours of Lines.—The degree of blackness at any part of the shading of a winged line, with reference to the background, is known as the *Contour* of the line at that point—so called because the energy-curve obtained by plotting the various intensities according to wave-length and blackness, is analogous to the gradient-curve obtained from the contour lines on a map.

Enhanced Lines, in a spectrum, are due to the normal atoms becoming ionised, losing one or more electrons as the combined result of higher temperature and altered pressure (*Saha Effect*); each element has its own ionisation conditions, thus the presence (or non-presence) of certain lines in stellar spectra affords a clue to the physical conditions in the stars' atmospheres.

Forbidden Lines are produced by possible, but very unlikely, 'transitions' (see page 24) in the atom, which cannot directly return to the ground state, but only through other transitions; an electric field, however, cancels the unlikeliness, and with a field of sufficient strength the lines become visible. The appearance of forbidden lines in a star's atmosphere indicates that it is dense, the electric field being due to the close ionised atoms and free electrons, but in a nebula they become possible as the result of the extreme tenuity—some 1/1000-millionth of an atmosphere—and 'weak' (*i.e.*, not too strong) radiation of very high energy, such as the short wave-length radiation from O and B stars.

Ultimate Lines.—Those fundamental lines of an element that alone persist under great rarefaction. When about the region of the spectrum which cannot ordinarily be observed, those that can be observed are known as *Raies ultimes.*

Interpretation of Spectra.—At very low pressures, as in the Giant stars (p. 20), for a given temperature the wave-length energy available is the same, and the violence of collision the same, as in dense stars; excited and ionised atoms are also present in both. But when an atom is ionised, the distances apart in a rarefied gas being great, there is less chance of its recapturing an electron, so that the proportion of ionised atoms is greater, and that of the neutral atoms less; the Giant star will, therefore, have stronger ionised-atom lines and weaker neutral-atom lines, than those in the spectrum of a dense star of about the same temperature; its lines will also be narrow and sharp—the '**c**' characteristic (p. 19). In dense stars, on the other hand, distances apart being small, ionised atoms soon recapture an electron, thus the neutral-atom lines are strong, the ionised-atom lines faint.

At the low temperature of the furnace spectrum, the lines of the excited atoms are faint (being chiefly those of the more-easily excited elements), while those of the normal (lowest energy-state) atoms are strong, the proportion of the latter atoms being the greatest. With rising temperature, owing to the more violent collisions and the greater supply of short wave-length quanta, the excited-atom lines grow stronger, owing to the ever-increasing quantity of atoms in that condition, and at last, at the arc spectrum temperature, ionised lines of the easily-ionised elements also begin to appear—some even appear in the furnace spectrum.

At a later stage, the neutral-atom lines disappear, those of the easily-ionised atoms first, the more refractory later. Thus the spark (lower-temperature) spectrum has faint neutral lines and strong enhanced or ionised lines, because ionised atoms now preponderate; faint lines of the atoms most easily doubly-ionised will also begin to appear in the lower-temperature spark spectrum.

At still higher temperatures, the ionised lines also disappear, being gradually replaced by the lines of doubly and trebly ionised atoms, and finally, at the highest obtainable spark temperature, and the still higher temperature of the O stars, hardly any lines are left in the visible spectrum except those of hydrogen and ionised helium—the latter of which has a very high ionisation potential. Lines of other elements, however, exist, but mostly in 'inaccessible' (unobservable) positions in the ultra-violet.

Planetary and Gaseous Nebulæ, on the other hand, in which the distances between the atoms is enormous, do not shine by their own light, but by absorption and re-emission of short wave-length radiation of O and B stars within them; they contain atoms which are doubly and singly ionised.

V. THE SUN, MOON, AND PLANETS.

The Sun, as an object for small telescopes, is of little interest unless sunspots are visible: special precautions are required in observing it so as not to injure the eyesight (see p. 40).

The disc of the Sun visible on ordinary occasions, known as the *photosphere*, presents a granular or 'rice-grain' appearance in large telescopes. Even in a small instrument of 2 or 3 inches aperture, the surface will show a mottled appearance, when the air is steady and definition good; but this mottling is of a coarser texture than that delicate granular appearance seen under higher powers with large instruments. *Faculæ*, *i.e.*, irregular, more or less streaky patches, somewhat brighter than the average surface, may generally be seen. They are elevations above the general level of the photosphere, and exist on every part of the disc, but are most numerous in the neighbourhood of sunspots. They are best seen near the limb or edge of the disc, since the photosphere in this region is perceptibly darker than at the centre of the disc, having only some 37 per cent of the brilliancy, according to Pickering. This is due to the absorption by the Sun's atmosphere of the light coming from within, which has to traverse a much greater depth of atmosphere at the limb, before reaching the Earth, than that coming from the centre: it therefore appears darker to us, contrasted with the faculæ, which have not lost so much light owing to their greater elevation. The darkening is specially noticeable in solar photographs.

The Sun's Rotation may be traced by the daily motion of the spots across the disc from east to west, the 'synodic' apparent rotation period, as seen from the Earth, averaging 27¼ days: spots may thus be visible for about a fortnight at a time. The sidereal or true rotation period is about 25 days near the Equator, and 27 days at 35°; the synodic rotation period, at these latitudes, varies in about the same proportion. The mean sidereal rotation period at present used in the *N.A.* and *A.E.* is 25·38 days (27·2753d. synodic), but a 25·2-day sidereal period, 27·1 synodic, is perhaps nearer the true value, being that favoured in the recurrence of sunspots, faculæ, flocculi, prominences, and magnetic storms. The Sun's axis of rotation is inclined 7¼° from the vertical to the Ecliptic plane (see p. 40).

Carrington's Series of Rotations (25·38 day), used for statistics, has as zero meridian the Sun's prime meridian that passed through the ascending node at 0h., G.C.T., Jan. 1, 1854; No. 1 began Nov. 9, 1853; 1101, 1936, Jan. 2·74 (17h. 46m).

Sunspots vary in size from small 'pores,' as the smallest are termed, to groups so large as to be visible to the naked eye, on occasion. A sunspot presents the appearance of a dark irregular spot, or *umbra*, surrounded by a less dark portion, or *penumbra*; the *umbra*, however, is only apparently dark by comparison with its surroundings, being actually brighter than the electric arc, though its darkest portion, the *nucleus*, has only about 1 per cent of the brightness of the average surface: very black, round spots, known as *nucleoli*, are often seen in the umbra. *Bridges* from the photosphere, often intensely bright, may frequently be seen gradually encroaching on and dividing up the penumbra and umbra; in large spots, these can easily be seen with a 3-inch telescope, or even less. The size of spots varies from about 500 miles to some 80,000 miles in diameter. Those over 15,000 miles are ***Naked-eye Spots***, visible without a telescope, when the Sun's brightness is sufficiently reduced by cloud, mist, or dark glass. The diameter of the spot, including the penumbra, may usually be roughly reckoned as being three times the diameter of the umbra.

The umbra is usually some 2000 to 6000 miles lower than the general surface, which results in the *Wilson Effect*, the apparent displacement of the umbra as a spot approaches the limb. On rare occasions, when of unusual size and depth, a spot is visible as a small notch on the Sun's edge when just coming into or going out of view.

Sunspots are never seen at the Sun's poles, and rarely within 5° of the equator. They occur mainly in two zones between 10° and 30° of N. and S. solar latitude. Spots in 45°-50° are rare, and no spot has yet been recorded beyond 60°. Sunspots have magnetic fields, and the polarity, + or −, of the 'preceding' or foremost spots of a group is opposite in the N. and S. hemispheres—which hemispheres may differ very considerably in their spottedness.

The Sunspot Period.—The spottedness waxes and wanes, a maximum being reached about every 11·1 to 11·15 years, on the average, but there is no definite period, intervals between maxima having varied from 7½ to 16½ years; the apparent 11-year cycle, however, is really a half-cycle, for the spot-polarity changes after every minimum.

The rise to maximum is usually more rapid than the fall, taking about 4½ years; minimum spottedness is reached about 6½ years later, when no spot may be visible for weeks. Large spots may appear at any part of the cycle.

Spoerer's Law states that the two spot-zones simultaneously move slowly from high N. and S. latitudes towards the equator. Nearing minimum—the end of each half-cycle—the spot-zones are near the equator; the new half-cycle begins when spots of opposite polarity break out in high latitudes, some time before the actual minimum is reached, and two or three years elapse before old-zone spots finally disappear. The new spot-zones gradually decrease in latitude, till, at the end of eleven years, they, in their turn, arrive near the equator; high-latitude spots of opposite polarity then appear, heralding the beginning of the second half of the cycle.

The variation of latitude is shown in a striking manner by plotting the spots of a cycle according to date and latitude. From its shape, this is known as a *Butterfly Diagram.*

Spots not on the centre are, of course, greatly foreshortened when near the limb.

Sunspots and Magnetic Storms.—The curves of sunspot activity, of terrestrial magnetic storms, and (on the whole) of auroræ, closely coincide, indicating some intimate connection not yet wholly explained. A large spot near the centre of the disc often coincides with a magnetic storm, but not always, and on the other hand the return of a certain area to the centre of the disc sometimes causes a magnetic storm, though no spot is visible.

Wolf's Sunspot Numbers give the relative 'sunspot activity' for any year, based on the number both of groups and of individual spots—the size of telescope used, and the observer, being taken into account. The numbers vary from 0 to about 150 at the highest maximum, and they have been calculated back to 1610 (See Memoirs R.A.S., vol. 43). A sunspot number of 100 is equivalent to a sunspot area of about 1/500th of the visible disc.

Prominences or *protuberances* are jets or clouds of glowing red gas which rise all round the Sun's 'limb' or edge from the *chromosphere*, a bright scarlet, irregular ring of light, some 5″ to 15″ in depth at different times, seen only during total eclipses, or by means of a spectroscope attached to the telescope (see p. 40). *The reversing layer* is a thin stratum of gas which is responsible for the dark lines in the solar spectrum, absorbing certain portions of the bright light from the layers beneath, and reversing them into dark lines. In solar eclipses, just before the Sun disappears, it shows the lines bright instead of dark—a phenomenon known as the *flash spectrum.*

Filaments are long dark prominences seen in projection on the Sun's disc. *Motion-forms* are apparent filaments over a sun-spot, but in reality only distortions of the hydrogen (C) line caused by high radial motion.

Flocculi, seen or photographed by the spectro-heliograph, in one particular wave-length of light (usually that of calcium, sometimes hydrogen), are small irregular clouds of either of these elements, which are seen all over the disc, and show the distribution of the element over it. There are both bright and dark flocculi: the latter may take the form of long dark wisps. The *Solar Reseau*, or *Reseau Photospherique*, is an as yet unexplained blurring or fuzziness of the solar granulation; it is not known whether it is of solar or terrestial origin. ('Reseau' also means the network of squares ruled on celestial photographs for measuring purposes).

The Corona, also seen only during total eclipses, is a mysterious, irregular, pearly ring of light surrounding the Sun. It is never quite the same, either in shape or extent, in successive eclipses, and appears to be partly gaseous, and partly meteoric, for it shines partly by reflected sunlight. It varies with the 11-year period of the Sun's activity, being more or less regularly distributed round the Sun at sun-spot maximum, while at sun-spot minimum there are large streamers, several degrees long, near the Sun's equator, with tufts or plumes of light near his poles. Its brightness varies, being at times uncomfortably bright, nearest the Sun, without a dark glass, especially when the Sun's and Moon's diameters are nearly the same, but on the average seems rather less bright than the Full Moon. The Corona spectrum has a characteristic green line (λ5304) due to oxygen, once ascribed to an unknown element 'coronium'.

Baily's Beads are sometimes seen for an instant before totality—a breaking-up of the thin disappearing crescent of the Sun into a series of bright moving points, like a string of shining beads.* Then, as totality begins, the prominences and corona appear until the Sun begins to emerge again; sometimes, however, they appear just before totality.

Shadow Bands or fringes, another eclipse phenomenon, are alternate light and dark bands, a few inches broad and 1 to 3 feet apart, that appear on white surfaces for an instant as totality begins: probably due to irregular refraction.

The Sun's Magnetic Poles are about 6° away (but perhaps this varies) from his rotation poles; they rotate in 31·29 days (31d. 7h.), and were on the Sun's central meridian on 25th June 1914.

The Sun's Temperature, that of a dwarf G0 star, is about 6000° K. (10,000° F.) near the surface. The *Solar Constant*, the amount of heat received by the Earth (on entering the atmosphere) from the vertical Sun, is 1·93 gram-calories per minute on each square centimetre; variations of one to five per cent seem to occur from day to day. The temperature of sunspots is about 4800°K.—1000° C. (1800° F.) less than that of the general surface.

Solar Motion.—The *Solar Apex*, or *Apex of the Sun's Way*, is the point on the star sphere towards which the Sun is travelling with a velocity believed to be about 19·5 kilometres (12·1 miles) per second. The position of the Apex is ascertained from study of proper motions, or radial velocities, but determinations differ, often by many degrees, different sets of stars giving varying results. In the main, however, there is agreement as to the general direction of the Apex being in Hercules or Lyra, about R.A., 18 hrs., Dec. 34° N. (or, as usually stated in degrees, R.A., 270°, Dec. 34° N.). The *Solar Antapex* is the point diametrically opposite on the star sphere, R.A. 6 hrs., Dec. 34° S.

Mean Daily Spotted Area of the Sun in millionths of the visible hemisphere (projected area, corrected for foreshortening).

Year.—	1918	1919	1920	1921	1922	1923	1924	1925	1926	1927	1928
Area. ...	1118	1052	618	420	252	55	276	830	1262	1058	1390
Mean Lat.	*12¾°*	*10¾°*	*10½°*	*8°*	*8°*	*15¼°*	*22¾°*	*20¼°*	*18¾°*	*15°*	*13½°*

Year.—	1929	1930	1931	1932	1933	1934	1935	1936	1937	1938
Area. ...	1242	516	275	163	88	119	624	1141	2074	2019
Mean Lat.	*10½°*	*9¾°*	*8¼°*	*4°*	*10¼°*	*23¾°*	*23¼°*	*20¼°*	*17°*	*14¾°*

Year.—	1939	1940	1941	1942	1943	1944	1945
Area. ...	1579	1039	658	423	295	126	...
Mean Lat.	*13½°*	*11¼°*	*10½°*	*9°*	*10°*	*21½°*	...

Sunspot Maxima and Minima (approx.; +, −, polarity of N. 'preceding' spots.

Minimum	1901·7 −	1913·6 +	1923·6 −	1933·8 +	1944·2 −	...
Maximum	1905·6 −	1917·6 +	1928·5 −	1937·4 +	1947·8 −	...

* Probably due to irregularities on the Moon's limb.

THE MOON

General Notes.—The Moon is the most interesting of all the heavenly bodies for a small telescope. In an opera-glass the dark portions visible to the naked eye are seen to be the smoother portions of the Moon's surface; the remainder of the surface is a mass of craters of every size, from some of which brilliant white streaks radiate for a great distance. The most striking views are obtainable when it is about its first or last quarter, when the lunar mountains near the *terminator* (or boundary between the bright and dark portions), cast long dark shadows which give a fine effect of contrast with the bright sun-lit parts. At the time of full Moon this contrast is lost, though the systems of *rays* or bright streaks are then most in evidence, and an interesting field of study is the total, or nearly total, disappearance of prominent objects (*e.g.*, Maginus) for 2 or 3 days before and after 'Full,' while others (notably the craters, properly so called, see p. 30) can still be located by reason of their being brighter than their surroundings. This disappearance is very noticeable in formations traversed by the rays or streaks, as in the S. W. portion of the Moon. A low power should be used at first, for a general view of the disc. (See note on 'Observing the Moon,' p. 40).

The Moon always presents the same side to the Earth, so that one side of the Moon is never seen at all. Owing, however, to what is termed the Moon's *libration*, or apparent swaying, due to the inclination of its axis to its orbit, and to other causes, we sometimes see a little more on one side or another, so that altogether about six-tenths of the surface is visible at one time or another. A full description of the Moon is quite beyond the scope of the present work, and the original works describing the features on the Moon's surface, such as Nasmyth's, Neison's, Goodacre's and Proctor's *Moon*, are now out of print. Current works are *Named Lunar Formations* (Müller and Blagg) and Wilkins and Moore's *Map the Moon.*

Lunar *plains*, the darker and smoother portions of the surface, were supposed by the early telescopists to be *seas*—which they much resemble under very low powers—and were named accordingly. More perfect instruments, however, revealed that the supposed seas were simply vast plains, by no means level, or smooth, possibly once the bottom of lunar oceans.

Lunar *mountain ranges* and peaks are much higher in proportion to the moon's diameter than terrestrial ranges are to the earth's diameter, some of them attaining a height of about five miles. The most conspicuous range is *The Apennines*, in the northern hemisphere of the moon, which rises like a wall from the *Mare Imbrium.* It is about 600 miles long, and its highest peaks attain a height of 3½ miles—the heights being found by measurements of their long sharp shadows, nearly 100 miles long.

Lunar *craters*, which are such a prominent feature in lunar landscapes, are of all sizes from a hundred and fifty miles in diameter downwards. Craters often have one or more conical peaks within the crater walls, of which *Tycho* and *Gassendi* are fine examples; the largest with a fairly level bottom, and often no central peak, and with lower bounding walls than the craters proper, are called *walled plains*, of which *Plato* is the best example. The interiors of the craters are usually lower than the surface outside, but sometimes the reverse is the case. Frequently an old crater will be seen that has been broken into by a later one.

Lunar *rills* are deep, winding, narrow valleys, resembling the bed of a dried up stream. Lunar *clefts* appear like cracks on the smoother portions of the surface. It is difficult to realise that these hairlike markings are sometimes fifty or a hundred miles long and up to 2½ miles in width. The greater number of clefts are to be seen only in pretty powerful telescopes. *Faults* are closed cracks in the moon's surface, and are numerous. They are visible owing to the surface on one side of them being higher than that on the other.

Lunar *rays* are the bright streaks which radiate from some of the principal craters. Unlike other lunar features, they are best seen about the time of full moon. The finest system of rays radiates from the great crater *Tycho*, in the southern lunar hemisphere. The strangest feature of these rays is that they are everywhere on the same level as the rest of the surface, and traverse unbroken both crater walls, valleys, and seas. No fully satisfactory explanation of their nature has yet been given.

Position Angle of the Moon's Axis.—This sways some 25° on each side of the hour-circle every month, the extremes being when her R.A. is about 0 hrs. and 12 hrs., *i.e.*, when crossing the celestial equator: it is about zero when her R.A. is 6 hrs. and 18 hrs. The amount is given in the 'Moon's Physical Ephemeris' in the *Nautical Almanac.*

Objects near the Limb. Those near the N. lunar pole are best situated for observation when the Moon has its greatest south latitude (about 5°), and *vice versa* for the S. pole; those near the west limb, when the Moon's actual longitude is E. of (*i.e.*, *greater* than), and those near the east limb when it is W. of (*i.e.*, *less* than) the mean longitude. The dates when any object near the limb will be nearest the centre, and thus most favourably situated for observation, can be ascertained from the *Nautical Almanac*, by finding the times when the favourable libration in latitude (p. 29) is about 6°, and that in longitude about 7°: the Moon, however, may be below the horizon, or the phase unsuitable.

Effects of Libration. At each recurring phase, though the positions and lengths of the shadows themselves have not changed greatly (lunar 'seasonal' changes being small, owing to the small inclination of the lunar equator to the Ecliptic, $1\frac{1}{2}°$), the Moon's latitude and longitude, &c., have altered. Libration has come into play, and we view the object and its shadow from a different position than formerly, the variation amounting at its maximum to over 20°, through the combined effect of the displacement in latitude and longitude. Except at rare intervals, therefore, we do not re-observe objects under anything like the same conditions. When viewing the Moon, it should also be remembered that it is only near the centre of the disc that we see objects in their true form and dimensions, as each object is more and more foreshortened the further it is away from the centre, and, on the limb, is seen only in profile.

The libration on any evening can be found from the *Nautical Almanac* in the 'Moon's Physical Ephemeris,' columns Earth's 'Selenographic Lat. and Long.' When the libration in longitude is +, the mean centre of the disc is displaced to the E., *i.e.*, the Mare Crisium is furthest from the limb. When the libration is −, the mean centre is displaced to the W., and the Mare Crisium approaches the limb. Similarly, when the libration in latitude is +, the mean centre is displaced to the S., *i.e.*, Plato is furthest from the limb, and *vice versa*, for −.

Best Altitude Conditions.—For any given age of the Moon, there is a certain date in the year about which more favourable altitude conditions obtain than at any other time, though it is modified to some extent by the Moon's changes in latitude. This is due to the fact that the Moon's average path coincides with the Ecliptic, so that on any given day, her altitude above an observer's horizon at culmination, will, on the average, be exactly the same as that of the Sun at noon on the date when he has similar R.A. The following Table indicates approximately the most favourable dates for observing the principal phases: (S. Hemisphere, transpose April, Oct.: and July, Jan.):—

N. Hemisphere:—	Moon 3-4 days old.	First Quarter.	Full.	Last Quarter.	25-26 days.
Most Favourable	End of April	Vernal Equinox	Winter Solstice	Autumnal Equinox	End of July
Least ,,	,, October	Autumnal ,,	Summer ,,	Vernal ,,	,, January

The Position of the Terminator on the Moon's equator, corresponding to various ages, can be approximately ascertained by means of the scale below the Map of the Moon on p. 31. It can be obtained more exactly from the 'Moon's Physical Ephemeris,' 'Sun's co-longitude' column, in the *Nautical Almanac* (in conjunction with a lunar chart having selenographic latitude and longitude lines), by using the following rule:—

Sun's Co-longitude. From:—		*Position of Terminator.*
0° to 90°, the figures in the Table give		the terminator's longitude E. of the central meridian (Sun rising).
90° to 180°, subtract the Sun's co-longit. from 180°: answer	=	,, ,, ,, W. ,, ,, ,, (Sun setting).
180° to 270°, subtract 180° from the Sun's co-longit. ,,	=	,, ,, ,, E. ,, ,, ,, (Sun setting).
270° to 360°, subtract the Sun's co-longit. from 360°. ,,	=	,, ,, ,, W. ,, ,, ,, (Sun rising).

Repetition of same Phase of illumination, near the same hour, may be expected in about 2 and 15 lunations, on the average, but there are variations—corresponding with the lengths of different lunations, which vary to and fro between $29\frac{1}{4}$ and $29\frac{3}{4}$ days. The mean lunation is just over $29\frac{1}{2}$ days, hence, on the average, in the second lunation similar phase falls in daylight; in the third, it is $1\frac{1}{2}$ hours later in the evening than the first, and so on. 1 mean lunation $= 29^d\,12^h\,44^m$; 2 lunations, $59^d\,1\frac{1}{2}^h$; and 15 lunations, $442^d\,23^h$. The mean interval from perigee to perigee, or mean anomalistic period is 27·55455 days, and does not recur at the same phase till after 14 lunations (about 1·13 yrs.), or about $1\frac{1}{2}$ months later in the following year, so that 'most favourable' conditions gradually disappear for a period.

Lunar Nomenclature. Lunar objects are generally referred to the *quadrant*, or quarter of the disc, in which they are found, numbered I to IV, as on the map. The principal formations have names of their own: other objects in the neighbourhood (also those *inside* or on a crater), not separately named, are denoted by the nearest crater name with a *Roman* letter added, for craters or depressions, or a *Greek* letter, for peaks or elevations—capitals denoting 'measured' points. Thus 'Aristoteles B' is quite different from 'Aristoteles,' being a small crater some 50 miles N. of the latter. Greek letters are also used for rills, in conjunction with the crater names.

Earthshine, popularly known as 'the Old Moon in the New Moon's arms,' is due to rays of light reflected from the Earth on the Moon's dark disc. It is stronger in the morning with Old Moon than in the evening with New Moon, and its variations are worth systematic study, as an index to the reflective power of the Earth's disc, which is lit up by the Sun. As the albedo of clouds is very high (p. viii), unusual brightness of Earthshine probably indicates that the sun-illuminated hemisphere of the Earth is much cloudier than usual, and *vice versa* when Earthshine is faint. Earthshine is best seen 3 to 5 days after New Moon in the spring, or before New Moon in the autumn, especially if the Moon is near perigee at the time, its brightness then being greatest. Earthshine is also known as '*lumière cendrée*,' or '*ashy light*.'

A very narrow ring of silver-white light, quite distinct from Earthshine, and encircling the whole lunar disc, is occasionally visible for short periods when the Moon is within 2 or 3 days of New.

Lunar Craters are classified by Neison as follows, but the classes merge gradually into one another, and near the border line either name may be used.

Walled Plains (*w* in Index), diam. 40-150 miles (65-240 km.), like *Plato.* Usually surrounded by a complex system of walls: floor usually not much lower than outside, and comparatively level; central mountain often absent. Mostly in S. hemisphere.

Ring Mountains (*mr* in Index), diam. 15-50 miles (24-113 km.), like Römer. Walls low and broken, probably ruined walled plains.

Ring Plains (*r* in Index), diam. 20-60 miles (32-97 km.), like *Copernicus*: comprise the majority of the larger lunar craters. More circular and regular than walled plains; single principal wall, generally; outer slope small, interior steep and usually terraced. Floor nearly always much lower than outside, and comparatively level. The deepest lunar formation is *Newton*, rim 23,000 feet (7000 metres) above the floor. In *Wargentin*, the floor is practically level with the top of the wall.

Crater Plains, diam. 10-20 miles (16-32 km.). Brighter, and with gentler outside slopes, than craters proper.

Craters proper (*c* in Index), diam. 5-15 miles (8-24 km.), like *Bessel.* Circular; outer slope steeper, but the interior falls more gradually than in crater plains. Floor small, with 'volcanic' cone; very bright near Full.

Craterlets, diam. 5 miles (8 km.) downward. Craters in miniature: merely a convenient sub-division, indicating very small craters.

Crater Pits, or 'Pits,' diam. as craterlets, but up to 11 miles (18 km.). Very shallow depressions, outside slope hardly perceptible. *Depressions* differ from crater pits in having no sign of walls whatever, and may be many miles or kilometers across.

Crater Cones. Steep conical peaks, diameter $\frac{1}{2}$-3 miles (1-5 km.), with narrow central opening, which is very difficult to see. They appear on mountain ridges, and on crater walls and floors, and are very bright near Full. For fuller details, see the reference books, given on page 28.

Lunar 'Seas,' Valleys, &c. The Sinus Iridum, with great bordering cliffs, rising in peaks over 16,000 feet high, is one of the finest objects on the Moon; it is best seen when the Moon is 8 or 9 days old.

Of the *valleys*, the Great Alpine Valley is the most notable. Most *clefts* or *rills*, and *faults*, are not visible in small instruments, but the Cleft of Hyginus, and that of Ariadæus just W. of it, can be seen in a two-inch telescope. The 'Straight Wall,' 60 miles long and 900 feet high, is a little E. of Thebit. Pico is a solitary peak on the Mare Imbrium.

The Brightness of different parts of the Moon is an interesting study: it is valued in 'degrees,' ranging from 1°, the darkest—found in Grimaldi and Riccioli—up to 10°, found in Aristarchus, the brightest object in the Moon; Proclus is 8°. 0° is black shadow. The floor of Plato undergoes curious changes in brightness as the Sun's altitude increases.

The varying colours of the Seas may also be studied. The prevailing tint of the Maria is grey, more or less dark, Mare Crisium being the darkest ($1\frac{1}{2}$°-3°), with a tinge of green. The brightest of the grey plains is Lacus Somniorum ($3\frac{1}{2}$°-4°); Palus Somnii, equally bright, is of a yellow-brown shade. The Mare Serenitatis, the centre of Mare Humorum, and part of the Sinus Iridum, have a dark greenish colour, and the Mare Crisium a lighter green; the Mare Frigoris is a yellowish-green.

Centres of Principal Ray Systems. Aristarchus, Aristillus, Byrgius A, Copernicus, Euler, Kepler, Messier, Proclus, Timocharis, and Tycho. Euclides and Landsberg A are surrounded by a 'nimbus,' or bright patch.

The Mean Centre of the Moon, or intersection of lunar meridian 0° with the lunar equator, can always be readily found, as it is approximately the point equidistant from the three craters, Herschel, Schröter, and Triesnecker. The lunar equator is very nearly the line drawn through Rhæticus and Landsberg; lunar longitude 0°, a line drawn through the centre of Walter and the E. side of Aristillus. But see note at foot of Map of the Moon as to curved lines.

Index, Map of the Moon. The diameters, given in miles, are approximate, as authorities sometimes differ, owing to irregular shape, &c. The letters Bc, Bb, &c., indicate the square in which the object will be found. *r*, *w*, *c*, etc., see above.

Name	Square	Diam.
Agrippa (*r*)	Bc	27m
Albategnius (*w*)	Bb	70
Alpetragius (*r*)	Cb	27
Alphonsus (*w*)	Cb	70
Anaximander	Cd	39
Apollonius	Ac	30
Archimedes (*r*)	Cc	50
Ariadæus (*c*)	Bc	5
Aristarchus (*c*)	Dc	28
Aristillus (*r*)	Bd	34
Aristoteles (*r*)	Bd	55
Arzachel (*w*)	Cb	65
Atlas (*r*)	Bd	55
Autolycus (*r*)	Bd	25
Bailly (*w*)	Ca	155
Bessel (*c*)	Bc	12
Birt (*r*)	Cb	9
Blancanus (*w*)	Ca	60
Bullialdus (*r*)	Cb	38
Burg (*r*)	Bd	28
Byrgius, & A (*r*)	Db	40
Capella (*r*)	Ab	30
Capuanus (*r*)	Ca	34
Cassini (*r*)	Bd	36
Catharina (*w*)	Bb	70
Clavius (*w*)	Ca	150m
Cleomedes (*w*)	Ac	80
Copernicus (*r*)	Cc	56
Crüger (*r*)	Db	30
Cyrillus (*w*)	Bb	65
Delambre (*r*)	Bb	32
Delisle (*mr*)	Cc	16
Encke (*r*)	Dc	20
Endymion (*w*)	Bd	78
Eratosthenes (*r*)	Cc	38
Euclides (*c*)	Cb	7
Eudoxus (*r*)	Bd	45
Euler (*r*)	Cc	19
Fabricius (*r*)	Ba	55
Flamsteed (*r*)	Db	9
Fracastorius (*r*)	Ab	60
Furnerius (*w*)	Aa	80
Gambart (*r*)	Cc	16
Gassendi (*w*)	Db	55
Gauss (*w*)	Ad	110
Godin (*c*)	Bc	23
Grimaldi (*w*)	Db	147
Hainzel (*w*)	Ca	55
Helicon (*r*)	Cd	13
Hell (*r*)	Ca	18m
Hercules (*r*)	Bd	46
Herschel (*c*)	Cb	25
Hevel (*w*)	Dc	71
Hippalus (*r*)	Cb	38
Hipparchus (*r*)	Bb	92
Hyginus & Cleft (*c*)	Bc	4
Kepler (*r*)	Dc	22
Lambert (*r*)	Cc	18
Landsberg (*r*)	Cb	28
Langrenus (*w*)	Ab	85
Letronne (*r*)	Db	50
Lindenau (*w*)	Ba	35
Linné (*c*)	Bc	2
Longomontanus (*w*)	Ca	90
Macrobius (*w*)	Ac	42
Maginus (*w*)	Ca	100
Mairan (*r*)	Dd	25
Manilius (*r*)	Bc	25
Marius (*r*)	Dc	27
Maskelyne (*r*)	Bc	19
Maurolycus (*w*)	Ba	75
Mersenius (*r*)	Db	41
Messala (*w*)	Ad	69
Messier (*c*)	Ab	9m
Moretus (*w*)	Ca	78
Mösting & A (*r*)	Cb	15
Newton (*r*)	Ca	143
Otto Struve (*w*)	Dc	150
Parry (*r*)	Cb	25
Petavius (*w*)	Ab	100
Philoläus	Cd	46
Piazzi (*w*)	Da	90
Picard (*r*)	Ac	21
Piccolomini (*r*)	Bb	57
Pico	Cd	...
Pitatus (*w*)	Cb	58
Plato (*w*)	Cd	60
Plinius (*r*)	Bc	32
Posidonius (*w*)	Bd	62
Proclus	Ac	18
Ptolemæus (*w*)	Cb	115
Purbach (*w*)	Cb	70
Reiner (*r*)	Dc	21
Reinhold (*r*)	Cc	31
Rhæticus (*r*)	Bc	25
Riccioli (*w*)	Db	106
Römer (*mr*)	Ac	30
Santbech (*r*)	Ab	46m
Schickard (*w*)	Da	134
Schiller (*w*)	Ca	113
Schröter (*r*)	Cc	25
Stadius (*r*)	Cc	43
Stöfler (*w*)	Ba	150
Taruntius (*w*)	Ac	44
Thebit (*r*)	Cb	32
Theophilus (*r*)	Bb	64
Timocharis (*r*)	Cc	23
Triesnecker (*r*)	Bc	14
Tycho (*w*)	Ca	54
Vendelinus (*w*)	Ab	90
Vieta (*r*)	Db	51
Vitello (*r*)	Db	28
Vitruvius (*c*)	Bc	19
Vlacq (*r*)	Ba	57
Walter (*w*)	Ba	90
Wargentin (*r*)	Da	54
Werner (*r*)	Bb	45
Wilhelm I. (*w*)	Ca	46
Wurzelbauer (*w*)	Ca	50
Zach (*w*)	Ba	46

SKETCH MAP OF THE MOON. (As seen in an inverting Telescope)

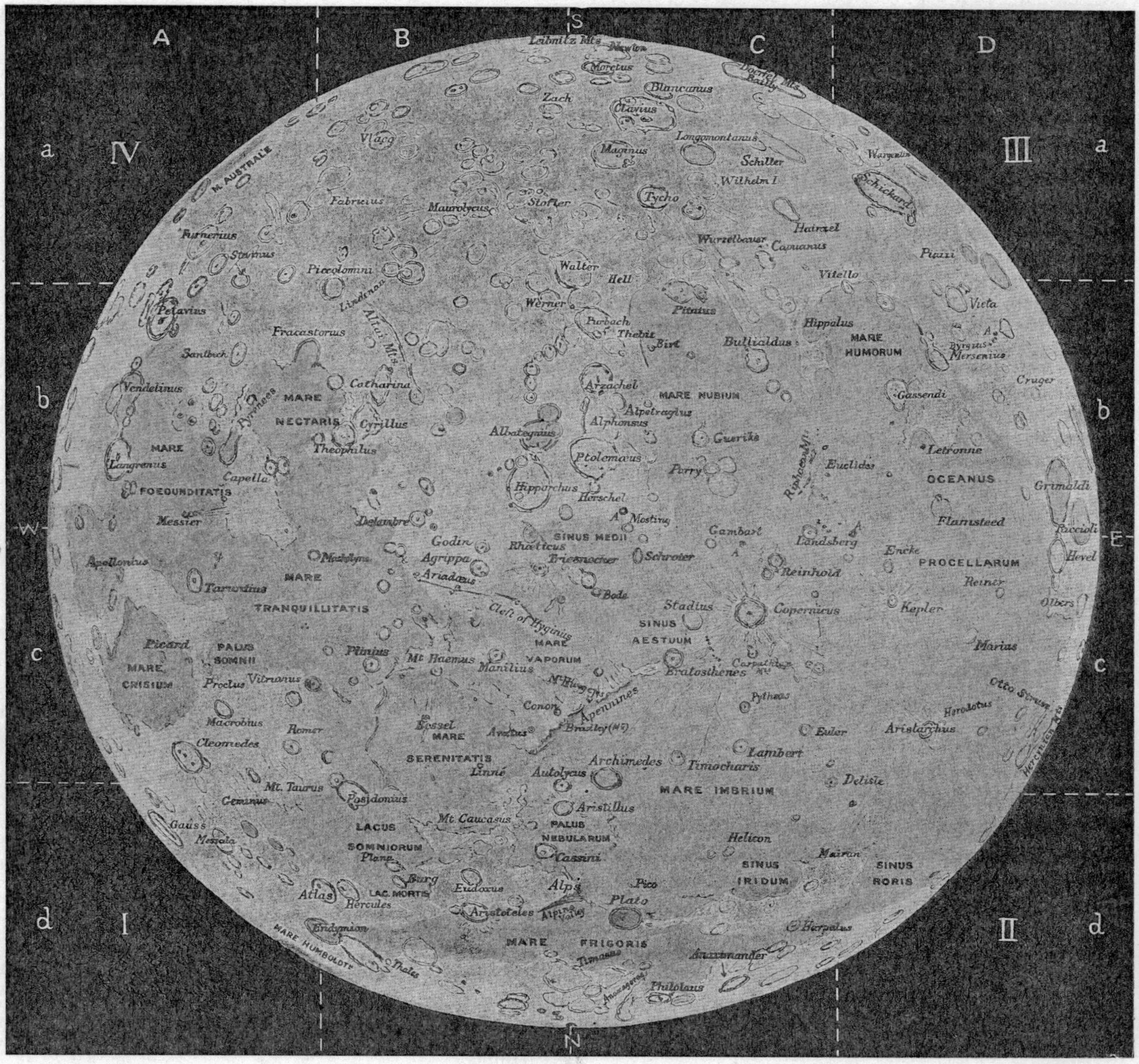

SCALE SHOWING APPROXIMATE POSITION OF THE TERMINATOR ON THE MOON'S EQUATOR AT VARIOUS AGES.

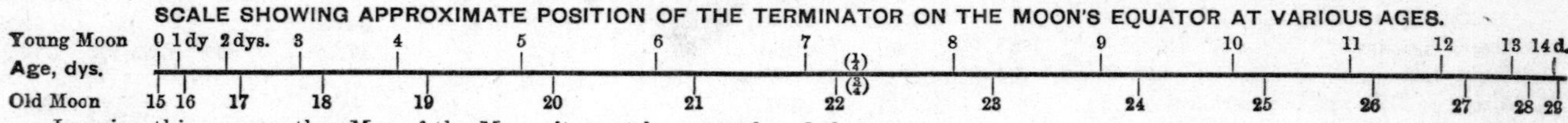

In using this or any other Map of the Moon, it must be remembered that :—

(*a*). Objects very near the limb in the Map may be completely out of sight or much foreshortened, owing to libration. The Mare Crisium and Grimaldi for instance, almost touch the edge at extreme libration.

(*b*). The lunar equator, and parallels of latitude, which are straight on the Map, are only seen thus when the libration in latitude is 0°, *i.e.*, when the lunar axis is in the position of mean libration ; at other times these lines are seen as ellipses of greater or less curvature, curved southwards when the libration in latitude is +, and curved northwards when the libration in latitude is –.

(*c*). Similarly the meridian of lunar longitude 0° is only seen as a straight line when the libration in longitude is 0° ; at other times it also is elliptical, convex W. or E. according as the Moon's libration is – or +.

(*d*). The mean centre of the disc is only seen in the centre when the libration in longitude and latitude are each 0°. At other times it may be displaced up to 7° 45′ in longitude and 6° 44′ in latitude, or as the combined result 10° 16′. The Moon's libration in longitude is 0° about perigee and apogee, and her libration in latitude about 0° when she is crossing the Ecliptic.

When the Moon's libration in longitude is –, the region exposed to view is on the E. limb, & Mare Crisium is nearer the limb, than mean position.
" " " + " " " W. " " " further from " " "
When the Moon's libration in latitude is – " " " S. limb, & Plato is nearer the limb than mean position.
" " " + " " " N. " " further from " "

LUNAR MOUNTAINS, &c.

		Height, ft.			Height, ft.
Alps,	Bd	12,000	Dœrfel Mts.	Ca	26,000
Alpine Valley	Bd	...	Hæmus Mt.	Bc	8,700
Altai Mts.	Bb	13,000	Leibnitz Mts.	Ba	30,000
Apennines	Cc	18,500	Pyrenees	Ab	12,000
Bradley, Mt.	Bc	13,600	Riphæan Mts.	Cb	2,700
Caucasus	Bd	18,500	Taurus Mt.	Ad	10,000

LUNAR SEAS (OR 'MARIA'), &c.

Mare Australe ...	Aa	Mare Nectaris ...	Ab	Lacus Somniorum	Bd
" Crisium ...	Ac	" Nubium ...	Cb	Palus Nebularum	Bd
" Fœcunditatis	Ab	" Serenitatis ...	Bc	" Somnii	Ac
" Frigoris ...	Cd	" Tranquillitatis	Ac	Sinus Aestuum ...	Cc
" Humboldtianum	Ad	" Vaporum ...	Bc	" Iridum	Cd
" Humorum ...	Db	Ocean. Procellarum	Dc	" Medii	Cc
" Imbrium ...	Cd	Lacus Mortis ...	Bd	" Roris	Dd

THE PLANETS.

The Nautical Almanac (N.A.), and **The American Ephemeris (A.E.)**, give much useful planetary observing information. Under 'Phenomena' are the dates of opposition, conjunction in R.A. with the Sun and Moon, elongations of Mercury and Venus, &c.; there are Occultation Tables, with latitude-limits of observability, and those seen at certain stations; also Sunrise, Sunset, Moonrise, Moonset, and Twilight Tables, for latitudes 0° to 60°. The 'Physical Ephemeris' Tables give the position angle of the axis, planetary meridian on the centre of the disc, magnitudes, configuration and eclipses of the satellites, &c.; also:—

Mars and Jupiter. The angular amount of phase, (always on the W. side from conjunction to opposition, and on E. side from opposition until conjunction) is given by column q; the linear (=areal) fraction of the disc illuminated, by column k. Column D⊕ gives the number of degrees the planet's N. pole (+), or S. pole (−), is turned towards the Earth: maximum about 25½° for Mars; 4° for Jupiter; 29° for Saturn; but largely nullified by foreshortening. 0° = both poles on limb.

Jupiter's Satellites. Configuration: ○ at the side indicates 'In transit'; ● 'In occultation or eclipse.' The Phase diagrams show the position of each satellite during the month by a * (change slight, except near opposition), of the points where the satellites disappear in, or emerge from the shadow†; c (or d) is the point of disappearance; f (or r), that of reappearance.

Saturn's Rings. Column B (Saturnicentric latitude of the Earth) gives the angular 'openness' of the rings, 0° when invisible, about 28° fully open. Column B' is the Sun's elevation above the ring-plane; the rings are invisible when B or $B'=0°$; and also when B (Earth) is + (North), and B' (Sun) is − (South), or *vice versa.* Position angle of axis is same as column P.

Hour of R.A. on the meridian at mean midnight (Sidereal Time), for each day; from this, that at other hours can be found.

Rising or Setting of Planets. From the *N.A.* time of meridian passage, subtract (or add) the semi-diurnal arc (see p. xiv).

Astronomical Terms; The Calendar. The student should read the very interesting article on these subjects in the Appendix to the British *N.A.*, which also contains, for the advanced, an elaborate *precis* of formulæ used in the Almanac.

Heliocentric longitudes and latitudes, and radius vectors, giving orbital positions and distances with reference to the Sun, are given annually in the *American Ephemeris.* The British *N.A.* publishes them for twenty years in advance, 1917-40 in *N.As.* 1915-17 (Mercury annually, till 1938): 1941-60, also 1900-1940, in special vols. Earth's heliocentric longitude, see p. 4.

General Notes.—The *Major Planets*, so called to distinguish them from the *Asteroids* or *Minor Planets*, none of which exceeds a few hundred miles in diameter, are Mercury, Venus, Earth, Mars, Jupiter, Saturn, Uranus, Neptune, Pluto. The first four, and Pluto, are sometimes distinguished as the *Terrestrial Planets*, as their sizes are comparable with that of the Earth, the others as the *Giant Planets.* They are always near the Ecliptic except Pluto, within the Zodiac (p. 3), and are readily distinguished from fixed stars, as they do not twinkle unless low down; their spectra are those of reflected sunlight, with bands due to methane in all the giant planets, and ammonia in Jupiter and Saturn (p. 35). Their constantly-changing positions are easily found by the R.A. and Declination given in almanacs.

Unlike the Moon, which souths about 38 to 66 minutes (mean, 50½) later each day, the *Superior Planets* (Mars, the Asteroids, Jupiter, and those beyond) south earlier, on the average, each night, appearing to move nearer the Sun daily when E. of him, but further away when W. of him, and being lost in his rays for some six weeks annually—Mars, and the asteroids in general, for months, biennially, having long synodic periods (see below).

The Superior planets are best seen when in opposition, southing about midnight; the *Inferior Planets* (Mercury, Venus), about the times of greatest elongation. Opposition or greatest elongation may occur at any time of the year, but the nearer they happen to one date in a certain month (Superior planets, that on which the Earth's heliocentric longitude is about the same as that of the planet's perihelion) the larger and brighter is the planet; many years, however, elapse before the most favourable conditions recur. For Magnitude variation, see pp. 17 and 41.

The Solar System (see also p. viii).—The figures below are mostly (or, based on) those of the *American Ephemeris*, to which refer (or to the yearly *B.A.A. Handbk.*) for greater precision. The larger of two diameters is the equatorial, the smaller the polar.

Sun.* Diameter, 865,370 miles, 1,392,700 km.; **Moon**, 2162 miles, 3480 km. **Density:** (water=1) Sun, 1·41; Moon, 3·34.

Planets.	Mercury	Venus	Earth	Mars	Jupiter	Saturn	Uranus	Neptune	Pluto	Sun	Moon
Angular diameter, Max.	12″·9	64″·0	...	25″·1	49″·8	20″·5	4″·2	2″·2	0·2	32′ 36″	33′ 31″
,, ,, Min.	4″·7	9″·9	...	3″·5	30″·5	14″·7	3″·4	2″·0	0·2	31′ 31′	29′ 22″
,, At Mean Dist.	6″·4	16″·0	...	6″·1	37″·9	17″·3	3″·8	2″·1	0·2	31′ 59″	31′ 5″
Oblateness or ellipticity	0	0	1/297th	1/70th	1/15·4	1/9·5	1/14th	1/40th	...	0	0·0006
Mass, Earth=1	0·04	0·83	1·00	0·108	318·4	95·2	14·60	17·16	0·83	333,400	0·012
,, Sun=1	1/8-millionth	1/403,490	1/329,370	1/3-millionth	1/1047	1/3502	1/22,869	1/19,314	1/400,000	1	...
Axis‡ or Equator, Inclination to orbit	32°	23°·45	25°·17	3°	26°·7	98°	151°	...	7°·17§	6° 41″	

Mean Distance from Earth:—*Inferior planets*, 1 Astron. Unit; *Superior*, =mean distance from Sun; mean opp'n distance, 1 unit less.
Aphelion and Perihelion Distances, $=\times a \pm ea$, when a=the semi-major axis (the Mean distance) in A.Us., and e the eccentricity.

Planet (Symbols, see p. xii)	Mean Distance fr. Sun.* Astron. Units	Millions of:— Miles	Kilom.	Diameter* Thousands of:— Miles	Kilom.	Density Water =1	Sun =1	Mean Periods. Sidereal, in years	Synodic, in years	Axial Rotation	Orbit: Epoch 1950. Eccen-tricity	Inclin. to Eclipt.	Longit. Asc. node	Longit. perihelion	Mean Motion (Sidereal) Daily	Yearly
Mercury	0·387	36·0	57·9	3·2	5·15	3·7	2·6	0·2408	0·3173	88 days	0·2056	7·00	47°·7°	76°·7	4°·09	...
Venus	0·723	67·3	108·3	7·85	12·63	4·9	3·4	0·6152	1·5987	22h 17m	0·0068	3·40	76·2	130·8	1·60	...
Earth	1·000	93·0	149·7	7·927 7·90	12·76 12·71	5·5	3·9	1·00004	...	23h 56m 4s	0·0167	0°	...	102·1	0·99	360
Mars	1·524	141·7	228·1	4·25	6·84	3·9	2·7	1·8809	2·1354	24h 37m 23s	0·0934	1·85	49·1	335·1	0·52	191½
Eros (433)	1·46	135·0	218·1	0·015	0·024	...	...	1·723	2·3031	5¼h	0·2229	10·84	303·6	121·9	0·54	209°
Jupiter	5·203	483·9	778·7	89·3 83·9	143·8 135·0	1·3	0·9	11·8622	1·0921	9h 50-55m	0·0484	1·30	99·9	13·5	0·08	30¼
Saturn	9·539	887·2	1428	75·0 67·8	120·7 109·1	0·7	0·5	29·4577	1·0352	10h 14-38m	0·0557	2·49	113·2	92·1	0·03	12¼
Uranus	19·19	1785	2872	33·2	53·5	1·2	0·8	84·0153	1·0121	about 10¾h	0·0472	0·77	73·7	169·9	0·01	4¼°
Neptune	30·07	2797	4501	30·9	49·8	1·6	1·1	164·788	1·0061	15h 40m	0·0086	1·78	131·2	44·2	0·006	2⅛°
Pluto	39·51	3675	5915	3·6	5·9	...	...	248·430	1·0047	...	0·2486	17°·14	109°·6	223°·2	0°·004	1¼°

* Distances and diameters given above correspond to a Solar Parallax of 8″·79. † Direction of motion is towards the figures.
‡ For the axis, to the *vertical* to orbit. § To Ecliptic (Moon, 1½°).

The Paths of the Planets on the Star Sphere. As seen from the Sun, these (their heliocentric paths) are, for ordinary purposes, unchanging, and each intersects that of the Earth (the same as the Ecliptic) at two practically fixed points, the nodes. The heliocentric paths are also approximately the average paths of the Superior planets, as seen from the Earth (see below).

Planets attain their greatest heliocentric latitude when about 90° longit. from the nodes, and remain longest (lengthens as the eccentricity) on that side of the Ecliptic in which aphelion lies than in the other, partly because the node-aphelion-node distance is greater (slightly, unless eccentricity is great), partly because the mean motion is slower. If the node-perihelion angle (ω) is *greater* than about 180°, aphelion is in the N. celestial hemisphere (Mars, Jupiter, Saturn, Neptune); if *less*, in the Southern (Mercury, Venus, Uranus, Pluto); in the former, the altitude at favourable oppositions is best for Southern, in the latter for Northern observers.

As seen from the Earth, the *Superior planets* reach a latitude above or below the Ecliptic at least equal to the inclination of their orbits, and each follows the heliocentric path more and more nearly the less its parallax—*i.e.*, the remoter the planet is from the Sun; thus their geocentric paths are confined to a very narrow strip on the star sphere—Mars excepted (see below).

Mercury and Venus, which circle the star sphere with the Sun, have the Ecliptic for their average path (approx.), and attain 5° and 9°, respectively, from it if max. heliocentric latitude occurs with Earth about heliocent. longit. 318° (*Merc.*), 166°, 346° (*Venus*).

The Earth's everchanging position in her orbit, may, as seen from her centre, displace the Superior planets from their heliocentric positions (*a*) E. or W. by an amount about equal to the Earth's *annual* parallax (p. 14) as seen from the planet; (*b*) N. or S. by a small amount—greatest about perihelion opposition, smallest about conjunction—except for near-by Mars, which at opposition may be some 3° to 5° N. or S. of the heliocentric path; Jupiter's maximum is about ¼°. And as the Earth's mean daily orbital motion of 1° exceeds those of Mars and the asteroids by ½° or more, and those of the other Superior planets by well-nigh 1°, (see Table, p. 32), when Earth and planet are on the same side of the Sun and in the same line, at opposition, the Earth outruns the planet, causing it apparently to retrograde on the star sphere—before and after opposition, also, for some time. The combined motions of the Earth and a planet make the latter's path on the star sphere, as seen from the Earth, a looped or zigzag curve.

Mercury is always so close to the Sun that, even when most favourably situated, he is only observable for about two hours (naked eye, ½ hr,) after sunset or before sunrise, and that at a very low altitude, especially in higher latitudes. His very eccentric orbit causes his greatest elongation (G.E.) from the Sun to vary from 18° to 28°—the latter one being at aphelion, when he is S. of the Celestial Equator, and best seen by Southern observers. In temperate latitudes he is most favourably placed near the Equinoxes, as an evening star in spring, some days before G.E.—one in April being best, or as a morning star in autumn, some days after G.E. (in the S. hemisphere, Oct. and April).

Mercury has phases like the Moon, and is mag. − 1·8 when in perihelion near superior conjunction (but very near the Sun); at G.E., the average is only + 0·2. Sidereal period 88 days; synodic, about 116 dys. (Rotation, see below).

Venus, the brightest of the planets, sometimes seen in broad daylight, may even cast a shadow; her faint markings (very doubtful if permanent features) are difficult to observe owing to lack of contrast, but her phases can be studied in a small telescope or good opera glass; examine in daylight—which diminishes the glare—or soon after sunset or before sunrise. Her greatest brilliancy is during the crescent stage—as an evening star about a month after, or as a morning star *before*, greatest elongation, which at maximum is 47°. (G.E. never occurs at nearest to Earth).

The maximum magnitude (− 4·4) occurs about every 8 years, when Venus is in perihelion near the end of December, and S. of the Celestial equator as a morning star, therefore more favourably situated for Southern observers; she is then twelve times brighter than Sirius; she is slightly fainter when in perihelion about the middle of March as an evening star, when Northern observers see her much higher above the horizon. Her apparent motion is so slow—the synodic period being about a year and seven months (584 days)—that she remains visible or invisible for several months, unlike Mercury, which rapidly disappears in the Sun's rays. Sidereal period, 224·7 days; rotation, see below.

A faint luminosity, like Earthshine on the Moon, occasionally reported as visible on the dark side, is now attributed to ocular causes.

Recurrence of Greatest Elongation.—For Mercury, the most favourable elongation occurs about every six years; for Venus about every 8 years. The intervals between greatest E. and W. elongation are very unequal:—

Greatest E. to greatest W. elongation, inferior conjunction between:—Mercury about 44 days; Venus 144 days.
„ W. „ E. „ superior „ „ „ „ 72 „ „ 440 „

Mars is of little interest in a small telescope except in or near opposition—when his angular diameter is 13″ to 25″; this occurs every 780 days on the average—nearly two years and two months, the longest (major) planetary synodic period; the sidereal period is 687 days. Favourable oppositions come every 15 or 17 years, the best about Aug. 26th (from 1924, very favourable), when Mars exceeds Jupiter in brightness, attaining mag. − 2·8, but as his disc is even then only half the diameter, little detail is seen in small telescopes. The mean and minimum opposition magnitudes vary between − 2·25 and − 1·0, while in conjunction with the Sun he is only 2nd magnitude. Except near opposition, Mars is more or less 'gibbous'—*i.e.*, not fully, but more than half-illumined—greatest when he is in quadrature (90° longitude, or 6 hrs. R.A. from the Sun); only 0·84 of the disc is then illumined. Mars has two tiny satellites.

On Mars' ruddy disc, dark greyish-green markings—once thought to be seas, but now supposed to be marshes or vegetation areas—can be seen, and one or other of the bright, white polar spots (probably snow-caps, perhaps partly hoar frost) is a striking feature; occasionally both caps are visible. The finer so-called 'canals'—an unfortunate translation of Schiaparelli's *canali*, 'channels,' not necessarily artificial—are invisible in small telescopes, and though some seem to result from real markings, the tendency is to regard them as partly due to ocular causes. Rotation period, 24h. 37·4m.

Rotation Periods of Mercury and Venus.—*Mercury's* rotation period is believed to be 88 days, the same as his sidereal one, so that he always keeps the same face to the Sun. That of *Venus* has now been determined by means of radio observations to be 22 hrs. 17 minutes.

Jupiter is a fine object for small telescopes, with his elliptical disc, darker at the edges than in the centre, and 'parallel belt' markings; when in quadrature (p. 5) the limb is very slightly shaded, owing to 'phase.' The rotation period is 9h. 50·5m. near the equator (System I., *N.A.*), and 9h. 55·7m. in the temperate zones (System II.).

For reference, the disc is divided into the *N. and S. Polar Regions*; the *Equatorial*, *Tropical*, and *Temperate Zones*, crossed by seven darker 'belts'—viz., the narrow *Equatorial Band*; the *Equatorial* (*N.* and *S.*), and *Temperate* (*N.*, *NN.*, *S.*, *SS.*) *Belts.*

The Great Red Spot, seen in 1857, first prominent in 1878, was an oval about 13″ by 3″ (30,000 by 7000 miles), and its rotation period has varied by several seconds. Bright red till 1881, by 1892 it had faded to a pale orange, and has since shown little colour. In 1919-20, remarkable and rapid changes occurred in this region, the Spot disappearing and re-appearing again. It has generally been seen in a 'hollow' or 'bay' in the S. side of the S. Equatorial Belt, and a dark marking, the *S. Tropical Disturbance*, periodically overtakes the Spot and accelerates its motion.

Jupiter's synodic period being about 399 days, in successive years oppositions take place a month later in the season, the most favourable being every 12 years, in Sept.-October; his magnitude is then – 2·5, compared with about – 2·3 at mean opposition. Minimum mag., when in conjunction with the Sun, about – 1·2. Sidereal period, 11·86 yrs.

Jupiter's Satellites or Moons.—Seven of these are seen only in great telescopes or on photographs. The other four (about mag. 6, and numbered from the planet I, II, III, IV) are visible in an opera glass: they are all eclipsed by Jupiter's *shadow* (not instantaneously), I to III once every revolution. Sometimes a satellite 'transits' or passes across the planet's disc, appearing, as it enters or leaves the disc, as a bright spot on a dark background (the limb or edge of the planet being darker than the centre), while later it may disappear, if the background is similar in brightness and colour; it may also show as a dark spot. The shadow also transits the disc as a dark spot, which is apt to be taken for the satellite itself; sometimes both satellite and shadow are seen transiting at the same time.

Occultations, when the satellites pass behind the *body* of the planet, are frequent, but of little interest, though, when Jupiter is in or near quadrature, the satellite may disappear, or re-appear, slightly away from the apparent limb owing to the 'phase'—which is on the west side before, and on the east side after, opposition.

Saturn is also a fine object for small telescopes. The disc is even more elliptical than that of Jupiter—seen fully only when the Earth is in the plane of the rings—but is only slightly darker at the edges than in the centre. Faint parallel-belt markings may be discerned, and occasionally bright or dark spots, but his special feature is the wonderful Ring system, divided in two by a dark line-like marking known as *Cassini's Division*; it is just visible in a 2½-inch refractor when the rings are fully open. The projecting ends of the rings are called the *Ansæ*; the one facing in the direction of the planet's motion, in the field of view, is the 'preceding' ansa, the other the 'following' one.

The principal rings are designated A (the outermost) and B which is brighter; A is divided by a narrow dark line known as *Encke's Division*, not easily seen. A third ring C, the dusky *Crape*, *Crepe*, *or Gauze Ring*, nearest the planet, requires at least a 4-inch telescope. The rings are not solid as was once supposed, but myriads of tiny bodies revolving round the planet; the actual thickness of the rings is not yet known; estimates vary from 10 to 50 miles.

Saturn Ringless.—Twice in the course of Saturn's 29½-year sidereal period, at intervals of 13¾ and 15¾ years (from 1936), the rings present their edge (*a*) to the Sun, (*b*) to the Earth, or (*c*) turn their unillumined side towards the Earth, and become invisible in ordinary telescopes—even in the largest telescopes, when edgeways to the Earth—for a day or two; Saturn is then in heliocentric longitude 172° or 352°, in the constellations Leo or Aquarius-Pisces. About 8-7 years later, when he is in the constellations Taurus or Sagittarius (long. 82° and 262°) the rings are fully open, and he is at his brightest (see p. 17). The most favourable conditions for brightness and openness are when Saturn is in opposition at the times of perihelion (longitude 91°), and greatest openness, which, for the same longitude, only occurs every 29-30 years (from 1943). The Earth is in longitude 82° and 91°, about Dec. 15 and 24, with Saturn N. of the Ecliptic, and in 262° about June 14, when he is S. of it: oppositions about these dates will therefore be favourable, but those in the observer's summer will be at low altitudes. As Saturn's synodic period is 378 days, oppositions recur only a fortnight later in the season each year, giving for some years a succession of the best brightness-conditions. At the time of ring-invisibility, the Earth may pass (or almost pass) through the ring-plane thrice in the course of a year, the central one being near longitude 172° or 352°, the others months before or after (see Table p. viii).

Saturn's magnitude varies with the apparent width of the rings; mean opposition about + 0·93, max. – 0·4; ringless, from 0·65 to 0·87. His rotation period varies with the latitude, averaging about 10½ hours. Herschel I. gives it as 10h. 16m.; Hall (1876) 10h. 14m. 24s., for lat. 10°; Denning (1903) 10h. 37m. 56s.* Sidereal period, 29·46 years.

Saturn has nine satellites; a very small telescope shows Titan, the brightest (mag. 8·3); a 3-inch, or even less, Rhea (mag. 10·0); a 4-inch, Tethys, Dione, and Iapetus (mags. 10·6, 10·7, 10·9, respectively); the others are mag. 12-15.

Uranus and Neptune are of little interest to the ordinary observer, being so distant that their small discs are visible only in telescopes over 4 inches, their satellites in large ones. Uranus, being mag. 6, is visible to the naked eye; Neptune, mag. 7, in an opera glass. Their maximum and minimum brightness differ only by about 0·5 and 0·2 magnitude, respectively: their angular diameters also vary very little. Uranus has five satellites, Neptune two.

Pluto, discovered 1930, has a very eccentric and highly-inclined orbit (17°); at perihelion (in 1989) he comes nearer the Sun than Neptune. His magnitude (seems variable, by 0·2-0·4 mag.) ranges from about 12¾ to 15¾. His diameter and mass, as determined by Prof. Brouwer of Yale from perturbations of Neptune, is about equal to that of Venus.

* In the Planet's north latitude 35°.

Planets X, O, P, &c. Ultra-Neptunian planets, suggested by planetary perturbations and cometary analysis. Pluto represents Lowell's 'Planet X' (1915, mass much less); for the others, see *H.A.*, vol. 61, *P.A.*, vol. 40, 1932.

The Asteroids, or Minor Planets, being very minute, are all invisible to the naked eye, except *Vesta* (oppos. mag. 6½); the largest *Ceres*, is 480 miles in diameter, but the great majority are well under 50 miles. They occupy the position where 'Bode's Law' (p. viii) indicates a planet ought to exist, and may possibly be the remains of one. Unlike the Major planets (except Pluto), their orbits vary greatly in inclination to the Ecliptic and in eccentricity *Hidalgo* (944) having an orbit-inclination of 43°, and an eccentricity of 0·65 (exceeded by that of *Adonis,* see below).

New asteroids may receive names, but are only numbered (symbolised thus, (3), roughly in the order of discovery) when a satisfactory orbit has been obtained : for the temporary nomenclature, see p. ix. Over 1500 asteroids are now listed.

Eros (433), diameter about 15 miles, and perhaps 8-shaped, or irregularly coloured, as its light varies, rotates on its axis in 5¼ hours. Its orbit is so eccentric that when nearest the Earth it is about half the least distance of Venus, or 14 million miles; it is then about mag. 7, but is usually beyond the reach of small telescopes, the mean opposition magnitude being mag. 10. The nearness of Eros makes it of great importance for accurate measurement of the Sun's distance.-

Amor (Delporte Planet 1932 EA), not more than 3 miles in diameter, approaches within about 10 million miles of the Earth—4 million miles nearer than Eros does. It may be in opposition twice in a year. Period about 2¾ years.

Apollo (*1932 HA*), a Reinmuth planet, about a mile in diameter, may transit the Sun, as its orbit comes slightly within that of Venus. At times it may come within 3 million miles of the Earth. Its period is about 1¾ years.

Adonis (*1936 CA.*), a second Delporte planet, in 1936 was only 1·38 million miles from us. The eccentricity (0·76) of its orbit is such that it comes close to the orbit of Mercury and travels out as far as that of Mars. It is probably under half a mile in diameter. Period about 2·57 years. Inclination of orbit, 1°26′. It was favourably placed for observation in June 1943, but search for it was unsuccessful.

Hermes, discovered by Reinmuth in 1937, approached nearer the Earth than any other known planetary body except the Moon, coming within 485,000 miles of us.

The *Trojan* (or *Jupiter*) *Group* of asteroids, named after heroes in the Trojan war, is noteworthy for its members revolving in stability equidistant (approx.) from the Sun and Jupiter, though their orbits are very near that of the latter.

Planetary Radiation.*—*The Insolation* of a planet is the total radiation it receives from the Sun; of this the planet *(a)* reflects much solar radiation of short wave-length, *i.e.*, the ultra-violet, visible, and shortest infra-red wave lengths up to say 1·4μ (= λ14,000); and *(b)* absorbs the rest, then re-radiates it as *Planetary Radiation* of long wave-length, *i.e.*, invisible low-temperature heat-rays, which may include the planet's own radiation, if any: thus *(b)* is the measured total radiation *less* the amount of *(a)*. A 1cm. water cell placed in the beam of the planet's radiation transmits (*a*) but absorbs (*b*), thus enabling the amount of the latter to be measured. As an atmosphere acts as a blanket, the planetary radiation of atmosphereless planets will be high; that of those with atmospheres will tend to be small, lessening the denser and cloudier the atmosphere. Quartz and fluorite screens, which transmit longer wave-lengths than the 1·4μ of the water-cell (to 4·1μ and 1·2μ respectively) are also used in these investigations.

Jupiter and Saturn emit 6 per cent of planetary radiation; Mars has about 50%, indicating a thin atmosphere; Venus, about 8% on the bright side. The Moon and Mercury give 74%, suggesting similar physical (atmosphereless) condition. The Moon's local radiation at first or last quarter is proportional to the distance from the illuminated limb, and is zero at the terminator. The difference in the radiation from the light and dark lunar areas is slight.

Planetary Temperatures.—The surface-temperature of the Moon varies greatly throughout the lunar day; under the vertical Sun it is 101°C. (214°F.), while during the long night it sinks to less than – 150°C. (– 238°F.). *Mercury* under the vertical Sun is about 685°K. (412°C., 774°F., above the melting point of lead), at perihelion, and 555°K. (282°C., 540°F.), at aphelion; his dark side must be very cold, practically no heat being measurable. *Venus* differs little on the bright and dark sides, her temperature being about – 23°C. (– 9°F.); we evidently only see the upper surface of a cloud-layer in the isothermal region. *Mars*, under the vertical Sun, is 21°C. (70°F.) at perihelion, but only – 6°C. (21°F.) at aphelion, when the temperature at the poles is about – 70°C. (– 94°F.). *Jupiter* and the other giant planets are evidently cloud-covered like Venus, but their temperatures are naturally lower, Jupiter being about – 130°C. (– 202°F.); *Saturn*, though much further from the Sun, some – 120°-150°C. (– 184°-238°F.), thus seemingly emitting some heat of his own; *Uranus* and *Neptune*, some – 190°C. (– 310°F.) and – 220°C. (– 364°F.) respectively.

Planetary Atmospheres.—The Asteroids, the Moon, and even Mercury (probably, the temperature being high), having masses too small to overcome the 'velocity of escape' (p. 24), are atmosphereless. If Mercury has an atmosphere as faint transient markings (perhaps dust from volcanoes) suggest, it is so tenous that the solar spectrum is unaffected.

Venus has carbonic acid gas in her atmosphere, but seemingly no oxygen or water vapour in the observable regions

Mars.—The density of his atmosphere at ground surface is estimated as not exceeding that of the Earth at a height of 11 miles, but it is probably much less; clouds form in it and disappear, and both oxygen and water vapour are believed to be present, and were reported as having been observed in 1924, but later observations failed to confirm them.

The Giant Planets' atmospheres, so far as they are penetrable, are probably largely composed of hydrogen, and all contain the not easily condensed methane (marsh-gas, CH_4), the quantity increasing the further the planet is from the Sun's warming radiation. Jupiter, with the highest temperature, and to a lesser extent Saturn, also contain ammonia.

* See Lowell Obs. Bulletin, No. 85, 1925.

Planetary Surfaces.—Only the cloudy upper regions of the Giant planets and of Venus are visible, but the actual surfaces of the Moon, Mercury, and Mars, are seen. The polarimeter curves of the three latter are strikingly similar to those of volcanic ash and pumice. From their albedos at different phases, the surfaces of Mercury and the atmosphere-less Moon seem to be very similar, as might be expected, and are rather rough; that of Mars seems to be fairly smooth.

Meteors or Shooting Stars are of all degrees of brightness, from the faintest, lasting an instant, to the *bolide* or brilliant *fireball*, lasting several seconds: those that reach the Earth are called *aerolites*. Meteors may appear in any part of the sky, but there are certain well-marked points on the star sphere from which showers of meteors come every year at regular dates, when the Earth returns to the same part of its orbit. These showers are named from the constellation in which lies their *Radiant Point* or *Radiant*—so called because the meteors of the shower appear to radiate in all directions from that point in the sky. Many hundreds of radiants are known; the Table on p. 43 gives a few of the principal showers that may be looked for, and the approximate position of their Radiants. Those interested will find a long list in Webb's 'Celestial Objects.' In colour, the average meteor is more or less white, and is estimated to weigh not more than a single grain, from brightness and velocity considerations.

The meteors for any particular radiant mostly exhibit the same general characteristics year after year. There are, however, considerable differences between various showers. In some, the meteors move very swiftly, in others, they move comparatively slowly; in some, the average meteor is faint, in others, a proportion of fireballs may be expected. Streaks or trails are characteristic of some showers, while occasionally a bright slow-moving meteor seems to travel in a wavy path. All these points should be noted in meteor observations, but in recording the appearance of a meteor, the unskilled should note that it is much more important to describe exactly its apparent path or track among the stars, from beginning to end, than its physical appearance. The same shower may also vary considerably in point of numbers, being quite conspicuous one year, and hardly visible the next, or for years in succession. On the other hand, some showers of considerable steadiness sometimes flash into great activity at intervals, the Leonids for instance.

Meteors are generally twice as frequent at 6 a.m. as at 6 p.m., because at the former hour we are facing in the direction of the Earth's motion in its orbit; in the latter, to the rear. They usually appear from 50 to 80 miles above the Earth's surface, and, on the average, disappear at 40 or 50 miles. (See Notes on observing meteors, p. 43).

Comets vary in brightness, most of them being visible only with the aid of a telescope. A comet is generally first discernible as a minute, faint, misty patch of light, so much resembling a nebula that it is only identified as a comet when found to be in motion, but sometimes even a very large comet escapes detection at first by approaching us in the line of the sun. The essential portion of all comets is the *coma* or head, the misty patch of light already mentioned. In addition a *nucleus* may develop as it approaches the sun, *i.e.* a bright flame-like or star-like appearance within the *coma*, and also a tail, or sometimes several tails—which always point more or less away from the sun, no matter whether the comet is approaching or receding from the sun. The tail usually appears as a curved hollow cone, decreasing in brightness as it widens out. Both nucleus and tail, when present, increase in size and brightness as the comet nears the sun, and decrease as it recedes from the sun; *envelopes*, or stratifications of the mist round the nucleus, especially on the side towards the sun, may also appear as the comet approaches perihelion. Neither nucleus nor tail, however, is necessarily present. Several comets are connected in some way with meteoric showers.

Periodic comets—those which revolve round the sun, and thus appear at regular intervals—are known by the name of their discoverer (as *Holmes' comet*), or discoverers at two different returns (as *Pons-Brook's comet*), or discoverer or investigator of the periodicity (as *Halley's* and *Encke's Comets*). Tempel I (1867), Tempel II (1873), indicate two discoveries by the same observer. *Biela's comet* (now lost), which divided in two, was known as Biela I and II.

The Zodiacal Light:—Except near the time of the equinoxes, this is not well seen in temperate latitudes, as its axis in the sky at other times is comparatively near the horizon. It appears as a faint, hazy, conical, beam, some 15°-20° wide at the base, which nearly follows the course of the Ecliptic (not the Celestial Equator) on the star sphere, for 90° or more from the horizon a little south (S. Hemisphere, north) of where the Sun is below the horizon; in its brightest parts, it is two or three times as luminous as the Milky Way, but towards its extreme limits it is always exceedingly faint. Its brightness seems to vary from time to time, and it is brighter when observed within the tropics than in temperate latitudes, partly owing to its being more nearly vertical to the horizon, and partly to the shorter duration of twilight. It is best seen Feb.-March (evening), Aug.-Sept. (morning) in the N. Hemisphere; in the S. Hemisphere, *vice versa*; the inexperienced are apt to mistake the glow of twilight for it. (See Notes on Observing). In a very clear atmosphere, the *Zodiacal Band*, a narrower extension, joins the *Gegenschein* (next page), thus extending the Light right round the star sphere. These phenomena are all usually attributed to sunlight reflected from meteoric bodies, their spectra being mainly that of sunlight, but two recent theories consider them, (*a*) a terrestrial 'tail,' like that of a comet, due to the Sun's light-pressure; (*b*) an atmospheric phenomenon at an immense altitude.

The 'Counterglow' or Gegenschein is a *very* faint round patch of light, 10°-20° in diameter (*i.e.*, larger than the 'Great Square of Pegasus' = α, β, γ, Pegasi and α Andromedæ), or 40°-60° according to another authority, situated on the Ecliptic at the point diametrically opposite to where the Sun is for the time being. It is very difficult to see, and cannot be distinguished if projected on the Milky Way: choose a moonless night of exceptional clearness, when the Ecliptic is highest above the horizon, viz., in December and January. According to Barnard, it is largest and brightest in September and October. (See a long paper by Barnard, in the *English Mechanic*, March 21, 1919). It also is probably due to sunlight reflected from meteoric bodies.

Occultations take place when the Moon or a planet passes in front of some celestial body, shuttting it out from view. The Moon frequently occults stars; the disappearance, or *immersion*, is always on the E. side of the Moon, the reappearance, or *emersion*, on the W. side: sometimes (but rarely) the Moon occults a planet. When the star is bright, the instantaneous disappearance and re-appearance are almost startling: very rarely, the star seems to hang for an instant on the limb, perhaps chancing on some irregularity parallel to the Moon's motion. Duration, see next page.

The Moon's (star) shadow is 2160 miles in diameter on the fundamental plane (p. 3), and has no penumbra; it sweeps across the Earth from W. to E., in the direction of the Earth's rotation, which makes occultations last longer than they would with a non-rotating Earth. The *N.A.* occultation list gives the parallels of latitude within which they are seen: near these limits, the small breadth of the shadow (oval, in general) confines visibility to a very limited district.

Eclipses occur when (*a*) the Moon passes in front of the Sun†; (*b*) a satellite enters its primary's *shadow* (the *body* blots out, in occultations), and becomes invisible, though nothing intervenes, because the Sun no longer illumines it.

In *Solar Eclipses*—which, strictly speaking, are really occultations of the Sun—the eclipse begins on the west side of the Sun's disc, and the shadow sweeps across the Earth's surface from west to east; in *Lunar Eclipses*, the eclipse begins on the east side of the disc, and sweeps over it westwards. The *umbra*, or *shadow*, is the dark shadow on that portion of the Earth in solar, of the Moon in lunar eclipses, which, for the time being, receives no direct light from the Sun. The umbra shades away into the bordering *penumbra* or partial shadow, which covers those regions of the Earth or Moon whence the Sun would be seen partially eclipsed: the edge between them is never sharply defined.

First Contact occurs, in a solar eclipse, at the instant when the discs of the Sun and Moon first appear to touch, *i.e.*, when the eclipse begins: *Last Contact* at the instant of the end of the eclipse. In the case of a lunar eclipse, we have two First Contacts—at the instant when (1) the penumbra, and (2) the umbra or shadow, first touch the Moon's disc; and similarly two Last Contacts, at the moment when (3) the shadow, and (4) the penumbra respectively leave the disc.

The *magnitude*, or extent, of partial and annular eclipses is indicated by expressing the proportion of the diameter eclipsed as a decimal of the full diameter, at the time, of the Sun's or Moon's disc; in solar eclipses it varies according to the locality, but in lunar eclipses it is the same at any place from which it is visible.

In a total lunar eclipse, the magnitude is indicated as the ratio to the Moon's diameter at the time taken as 1; any eclipse less than 1 will be a partial one, while the maximum will be about 1·8, but this only occurs when the Moon is simultaneously in perigee and on the Ecliptic. The further the Moon is from the Ecliptic, the shorter is the duration of totality, and the nearer the points of first and last contact to the lunar poles.

Lunar Eclipses, when total and central, may last as long as 3 hours 48 minutes from first to last contact of the umbra, or up to 6 hours including the penumbral stage; the maximum duration of totality is 1 hour 42 minutes. Usually the Moon does not altogether disappear from view, even at mid-eclipse, but shines with a dull reddish-orange or greyish light, being illuminated by sunlight refracted by the Earth's atmosphere: the colour and brightness depend on the amount of water vapour and clouds present in the Earth's atmosphere at the time. On rare occasions the clouds intercept all or nearly all the rays that would be refracted, so that the Moon becomes nearly or altogether invisible.

Solar Eclipses, both total and annular, are rarely visible from any given place, the 'expectation' being only one in 360 years. Some 3 or 4 hours elapse between first and last contact, but totality never exceeds 7 m. 40 secs., and annularity 12½ minutes: both are usually much less. At the equator, both totality and contact-interval last about a quarter longer than at lat. 50°. The width of the zone of totality averages less than 100 miles, but where the Sun is in the zenith it may be about 167 miles.* Partial solar eclipses are of little interest, the Sun merely appearing notched; the temperature may fall perceptibly, however, and about mag. ·97, Mercury, Venus, and stars may appear.

Transits of Mercury and Venus.—Transits of *Venus* happen twice at the short interval of eight years, and then do not recur for over 100 years (105½ and 121½ alternately). Last transits, 1874, 1882; next transits, 2004, 2012.

Mercury transits the Sun about four times in 33 years, and *at the same node* at intervals of 7, 13, 33 or 46 years. The transits always happen at the descending node in May, or at the ascending node in November. Transits take place in May, 1957 and 1970, and in November, 1953, 1960, 1973, 1986, and 1999. (See Note on Transits, p. 42).

* See Track Charts in the *N.A.* † Or, in binaries, one star passes before the other.

Duration of Occultations.—The Moon's mean daily motion among the stars is 13°·18, or 0°·55 per hour, as seen from the Earth's centre. The Moon's mean angular diameter being 0·518°, for a central occultation her (star) shadow takes nearly an hour, on the average, to pass the Earth's centre, and still longer a point on the Earth's surface, where by her rotation, an observer is being carried in the same general direction as the shadow is travelling. At the Earth's equator the speed is about 1030 miles, and at latitudes 45° and 52°, 734 miles and 640 miles per hour, respectively: the duration of an occultation, therefore, shortens with increasing latitude, but in finding the actual duration, the Moon's varying velocity and angular diameter, and other factors, have to be taken into account. The track of the centre of the shadow may take strange curves, very similar to those of the tracks of various solar eclipses given in the *N.A.* In the latitude of Greenwich, some central occultations may last about 1½ hours.

Occultation Period.—Owing to the westward motion of the Moon's node along the Ecliptic (about 1½° per nodical month), the Moon's monthly path among the stars is always changing, circling the star sphere back to the same node in 18·59 years. *On the average*, therefore, each star within about 6¼° of the Ecliptic has the chance of being occulted twice during that interval, when it is passed successively by the ascending and descending quadrants of the Moon's path. These 'passings' are at average intervals of 9¼ years for stars on the Ecliptic itself; for other occultable stars the interval between the passings shortens as the distance from the Ecliptic increases (with a correspondingly longer interval to the next pair), till, at the occultable limit, the two passings coincide. But the intervals are not constant, owing to the varying inclination of the Moon's orbit, the node's irregular and sometimes (as regards the mean) reversed motion, &c., so that an occultation *may* be repeated during many months—or even some years, for stars near the occultable limit, where the monthly paths are closely crowded—before the path finally departs from the star.

Twilight, from ancient times, has been reckoned as ending when the Sun's centre is 18° below the horizon, 6th magnitude stars then being visible in the zenith; it has no definite duration, however, as meteorological conditions may modify it. The glow, in its later stages is a segment of a circle, brightest vertically over the Sun. Directly opposite, the indigo-blue segment of the unilluminated atmosphere rises from the east as the Sun recedes from the horizon.

Twilight lengthens with distance from the Equator, and is shortest all over the Earth about the Equinoxes. The total variation never exceeds half an hour below latitude 40°, and in higher latitudes, some 10-20 minutes during autumn, spring, and winter; but above lat. 40°, in summer twilight lengthens, till it lasts all night above 50°. *Civil, Nautical*, and *Astronomical Twilight* (British *N.A.*) end when the Sun's centre is 6°, 12°, and 18° below the horizon—the first about the limit when "ordinary outdoor operations become impracticable without artificial light." Table p. xiv.

Twinkling of Stars.—Though purely atmospheric in its origin, this phenomenon is of interest to astronomers, as it is affected by the nature of the light emitted by each star, *i.e.*, by its spectrum. White stars (Types B and A) twinkle most; yellow stars (Types F to K) slightly less, and red stars (Type M) least of all. Twinkling is least at the zenith, and in settled and calm weather; and greatest toward the horizon, and in unsettled and stormy weather: there is also a seasonal waxing and waning from mid-summer to mid-winter and *vice versa*. Planets do not usually twinkle except when near the horizon—supposed to be due to the fact that they have discs of an appreciable size.

The Green Flash, or 'Green Ray,' occasionally seen for a second or two before the instant of sunset or sunrise, is a beautiful solar phenomenon, due, like twinkling, to atmospheric causes; it is more often visible if an opera-glass is used. The general conditions required are a distant, sharply-defined, and low (preferably sea) horizon: avoid looking at the Sun till the last moment. Cool weather and absence of red tints seem to favour visibility. Sometimes it takes the form of a *white* flash followed by a deep blue one. While the duration is usually only a second or two, it tends to lengthen with increase in latitude, especially if the horizon is nearly parallel to the Sun's motion. In the Antarctic, it has been observed for 30 minutes. *A Red Flash* is sometimes seen as the Sun's *lower* edge emerges from a dark cloud near the horizon: it may last minutes if the cloud's motion is nearly the same as the Sun's.

Auroræ are believed to originate in the Sun. There is general agreement between the sunspot maximum and minimum and their greatest and least frequency, and though no definite relationship with sunspots has yet been demonstrated, magnetic storms and auroræ frequently occur when large spots are on or near the Sun's central meridian: they may be due to rays shot out from certain areas of the Sun's surface—not necessarily radially, or from where a sunspot is seen. Auroræ appear in various forms: diffuse areas, arcs, rays, beams, curtains, patches, &c. (details see p. 44). The ordinary height is some 87 to 300 kilometres (55-180 miles), but altitudes of 1000 km. (620m.) have been recorded.

Auroræ are most frequent about the time of the equinoxes—especially just after.* In Europe, some thirty may be seen annually on the line Inverness-Oslo; south of that line the number rapidly falls off, and south of the latitude of Paris, they appear only at long intervals. In America the corresponding limits are Quebec-Alaska, and Washington.

The colour of Auroræ is ordinarily faint white, silvery or delicate green in the brighter parts; red may appear, especially in the diffused type, or towards the lower edge of other types, and may pass into yellow-green. The auroral spectrum (also that of the night sky, faintly), has a characteristic green line—λ5577—due to oxygen and nitrogen.

Luminous phenomena, simulating auroral forms, also occur (rarely) near or even at ground level, and owing to undoubted theoretical difficulties (in our present state of knowledge) are usually attributed to mist or optical illusion. These explanations, however, do not account for the apparent absence of reports of such illusions from the regions of lesser auroral activity, where they are equally likely to occur, nor do they satisfy an actual witness of a 'low aurora.'

* See 'Auroræ,' Encyclo. Brittannica., 11th edition.

VI. HINTS ON OBSERVING, &c.

Atmospheric Conditions.—To get the best results, objects should be viewed when they are as far as possible above the horizon, *i.e.*, when near culmination. Satisfactory observations cannot be made of objects at low altitudes, owing to the increased intervening thickness of the atmosphere, and the haze and mist which so often obscure the horizon. The nights when the sky is darkest, and the stars most brilliant, are not always the best for observations. Faint and ill-defined objects, such as some nebulæ, may, however, often be seen to advantage on such nights.

During a slight haze, the air is often very steady, and splendid views of bright objects may then be obtained. If the stars twinkle much, it indicates that the air is unsteady and not altogether satisfactory for observation.

Viewing Faint Objects.—The eye becomes much more sensitive to faint impressions after it has been kept in the dark for a considerable time. A slight change of focus is often restful to the tired eye.

Very faint objects, otherwise invisible, may sometimes be detected by averted vision: the eye is directed to another part of the field, while the attention is fixed on the spot where the object is supposed to be.

Making Notes: Consulting Charts, &c.—A bull's-eye lantern with a slide to shut off the light is of great use. A cycle lamp may be utilised by the occasional observer. A photographic red lamp is even better, as it does not affect the sensitiveness of the eye. It may be placed on a support at some distance from the observer, and so directed as to throw a *faint* light on the book or card, when notes or sketches are being made at the telescope. A strong light should be avoided, as it makes the eye less sensitive for observation.

A small table to hold the maps and other books, with a lantern having a shade to throw the light downwards, lest the direct rays of light should reach the eye, is almost a necessity; a special shelf may be fixed up in an out-house.

All observations should be written down at the time, when they are made. The notes should be clearly worded, and should have entered on them the year, month, day, hour, and minute of the observation, together with the aperture and power of the telescope, and the state of the air. In Earthshine observations, the temperature, barometer reading, and direction of the wind should also be noted, as meteorological conditions have some influence on the brightness.

Direction in an Inverting Telescope.—In the inverted view of an object, as seen in astronomical telescopes (except 'Gregorians'), to observers in the Northern Hemisphere the upper part of the field of view is south, while the lower part is north; east is on the right hand of the object, and west on its left side.

To observers south of the Equator the reverse is the case; the upper part of the field is north, and the lower south; east is on the left hand of the object: west, on its right.

For circumpolar stars, however (*i.e.* those a less number of degrees from the Pole than the observer), the rule does not hold, as the observer is facing the other way, and objects on opposite sides of the Pole are moving in opposite directions.

North Preceding, &c.—To get over these difficulties in describing how to find a celestial object in the field of view, the phrases 'North (or South) preceding,' 'North (or South) following,' a certain star, are commonly used. *North* (or *South*) indicates that the object is nearer the North (or South) celestial pole than the star referred to; *Preceding* that its Right Ascension is *less* than that of the reference star, and *Following*, that its R.A. is *greater*, thus indicating the

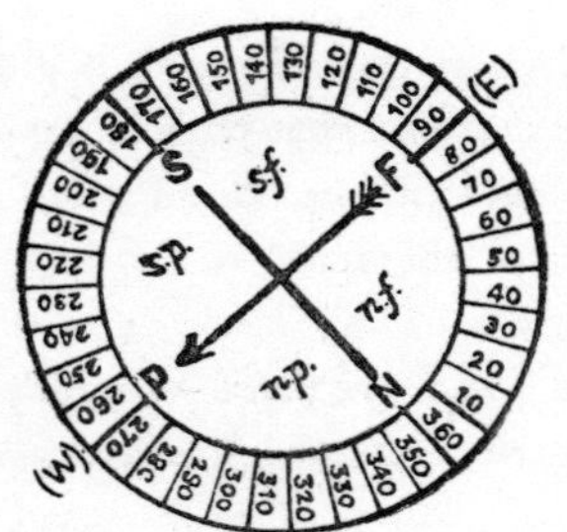

Between rising and culmination.
(*Angle depending on latitude of observer and declination of star*).

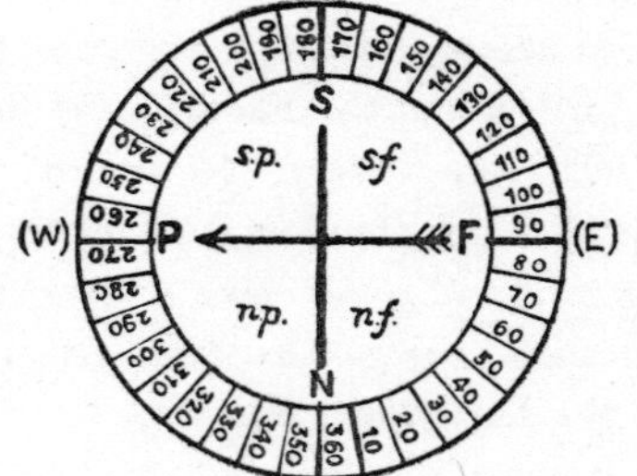

Southing or culminating.
(*Upright*).

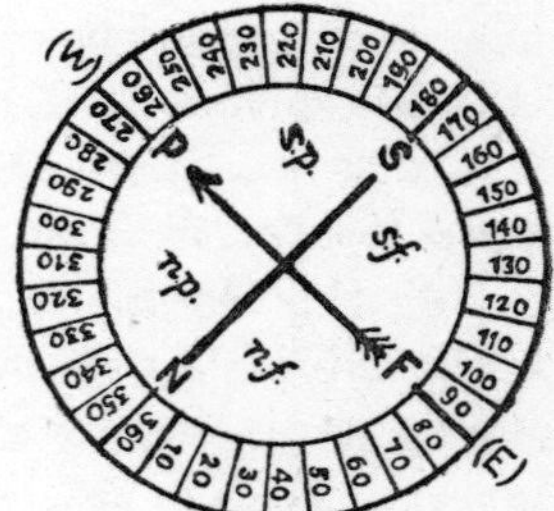

Between culmination and setting.
(*Angle depending on latitude of observer and declination of star*).

n.p.=North preceding. *n.f.*=North following. *s.p.*=South preceding. *s.f.*=South following. *P*=West. *F*=East.

direction in which to find the required object. The annexed diagram indicates how the hour-circle—which coincides with the line SN in the diagram—lies with respect to the horizon in an inverting telescope, when in different positions, and how a Position angle (P.A.) will in consequence occupy varying positions in the field of view.

In the diagram, the arrow denotes the apparent path of a star with reference to the horizon, as it crosses the field of view of a fixed inverting telescope in the N. Hemisphere. This path will be horizontal only when the object is on the meridian, but the relative positions remain unchanged. In the S. Hemisphere, invert the whole diagram.

Observing the Sun.—It is extremely dangerous to attempt to view the Sun unless proper precautions are taken: blindness may be the penalty of rashness or ignorance. A perfectly safe method is to support a smooth, white card, at the distance of about a foot from the eye-piece, and to focus the image of the Sun projected on it. The screen should be held in a covered frame-work or box, and the picture of the Sun viewed through a hole in one of the sides. If, on the other hand, the Sun is viewed directly through a dark-glass cap, a larger aperture than 2 inches cannot safely be used in the heat of summer. A stop made of a card, with a circular hole of 2 inches or less in diameter, should be fitted over the object glass of a larger instrument, to reduce the amount of light and heat transmitted: this, however, tends to reduce the sharpness of the definition. A special solar eye-piece can be obtained which enables full apertures to be used with safety.

Observing Prominences, by the spectroscope. The edge of the Sun's image should be made to fall on the nearly-closed slit of the spectroscope—which must be one of considerable dispersive power. The telescope should then be driven (preferably by clockwork) so as to keep the image in the same position. The spectroscope is next focussed on one of the hydrogen lines of the spectrum, and, on the slit being opened, the prominence will be seen. Good views may be obtained in this way, using a 3-inch telescope with a spectroscope having several prisms.

Observing Sunspots.—In studying their motion across the disc from east to west (see note, p. 39, as to direction in inverting telescopes), the position angle (p. 5) of the Sun's axis requires to be taken into consideration, as the apparent path varies according to the time of the year. The spots only move in straight lines across the disc about June 5 and December 7, on which dates alone the solar equator is seen as a straight line on the disc, dividing it into two hemispheres, with the poles exactly on the limb. At all other times, one pole alone is visible—very near the limb owing to foreshortening—and the solar equator lies on one side or other of the apparent centre of the disc, and is curved downwards or upwards, as are also the paths of the spots: maximum curvature northwards, about March 7; southwards, about Sept. 8. Sunspots take about a fortnight to traverse the disc from limb to limb, and will reappear after the same interval if they survive. Naked-eye spots **have a diameter not less than about 1/60th of the disc (31″).**

The variation of the position angle of the Sun's axis during the year (for the *North* pole) is about as follows :—

Jan. 5,	July 7,	0°	Feb. 23,	May 19,	20° W.	July 7,	Jan. 5,	0°	Aug. 28,	Nov. 20,	20° E.
,, 16,	June 26,	5° W.	Mar. 7,	May 8,	23° W.	,, 19,	Dec. 26,	5° E.	Sept. 8,	Nov. 9,	23° E.
,, 27,	,, 15,	10° W.	,, 18,	Apr. 26,	25° W.	,, 30,	,, 16,	10° E.	,, 21,	Oct. 30,	25° E.
Feb. 8,	June 5,	14° W.	April 8,	...	26° 42′ W.	Aug. 13,	Dec. 7,	14° E.	Oct. 11,	...	26° 42′ E.

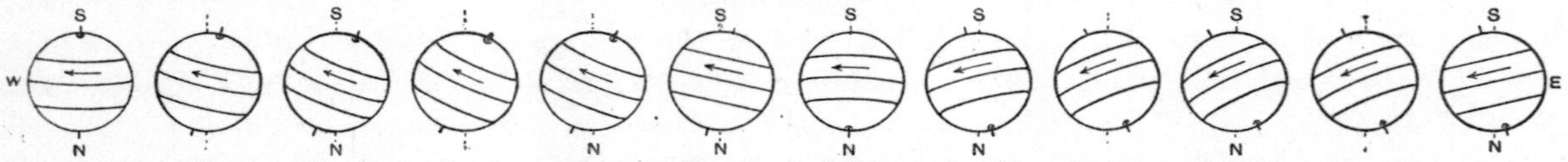

Jan. 5 Feb. 8 Mar. 7 Apr. 8 May 8 June 5 July 7 Aug. 13 Sept. 8 Oct. 11 Nov. 9 Dec. 7

The distance of the Sun's visible pole from the limb has necessarily been exaggerated in the diagram. N, S, indicate the line of the hour circle, N showing North in an inverting telescope—nearest the horizon in the N. Hemisphere. In the S. Hemisphere, hold the book upside down.

Near the times of the greatest inclination of the axis to the hour-circle, spots just appearing on the limb in the high spot-latitude of 45°, are, by the inexperienced, apt to be taken as being near the poles.

The number of degrees the solar equator is below or above the centre of the disc on various dates, is given in the *Nautical Almanac*, column B_0, 'Heliographic Latitude of the Earth,' + indicating that the spot-path is curved southwards, and − that it is curved northwards. The longitude of the spot on the surface can be found when it arrives half-way across the disc, from the column L_0, 'Heliographic longitude of the centre of the disc.'

Observing the Moon.—With a low power, and a fair-sized telescope, the glare of the Moon is very trying to the eye, and a tinted glass, mounted in the same way as the dark glass of the solar eye-piece cap, may be used. Reducing the aperture affects the sharpness of the definition. When the Moon is in perigee, the brightness is appreciably greater than when she is in apogee, the ratio being nearly as 4 is to 3. Best-seen conditions of each phase, see p. 29.

Observing Lunar Eclipses.—Mid-winter eclipses have the best altitude conditions, mid-summer ones the least favourable, for the reason given p. 29. First contact is always on the E. side of the disc, and through the telescope the Earth's shadow may be seen sweeping slowly across it, but the edge is not sharply defined. It should be noticed that from first to last, the 'preceding' edge of the umbra is always uniformly convex, unlike the dark terminator of the young Moon, which, though convex at first, daily grows less convex, till, at First Quarter, it is straight, and finally becomes increasingly concave. Similarly, the 'following' edge of the umbra is also always convex. Phenomena that may be noted are the visibility or otherwise of the rays, and of prominent craters, &c., such as Aristarchus and Copernicus: also the variations of colour as the eclipse progresses, on different parts of the disc.

Observing the Superior Planets.—In temperate latitudes, summer observations of these planets are always conducted under unfavourable conditions as to altitude; in winter, the altitude conditions are the most favourable. This results from the planets being always near the Ecliptic, so that their highest altitude above the observer's horizon at culmination is much the same as that of the Ecliptic where it cuts his meridian. At mid-summer, midnight culmination is at its lowest, and in mid-winter at its highest. Thus observers in the Northern hemisphere, outside the tropics, are better situated for observing the oppositions between October and March, than those in the Southern hemisphere, while observers in the latter are better placed for seeing oppositions between April and September.

A curious effect of the two-year synodic period of Mars is, that for some eighteen months or so in succession, he is visible at some time or other every night, then becomes lost in twilight and daylight for some four or six months.

The angular diameter, or semi-diameter, of a planet's disc on any date, will be found in almanacs: the diagram indicates, on a uniform scale, the range of changes, and relative sizes, of the discs, and the favourableness, or otherwise, of the size of the disc can easily be inferred by reference to the mean diameter.

Saturn. Min. 15″ Mean. 18″ Max. 21″. Uranus. 3½″. Mars. Min. 3½″ Mean. 15″ Mean. opp. 19″ Max. 25″. Jupiter. Min. 30″ Mean. 40″ Max. 50″.

Observing Mercury and Venus.—The most favourable seasons of the year are indicated on page 33. For Mercury, Southern observers have the best conditions, as his maximum elongation occurs when he is in S. Declination.

Observing Occultations.—Beginners will probably be rather puzzled to know the direction in which the Moon will approach the star, owing to the varying position of the Moon's axis with respect to the horizon: the direction, however, is approximately at right angles to the line joining the cusps, or horns of the Moon.

The Moon's mean hourly motion being fully ½°, the rate of approach is about a quarter of the Moon's diameter in 14 minutes, or the apparent diameter of Hipparchus in about 2¾ minutes, or of Copernicus in about 1½ minutes. The time, however, is modified by the latitude of the observer, &c.

Observing the Zodiacal Light.—As the axis of the Light approximately coincides with the Ecliptic, the most favourable conditions in temperate latitudes are when the Ecliptic is most nearly vertical to the horizon soon after sunset, or before sunrise, which in the evening is before the Spring equinox, and in the morning after the Autumnal equinox, of each hemisphere. The nearest approach to verticality is always when 6 hrs. R.A. is on the meridian (N. Hemisphere), or 18 hrs., (S. Hemisphere); at that instant, too, both the direction of the lowest portion of the Light, also the verticality, are most easily found, as the Ecliptic then intersects the horizon exactly due west and due east,* and its angle with the horizon is equal to the co-latitude of the observer *plus* 23½°.

The Zodiacal Light proper cannot be longer above the horizon than six hours after sunset, or before sunrise, as its extension from the Sun is reckoned as about 90°, but of course it will only be distinguishable for a much shorter period, twilight preventing observation for perhaps an hour after sunset, in the higher temperate latitudes; and the haze of the horizon obscuring its faint extremity for long before setting. For brightness, compare with Milky Way.

The Table below gives the approximate dates and hours when the Ecliptic is most nearly vertical during the short observing season. The dates at the top are for the N. Hemisphere; those at the foot (in italic) for the S. Hemisphere. The position of the foot of the Light on the horizon for three or four hours after (or before) the hours mentioned is easily found, as its movement in azimuth westwards, may be taken as about 6° per hour, over that period; similarly, the decrease per hour in inclination after (or before) greatest verticality is, roughly, 2°.

Feb. 5	Feb.12	Feb.20	Feb.27	Mar.7	Mar.14	Mar.22	Sept.22	Sept.29	Oct.7	Oct.14	Oct.22	Oct.30	Nov.7
9 p.m.	8·30	8 p.m.	7·30	7 p.m.	6·30	6 p.m.	6 a.m.	5·30	5 a.m.	4·30	4 a.m.	3·30	3 a.m.
Aug. 6	*Aug.13*	*Aug.21*	*Aug.29*	*Sept.6*	*Sept.13*	*Sept.21*	*Mar.23*	*Mar.31*	*Apr.8*	*Apr.15*	*Apr.23*	*Apr.30*	*May 8*

Observing the Milky Way.—The Milky Way circles round the Celestial poles once each sidereal day, its central line passing within 27° of the N. pole, in the W of Cassiopeia, and within 27° of the S. pole, near *α* Crucis.

In the N. hemisphere, in the latitude of Britain and the U.S.A., it passes through or near the zenith during the hours when R.A. 22 hrs. to 4 hrs. are on the meridian; thereafter it approaches the horizon, till, when R.A. 13 hrs. is on the meridian—and for some time before and after—it lies so close along the N. horizon for most of its visible length that it is hardly observable, after which its altitude begins to increase again. The Cassiopeia-Argo section is visible to its maximum extent when R.A. 8 hrs. is on the meridian, and the Cassiopeia-Scorpius section when R.A. 16h. is on the meridian, but the portions near the horizon are not well seen. For favourable observing times, consult Table p. xiv.

In the S. hemisphere, in the latitude of Cape Colony and Southern Australia, the corresponding phases are:—overhead, R.A. 10 hrs. to 16 hrs. on the meridian; on the horizon, R.A. 1 hr. on the meridian. The Crux-Cygnus and Crux-Perseus sections are visible to their maximum extent when R.A. 20 hrs. and R.A. 4 hrs., respectively, are on the meridian.

* The compass-direction requires correction for the magnetic variation; see 1-inch Government Maps.

Observing Variable Stars.—The 'variable' is compared with neighbouring stars of similar brightness and of known magnitude. Two comparison stars are found, one rather brighter than the variable, the other slightly fainter; the magnitude of the variable will be between those of the comparison stars, and the nearer their magnitudes, the more accurate the result. Except for rough estimates, a catalogue of magnitudes is required, or a special star chart, such as those for Novæ and interesting variables given from time to time in the British Astron. Association Journal, or 'sequences,' *i.e.*, lists of standard stars, arranged in order of magnitude for this purpose.

The dates of maxima and minima are recorded by the Julian Day (J.D.)*—which begins at *noon*, not midnight, (p. 9)—and decimals of a day, but observations cannot always be made, as the date may fall when the star is near the Sun, or during moonlight. The annual B.A.A. Handbook gives useful observing information, dates of maxima, &c.

It is important, where possible, (*a*) to observe the star when at its highest altitude; (*b*) that the comparison stars be about the same altitude, so that atmospheric absorption (see below) will equally affect their magnitudes; (*c*) that they be as nearly as possible similar in colour to the variable, as it is very difficult to estimate correctly the real relative brightness of two stars differing widely in colour, as, for instance, in the case of Betelgeuse and Rigel. For a curious optical phenomenon—known as the *Purkinje Effect*—comes into play, namely, that if red and green lights, appearing equally bright, are increased or decreased in the same ratio, in neither case will they now appear of equal brightness; the red will seem the brighter when the light is increased, but the green when the light is decreased.

Estimating Magnitudes: Atmospheric Absorption.—For accurate valuation of the magnitudes of bright variable stars, if the comparison stars are not about the same altitude, allowance must be made for the difference, as atmospheric absorption diminishes the brightness (apart from haze) by approximately the following magnitudes:—

Zenith distance.	47°	58°	64°	69°	71°	73°	75°	77°	79°	80°	84°	86°	88°	89°
No. of mags. diminished.	$\frac{1}{10}$th	$\frac{2}{10}$ths	$\frac{3}{10}$ths	$\frac{4}{10}$ths	$\frac{5}{10}$ths	$\frac{6}{10}$ths	$\frac{7}{10}$ths	$\frac{8}{10}$ths	$\frac{9}{10}$ths	1 mag.	$1\frac{1}{2}$m.	2m.	$2\frac{1}{2}$m.	3m.
Altitude above horizon.	43°	32°	26°	21°	19°	17°	15°	13°	11°	10°	6°	4°	2°	1°

Comet Seeking.—In searching for comets, a telescope of fairly large aperture and of short focal length, with an eye-piece of low power having a large field of view, should be used. The observer should slowly 'sweep' (*i.e.*, move the telescope in a horizontal direction) for some distance, a careful watch being kept all the time. At the end of the sweep the telescope is *slightly* raised or lowered, and an overlapping sweep is taken in the opposite direction. This process is repeated continuously. Should a nebulous-looking object be noticed, the comet-hunter must look in his catalogue of nebulæ to see if the object can be identified. If not, he should draw a careful sketch of its position among the neighbouring stars. If in the course of time any movement can be detected, and the place of the suspected object does not agree with that of any known comet, its position should be determined as accurately as means will allow, and a telegram giving particulars should be sent to Greenwich (or the corresponding) Observatory.

Observing Transits.—There are four contacts: *external contact,* at ingress and egress, *i.e.*, entering or leaving the Sun's or planet's limb; and *internal,* when entering completely on or beginning to depart from, the disc.

The Black Drop, seen at internal contact when Venus (sometimes Mercury) is just touching the Sun's limb, is a curious drawing-out of the planet's black disc to the Sun's limb, in a broad band or ligature, which gives it the appearance of a drop of black ink hanging internally from the Sun's limb. In a few seconds the band contracts, then breaks: this renders the instant of internal contact uncertain. A very narrow brilliant circle of light is sometimes seen surrounding Venus near first and last contacts; it is probably due to sunlight refracted by her atmosphere.

Observing Nebulæ.—These faint objects lose least light by atmospheric absorption when near the zenith, hence those showing a preference for the Galactic plane are most favourably situated when the Milky Way is nearly overhead, but those showing a preference for the Galactic poles, when the Milky Way lies near the horizon. Suitable times for observation can be found by the notes on p. 11, along with the Table of Sidereal Time on p. xiv.

Observing Earthshine.—The degree of visibility of the outlines of the Maria, and of Aristarchus, Copernicus, and other prominent craters, affords a good index of the state of the atmosphere. The thermometer and barometer readings, and direction of the wind should be noted, as meteorological conditions have some influence on the brightness.

Observing Novæ.—The following changes generally occur in the spectra and colour; there may be considerable variations from the normal, some stages missing, and individual peculiarities. I. A. U. Notation (1922, 1928) below.

1. Continuous spectrum : ... ... White
2. Hydrogen lines double: bright & dark lines: „
3. Lines widen : continuous spectrum fades.
4. Nebula lines appear : ... ... Yellow
5. Hydrogen lines brighten up : Red
6. Hydrogen lines fade : ... Orange
7. Nebula lines more prominent than hydrogen ones, ... Bluish
8. Star now a planetary nebula.
9. Nebula lines fade: spectrum now faintly continuous, bright Wolf-Rayet bands.

Qa; absorption lines and bright bands (faint). **Qb**; stronger absorp. lines (mainly enhanced metallic, many double) and bright bands. **Qc**; absorption metallic lines of *O*, *N*, *He*, enhanced metallic lines predominating. **Qd**; as Qc, but gaseous lines predominating. **Qu**; broad nebulous emission bands near λλ3480, 4515, 4640. **Qx**; bright bands (enhanced *O*, *N*, *He*); absorption lines faint. **Qy**; as Qx, bright nebular bands. **Qz**; bright nebular and weak Wolf-Rayet bands. **Qz-O5**; as Qz, Wolf-Rayet bands strong.

Combination spectra indicated by combining the small letters, placing the most prominent first.

* Sometimes J.A.D.—Julian Astronomical Day.

Observing Meteors.—Showers from radiants within or near the circle of the 'always-seen' stars of any locality are observable all night, more or less, but the observing interval shortens as the distance from that circle increases, until, for the more remote, should the culmination-hour be many hours after midnight, the shower is never observable from that latitude except for a few hours before sunrise. Thus the November Leonid shower is only a morning one as the radiant culminates about 6 a.m., and only rises about midnight. Some meteors from a radiant just below the horizon *may* be visible, however. The possible observing-hours can be found from the star Table on page xiv.

The following are the important points to note:—Date; Greenwich Mean Time (G.M.T., U.T.) of appearance; R.A. and Dec. of beginning and end of flight, and duration in seconds; colour and stellar magnitude, stating comparison star; path, if straight or wavy; streak or train, if any, and the colour, duration, direction and speed of drift; any other notes. A *streak* is the faint, phosphorescent narrow band, sometimes coloured, which endures for a time along the path of some meteors: a *train*, a spark-like and usually quickly-disappearing appendage. The R.A. should be stated in degrees (see conversion Table below), and the observation communicated to the Director, Meteor Section of the British Astronomical Association, London, or to the American Meteor Society. Cambridge, Mass.

For counting seconds, the well-known photographic rule 'One, two, three, ONE; one, two, three, TWO; &c.', pronounced rapidly but distinctly, gives very near results.

List* of Important Showers.—The Radiant position may change a degree or two on successive days, and a look-out should be kept before and after the dates given, as leap year adjustments cause small variations. For a Radiant on every night of the year, see B.A.A. Handbook, 1922; and list of 1000 radiants, *Mem. R.A.S.*, vol. 53.

The column headed 'Cul.' gives the Radiant's approximate hour of culmination on the central date, 'a' denoting a.m.; 'p' p.m.

Date.	Shower.	Cul.	Radiant. R.A. = h. m.	Dec.	Speed, &c.	Date.	Shower.	Cul.	Radiant. R.A. = h. m.	Dec.	Speed. &c.
Jan. 2-3	**Quadrantids**	9a	230°=15 20	53° N	Medium.	Aug. 10-12	**Perseids** [1]	6a	45°= 3 0	57° N	v. swift.
„ 17	κ Cygnids	12a	295° 19 40	53° N	slow, trained.	„ 12-Oct.2	α Aurigids	6a	74° 4 56	42° N	v. swift, streaks.
Feb. 5-10	α Aurigids	8p	75° 5 0	41° N	v. sl., fireballs.	Aug.-Sept.	Lacertids	12p	332° 22 8	49° N	medium, short.
Mar. 10-12	ζ Boötids	3a	218° 14 32	12° N	swift, streaks.	„ 10-20	κ Cygnids	10p	290° 19 20	54° N	„ bright.
Apl. 20-22	**Lyrids**	4a	271° 18 4	33° N	do	„ 21-23	o Draconids	9p	291° 19 24	60° N	v.slow: max. 1879.
May 6	**γ Aquarids**	7a	334° 22 16	2° S	v. swift [3].	„ 21-31	ζ „	7p	263° 17 32	62° N	slowish, bright.
„ 11-24	ζ Herculids	1a	247° 16 28	28° N	swift, white.	Sept. 7-15	ε Perseids	5a	61° 4 4	35° N	swift, streaks.
„ 30	η Pegasids	6a	333° 22 12	27° N	v. sw., streaks	Oct. 2	Quadrantids	3p	230° 15 20	52° N	slow. In 1877.
June 2-17	α Scorpiids	12p	253° 16 52	22° S	v.sl., fireballs.	„ 12-23	ε Arietids	1a	42° 2 48	21° N	v. slow, fireballs.
„ 27-30	ι Draconids	9p	228° 15 12	57° N	v. slow [4].	„ 18-20	**Orionids**	4a	92° 6 8	15° N	swift, streaks.
„ -Sept	γ do	9p	269° 17 56	48° N	slow, trained.	„ 30-Nv.17	ε Taurids	1a	64° 4 16	22° N	slow, fireballs.
July 18-30	α Cap'cornids	12p	304° 20 12	12 S	v.sl., bright [5].	Nov. 3-15	e „	12p	55° 3 40	13° N	v. slow, bright.
„ -Aug	α Cygnids	12p	315° 21 0	48 N	sw., last long.	„ 13-15	**Leonids** [2]	6a	150° 10 0	22° N	v. swift: period
„ 25-Au. 4	α-β Perseids	7a	48° 3 12	43 N	v. sw., streaks	„ 17-27	**Andromedids**	10p	25° 1 40	43° N	v. slow [6]. [33⅓yrs
„ 25-30	δ Aquarids	2a	339°=22 36	11 S	sl., long paths.	Dec. 10-12	**Geminids**	2a	112°= 7 28	33° N	med'm, white, rich

Notes. [1] The Perseids are visible during July and Aug. (a rich display, max. Aug. 10-12): the radiant moves from about 2° +41° to 68° +61° (Androm. to Camelop.). [2] The Leonids, or November meteors, are seen at their best about every 33 years: plentiful in 1799, 1833, and 1866, but the 1900 display was not brilliant owing to the disturbance of their orbit by Jupiter. [3] Long paths, before sunrise; Halley's comet. [4] Pons-Winnecke's comet. [5] Comet 1881 V. [6] Biela's comet.

R.A. Hours & Minutes converted into Degrees, or vice versa; **1 min. = ¼°.** (Reads continuously *across* page).

hrs.	0m.	4m.	8m.	10m.	12m.	15m.	16m.	20m.	24m.	28m.	R.A.	30m.	32m.	36m.	40m.	44m.	45m.	48m.	50m.	52m.	56m.	hrs.
0	...	1°	2°	2½°	3°	3¾°	4°	5°	6°	7°	0h.	7½°	8°	9°	10°	11°	11¼°	12°	12½°	13°	14°	0
1	15°	16	17	17½	18	18¾	19	20	21	22	1	22½	23	24	25	26	26¼	27	27½	28	29	1
2	30	31	32	32½	33	33¾	34	35	36	37	2	37½	38	39	40	41	41¼	42	42½	43	44	2
3	45	46	47	47½	48	48¾	49	50	51	52	3	52½	53	54	55	56	56¼	57	57½	58	59	3
4	60	61	62	62½	63	63¾	64	65	66	67	4	67½	68	69	70	71	71¼	72	72½	73	74	4
5	75	76	77	77½	78	78¾	79	80	81	82	5	82½	83	84	85	86	86¼	87	87½	88	89	5
6	90	91	92	92½	93	93¾	94	95	96	97	6	97½	98	99	100	101	101¼	102	102½	103	104	6
7	105	106	107	107½	108	108¾	109	110	111	112	7	112½	113	114	115	116	116¼	117	117½	118	119	7
8	120	121	122	122½	123	123¾	124	125	126	127	8	127½	128	129	130	131	131¼	132	132½	133	134	8
9	135	136	137	137½	138	138¾	139	140	141	142	9	142½	143	144	145	146	146¼	147	147½	148	149	9
10	150	151	152	152½	153	153¾	154	155	156	157	10	157½	158	159	160	161	161¼	162	162½	163	164	10
11	165	166	167	167½	168	168¾	169	170	171	172	11	172½	173	174	175	176	176¼	177	177½	178	179	11
12	180	181	182	182½	183	183¾	184	185	186	187	12	187½	188	189	190	191	191¼	192	192½	193	194	12
13	195	196	197	197½	198	198¾	199	200	201	202	13	202½	203	204	205	206	206¼	207	207½	208	209	13
14	210	211	212	212½	213	213¾	214	215	216	217	14	217½	218	219	220	221	221¼	222	222½	223	224	14
15	225	226	227	227½	228	228¾	229	230	231	232	15	232½	233	234	235	236	236¼	237	237½	238	239	15
16	240	241	242	242½	243	243¾	244	245	246	247	16	247½	248	249	250	251	251¼	252	252½	253	254	16
17	255	256	257	257½	258	258¾	259	260	261	262	17	262½	263	264	265	266	266¼	267	267½	268	269	17
18	270	271	272	272½	273	273¾	274	275	276	277	18	277½	278	279	280	281	281¼	282	282½	283	284	18
19	285	286	287	287½	288	288¾	289	290	291	292	19	292½	293	294	295	296	296¼	297	297½	298	299	19
20	300	301	302	302½	303	303¾	304	305	306	307	20	307½	308	309	310	311	311¼	312	312½	313	314	20
21	315	316	317	317½	318	318¾	319	320	321	322	21	222½	323	324	325	326	326¼	327	327½	328	329	21
22	330	331	332	332½	333	333¾	334	335	336	337	22	337½	338	339	340	341	341¼	342	342½	343	344	22
23	345	346	347	347½	348	348¾	349	350	351	352	23	352½	353	354	355	356	356¼	357	357½	358	359	23

* List of S. Hemisphere Radiants, see *M.N.*, vol. 95, p. 709, 1935.

Observing Auroræ (see also p. 38).—Those in favourable latitudes should watch during the more active portion of the sunspot period, or when there is considerable solar activity, especially near the equinoxes.

Arcs and *Bands* stretch across the sky, and may have considerable persistence; the latter appear like portions of arcs. *Rays* or streamers seem to flicker, and are more or less radial to the band or arc; *Beams* are long bright rays, of exquisite green or red, like search-lights. *Curtains* have curious convolutions, and are more or less parallel to the horizon, the lower edge being most continuous. *Patches* are isolated oval or globular areas resembling faint but quite transparent clouds; *Diffuse Auroræ* are large areas, often coloured, with no definite outline. *Coronæ*, rare, but exceedingly fine, are large starfish-shaped ovals, with dark centre, from which bright narrow flickering bands may extend to the horizon. The *Dark Segment* is the gloomy portion of the sky beneath the arch or streamers, in which the stars may be hardly or not at all visible. Various types may be seen during a display.

In N. temperate latitudes, the centre of disturbance is in a northerly direction—not necessarily in the direction of the magnetic pole, as is often supposed; a patch, arc, or corona may be overhead, or even south of it. Rays often appear to flash or flicker, and in arcs and bands a flickering from side to side is sometimes seen—not always in the same direction—and portions may suddenly brighten up and become centres from which the disturbances appear to travel.

The chief points to notice are the type, colour, brightness as compared with the Milky Way, height of lower edge above the horizon, and width; direction of the centre of the disturbance (allow for 'magnetic variation' of the compass), and times of the various phases. Also note the barometer and thermometer readings, and direction and force of the wind.

The angular breadth and length of persistent arcs, bands, and patches, should be carefully gauged by reference to the distance between neighbouring stars; also the angular distance, from well-known stars, of the upper and lower edges. The notes should be repeated at intervals, the times being carefully noted, as the height and distance of the aurora might be calculated from simultaneous observations (send notes to the B.A.A., Auroræ Section, London).

VII. THE CARE AND USE OF THE TELESCOPE.

Astronomical Telescopes are of two kinds—refracting and reflecting. Both varieties are rated according to their 'aperture,' as the *clear* diameter of the large lens in refracting telescopes, or of the mirror in reflecting telescopes, is called.

The larger the aperture, the more powerful the telescope in 'light-gathering' power, *i.e.*, in rendering visible faint objects; and, as this power (theoretically) increases in proportion to the *square* of the diameter, a telescope of 3 inches aperture is twice as powerful as one of 2 inches, while a 4-inch has nearly twice the power of a 3-inch, or four times that of a 2-inch (actual ratios, 4, 9, 16). In refractors, however, the theoretical power falls off rapidly with increasing diameter, the ever-thickening object-glass absorbing more and more light, though reflectors under 10 ins. are not quite so powerful as refractors of equal size. For astronomical purposes, a 3-inch telescope is about the smallest that can be used with satisfaction, though pleasing views of many objects may be obtained with smaller telescopes of good quality.

Diam. Object Glass (clear aperture)	1 in.	1½ in.	2 in.	2½ in.	3 in.	3½ in.	4 in.	4½ in.	5 in.	6 in.	8 in.	10 in.	12 in.
Closest star divided (approx.)	4·56″	3·04″	2·28″	1·82″	1·52″	1·30″	1·14″	1·01″	0·91″	0·76″	0·57″	0·46″	0·38″
Faintest star shown („) mag.	9·0	9·9	10·5	11·0	11·4	11·7	12·0	12·3	12·5	12·9	13·5	14·0	14·4

THE REFRACTOR essentially consists of two convex lenses—(i) a large one of considerable focal length, known as the *object glass*, which forms at its focus an image of the distant star or other object, and (ii) a small lens of much shorter focal length: this is called the *eye-piece*, and is used to magnify the image formed by the object glass.

The Object Glass is the most important part of the refractor, as its excellence depends on the accuracy of the curves of the lenses, the highness of their polish, and their transparency. In all astronomical telescopes worthy of the name, the object glass is 'achromatic'; that is to say, it is composed of two (sometimes three) lenses of equal size, but made of glasses of different density. These are so proportioned as to form an image almost free from the false colours which are inevitably present when a bright object is viewed through an object glass consisting of a single lens. A good object glass requires to be treated with the most scrupulous care. Follow carefully the notes on p. 49.

THE REFLECTOR.—In this form of telescope a large, concave, parabolic-curved mirror takes the place of the object glass of the refractor. The large mirror is held in a cell at the lower end of the large tube. The rays of light from the object pass down the tube and are reflected back. The reflected, convergent rays are intercepted—

(1) In the 'Newtonian' form of telescope, either by a small, elliptical, plane mirror ('flat'), or by a right-angled totally-reflecting prism, which reflects them at right angles through the side of the telescope to the eye-piece.

(2) In the 'Cassegrainian' form, by a small convex mirror, which reflects them back again, through a hole in the centre of the large mirror to the eyepiece; or (3) in the 'Gregorian' form, by a small concave mirror.

The Newtonian and Cassegrainian forms, like refractors, give an inverted image; the Gregorian, an *erect* image. The Cassegrainian form gives a greater focal length and larger image than Newtonians of the same aperture and length, but its field of view is smaller and the image fainter. Great telescopes are sometimes designed to use both forms.

Mirrors are usually made of glass, on which a film of silver is deposited chemically; this is very easily tarnished (p. 49), and vaporised aluminium is now often used, which is about as efficient as fresh silver, lasts years with little deterioration, and reflects the ultra-violet rays and blue end of the spectrum better—of great advantage photographically—but the red and infra-red rays less efficiently. Stainless steel mirrors last well, but only give 65% efficiency, compared with the 90% average of fresh silver.

An unsilvered glass mirror and 'flat'—which reduce the sunlight and heat reflected by some 90%—enable solar observations to be made with fairly large apertures, giving improved definition; a dark glass or solar eyepiece, however, is still necessary.

Eye-pieces.—These are used to magnify the image formed by the object-glass or the large mirror. For very high powers, and in special cases, a single lens is sometimes used to minimise loss of light, but generally an eye-piece consists of two lenses—a *Field lens*, furthest from the eye; and an *Eye lens*, nearest the eye. These are mounted in a short tube which screws or, preferably, slips into the focussing-tube of the telescope.

Positive and Negative Eye-pieces.—Eye-pieces are of two types:—*(a) Positive*, in which the image-plane is outside the eye-piece—between it and the object-glass or mirror—so that it can be used with a micrometer. *(b) Negative*, which cannot be employed with a micrometer, as the image-plane lies inside the eye-piece.

Inverted Image.—All astronomical eye-pieces show the object inverted (unless used with Gregorians), but this is of no disadvantage in practice. To make the object appear right way up requires additional lenses, or prisms, which absorb light, making the image fainter with no compensating gain. Among many varieties of eye-pieces are the:—

Huygenian eye-piece (negative).—The most common form, two plano-convex lenses having their flat surfaces towards the eye. Note that, though negative, fine cross-wires can be inserted on its diaphragm, at the focus of the eye lens, for use in a "finder" (p. 46), or for "guiding" in celestial photography—using cement, or threading through small holes.

Ramsden eye-piece (positive).—Two plano-convex lenses with their plane faces outward. Field of view "flatter" than that of the Huygenian, *i.e.*, not so blurred round the edges when the centre is sharply focussed. Performs well on planets.

Tolles Solid Ocular (negative) is practically a Huygenian eye-piece made out of a single glass cylinder, the foci of its curved ends falling inside it. Transmits more light than the Huygenian, and gives very good definition when well made.

Orthoscopic eye-piece (positive) contains a triple field lens and a simple eye lens. It yields a flat field free from distortion, and is specially recommended for medium and high powers. ('Orthoscopic' means giving a correct image.)

Kellner eye-piece (positive). A convex or plano-convex field lens with a much smaller over-corrected plano-convex achromatic eye lens. Field very large, colourless, and 'orthoscopic'; low powers are suitable for comets and scattered objects.

Monocentric eye-piece (positive).—A triple cemented lens, particularly recommended for the critical study of lunar and planetary detail, as it gives exquisite definition, and freedom from 'ghosts': its small field is its weak point.

Barlow Lens.—A concave or concave-meniscus lens of about 3 inches negative focal length, mounted in a short tube—made a sliding fit—inside the eye-piece draw-tube, and placed between the objective and eye-piece, 4 or 5 ins. from the eye-piece.

It increases considerably the focal length of the object-glass or mirror, giving an image of double the size, more or less, according to its distance from the eye-piece. This valuable device, at the cost of a slight loss of light, and a tendency to form 'ghosts,' gives a flatter field and an increase of the powers of all eye-pieces used, thus doubling the set at small expense.

The magnifying power of a telescope depends entirely upon the ratio of the focal length (f_1) of the object-glass to that of the eye-piece (f_2), the formula being $f_1 \div f_2$; thus, with an object-glass of 36 inches focal length, and an eye-piece having a focal length of ½ inch, the magnifying power will be 72 diameters, or "power 72" as it is termed. Note that, as the power is increased: (*a*) the image gets fainter, and the area included less; (*b*) stars pass more quickly across the field; and (*c*) the atmospheric disturbances are also magnified, as well as any vibrations of the stand or ground.

It is advisable to have at least three eye-pieces of different power:—

(1). One of low power with a large "field," (that is, showing a considerable area of the sky), for viewing comets, large and scattered clusters, and extended nebulæ, magnifying 8 or 10 times per inch of aperture. Thus, on a 3 in. telescope the power may be from 25 to 30, or for a 4-inch, 32 to 40. For average eyes, aperture × 4 gives *lowest* useful power.

(2). One of moderate power, magnifying 25 or 30 times to each inch of aperture = 75-100 for a 3-inch, 100-120 for a 4-inch.

(3). One of high power, magnifying 50 or 60 times to each inch of aperture = 150-180 " " 200-240 " "

When experience has been gained, the observer may sometimes use eye-pieces of still higher powers—the extreme limit of useful power being about 100 diameters per inch of aperture—but, as a rule, to advantage only on close double stars, when the telescope is of fine quality, and atmospheric conditions most favourable. Such nights are very rare.

To find Focal Lengths.—(*a*) *Object-glass or Mirror.* Remove the eye-piece and stretch a piece of semi-transparent paper over the end of the draw-tube. Point the telescope at the Moon, and focus her image on the paper screen; the measured distance between the back of the object-glass and the screen—in Newtonians, between the centres of the surfaces of the large mirror and flat, and thence to the screen—is, for practical purposes, the focal length required.

(*b*) *Huygenian Eye-piece.*—Divide twice the product of the focal lengths of the two lenses by the sum of their focal lengths; the quotient is the focal length of an equivalent single lens.*

To find the Power of an Eye-piece.—Make a scale with plainly-marked equal divisions. Set this up at a considerable distance away, and, holding both eyes open, view the scale through the telescope with one eye and directly with the other. The number of divisions on the scale, covered by the magnified image of one of them, is equal to the magnifying power of the eye-piece used. For low powers, a distant brick wall will serve as a scale.

Another method.—Focus the telescope on a star. Next morning, without altering the focus, point the telescope to the bright sky. When the eye is placed about 10 inches behind the eye-piece, there will be seen a small, clearly-defined disc of light. Measure the diameter of this disc by means of a Berthon Dynamometer (see p. 47) placed against the eye-piece—a pocket lens, of low power, should be used as an aid in doing this. The magnifying power of the eye-piece is found by dividing the clear diameter of the object glass by the measured diameter of the bright image.

To find the Diameter of the Field of an eye-piece, observe how long a star situated near the equator (for instance, δ Orionis, or γ Virginis) takes to pass centrally across the field from one side to the other. This time, expressed in minutes and seconds, when multiplied by 15, will give the diameter of the field in minutes and seconds of arc.

* When the distance apart of the lenses d is equal to half the sum of their focal lengths, $(f_1+f_2)\div 2$; the Rev. W. F. A. Ellison points out that as this distance is not always kept to, the correct formula for all combinations is:— Focal length $= \frac{f_1 \times f_2}{f_1+f_2-d}$.

TESTS.

The actual performance of a telescope on a celestial object is the only really satisfactory test. Seen through a telescope bearing its highest power, a fixed star of the second magnitude should appear as a minute, well-defined, circular disc of light, almost a point, and surrounded by one or two thin, concentric, bright rings. There should be no false rays of light, and the rest of the field should be uniformly dark. The telescope should not, however, be condemned too hastily, as an inferior eye-piece, or the state of the air (see p. 39), may be responsible for apparent defects in the object glass. A close double star with very unequal components forms a most severe test. A telescope of the finest quality should separate a double, consisting of two 6th magnitude stars, whose distance from centre to centre in seconds of arc is equal to 4·56 divided by the aperture expressed in inches. (see Table p. 44).

ACCESSORIES.

Stands.—Much depends upon the rigidity of the telescope stand, and good observations must not be expected from the open window of an ordinary room, as the vibration of the floor, and the mixed currents of air, set the object being viewed dancing. For small telescopes, the ordinary, alt-azimuth, tripod garden stand is most convenient. An iron pipe of about 4 inches diameter, partly sunk in the ground, and rammed full of clay to deaden vibration, forms a good support for a telescope of moderate size.

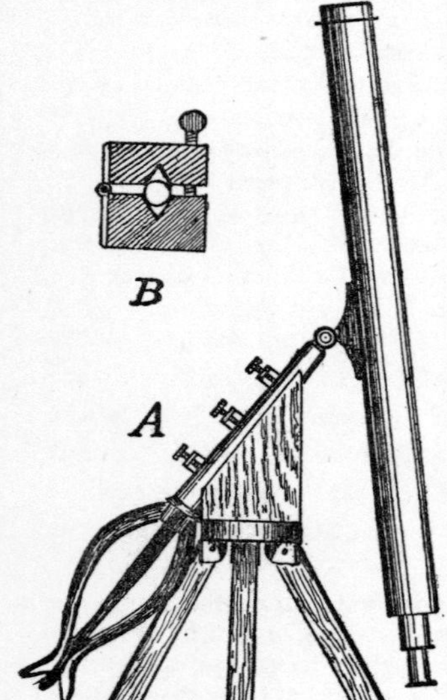

The Equatorial Stand is of enormous advantage, but is rather expensive. It has one of the pivots, or axes, which carries the telescope, directed towards the celestial pole, (being adjustable for latitude). The result is that a star may be followed by a single circular movement of the telescope, instead of the instrument having to be moved both in altitude and azimuth. A make-shift is to screw to the stand top a wooden block cut off at an angle, as shown in the illustration (A), and which has a V-groove, with sides at an angle of 60°, cut along the inclined face, for receiving the pillar. The claw legs of the stand, folded up, will act as a counterpoise, and two or three screw clamps will keep the pillar firm. A piece of hard wood (not shown in the illustration), also V-grooved, should be interposed between the point of the screws and the pillar, to prevent damage when tightening up the screws. A somewhat simpler construction is to hinge this upper block at one side to the lower block, and pass the screws through both blocks at the other side, as shown in the illustration at (B).

The angle of the sloping top, from the vertical, must be the latitude of the observer subtracted from 90°. Thus, for latitude 52° it will be 90° − 52° = 38°.

Finder.—A finder is a small telescope fixed by supports to the body of the larger instrument. When high powers are used, this adjunct is a necessity, and in all cases it adds much to the comfort of observing. The finder may be roughly adjusted by day on a distant weather-cock or some other definite object. To improve the adjustment, bring the polar star into the centre of the field of a low power eye-piece on the large telescope; then alter the direction of the finder, by means of the adjusting screws, until the star image is in the centre of the field of the telescope, and also bisected by the cross wires of the finder at the same moment. Now replace the low-power eye-piece by one of high power, and perfect the adjustments in the same way. For small telescopes up to 3-inch, 'sights' similar to those on rifles can be arranged (painted white), which will be found of some service.

Dew-cap.—To guard against the deposition of dew on the object glass, make a tube of tin, cardboard, or some such material, about 9 inches or 1 foot long, and of such a diameter as to fit closely, but not too tightly, on to the object glass end of the tube. The inside of the dew-cap should be covered with black velvet, or painted with a mixture of lamp-black and size. Black blotting paper is also suitable.

Star Diagonal.—An L-shaped tube containing a right-angled totally-reflecting prism. One end of the fitting screws into the focussing-tube of the refractor, while the other end is screwed to receive an ordinary eyepiece. Its use prevents awkward positions of the body when viewing objects at high altitudes, but results in some loss of light and definition. A special diagonal is made for the Sun, which only requires a light shade glass (see note on p. 49).

Berthon's Dynamometer (or measuring gauge) is a little instrument used for measuring the diameters of small objects. It has two flat metal sides, the internal straight edges of which meet towards the end, and are inclined to each other at a small angle. One of the edges is graduated from 0 to $\frac{2}{10}$ of an inch. The figures on the scale denote the width of the gap between the two straight edges. To measure the diameter of any small object by means of this little appliance, it is only necessary to see at what part of the scale the object *just* fills the space between the internal edges of the gauge, and then take the reading from the scale. The scale is divided into 20 long divisions of ·01 or 1/100ths of an inch. These are subdivided into five parts, each equal to ·002 or 1/500ths of an inch. The first two long divisions are again divided into parts equal to ·001 or 1/1000ths of an inch.

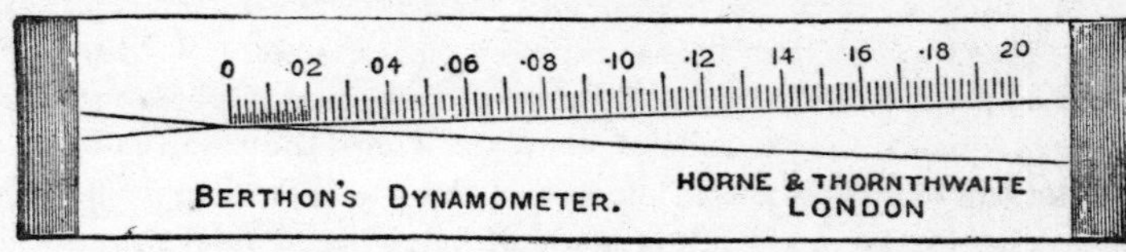

Telescope House.—A tall folding clothes-horse, with a sheet fixed to it, and stayed by tent-ropes, forms a fair substitute, which will, to some extent, shield the telescope from vibration by the wind, and add to the observer's comfort.

TO CONSTRUCT A SIMPLE EQUATORIAL OR ALT-AZIMUTH STAND.

By following the directions and studying the diagrams given, any handy amateur, with the aid of a few simple tools, will be able at a very low cost to construct an efficient equatorial or alt-azimuth stand for a 3-inch or smaller refracting telescope. If made on a larger scale and of considerably thicker materials, the equatorial head here described, mounted on short, strong, fixed legs, would do equally well for a reflecting telescope of moderate size.

The Legs.—Take 3 deal boards about 6 to 6½ feet long, 5 inches wide, and 1 inch thick. Mark a point 2 inches from an edge at one end of the board and another point 3 inches from the same edge at the other end. Join the points found with a straight line and saw along it. This will divide the board into two equal flat pieces, each 1 inch thick, and tapering from 3 to 2 inches in width. These two pieces are joined together at distances of 1 inch and 9 inches from the narrow bottom end by 1¾-inch screws (No. 9 or No. 10, about $\frac{3}{16}$ inch diameter). The two laths are kept apart by blocks of hardwood cut from a piece having a 2 inch square section, and held in place by screws. Thus the leg is formed as shown in Fig. 1, which is on a scale three times less than that of Figs. 2, 3 and 4. The laths should not be screwed together until the brass plates mentioned later on have been fitted. A metal plate (*p*) sawn or filed to a blunt point, may be screwed to the *inner* side of the foot, with the point projecting.

The Top of the Stand.—This is best made from an iron casting, for which a wooden pattern will be required. The pattern is made of ¼-inch mahogany fretwood, cut to the shape shewn in Fig. 2, and strengthened by having a 4-inch bevelled disc of the same material glued and screwed on to it, so that the central part is ½ inch thick. Each of the three projecting parts of the casting is either drilled with two ¼-inch holes, each ¼-inch distant from the 3-inch edge, to receive ¼-inch bolts, or, as an alternative, $\frac{3}{16}$-inch holes may be drilled, and tapped ¼-inch Whitworth to receive metal screws. A ⅜-inch hole is drilled through the exact centre of the disc. Instead of the casting, a piece of tough, hardwood, such as beech, cut to the same shape, but at least 1¼-inches thick, may be used.

The Leg Pivots.—Cut a 12-inch length of ½-inch *square* brass bar into three equal pieces. In a lathe, turn half-an-inch at each end into a blunted cone (C, Fig. 2), the small outer end being ⅜-inch in diameter. If no lathe, file the ends to the same shape as carefully as possible. These bars are now drilled with ¼-inch holes to correspond to the holes in the top, and are then screwed or bolted to the underside of the iron top.

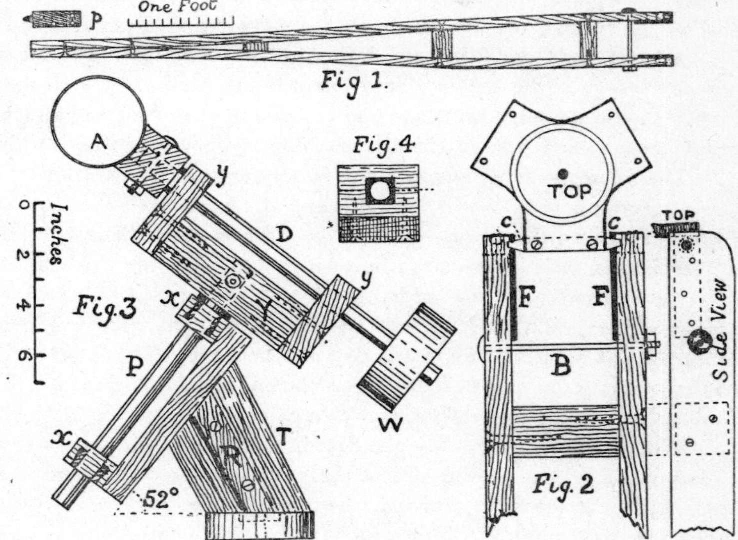

The Hinge Plates.—To the top inner side, and towards the back of each of the laths forming the legs, is firmly screwed a flat, brass plate, 4 inches long, 1 inch wide and $\frac{3}{16}$-inch thick (Fig. 2, F, and side view). The plate is flush with the top of the leg, which is rounded off at the outer top corner, and has in it near the top a ⅜-inch hole slightly enlarged, and coned to fit over the conical pins at C. B is a ¼-inch bolt 6½ inches long, having a nut, bearing on a washer, which nut on being screwed up makes the hinge firm, and adjustable for wear.

The Equatorial Head (Fig. 3).—For this some pieces of oak or strong hardwood a full inch thick are required. The base is circular, and has, centrally fixed by screws in a recess in the bottom, a plate with a $\frac{3}{8}$-inch Whitworth tapped hole, to receive a screw which clamps the head to the stand. This plate might be fixed in a recess on the upper side of the round base before the angle piece next referred to is fixed in position.

Fixed to the base is the trapezoid or angle piece of 1-inch wood (T). Strong glue and $2\frac{1}{2}$-inch No. 12 screws should be used for fixing the parts. The top of this piece must be cut off at such a slope that the angle which it makes with the base is equal to the latitude of the place where the stand is to be used. A piece of wood 8 in. × 3 in. × 1 in. is screwed to the top of the trapezoid piece, and the whole is strengthened by adding the side pieces (R) which are 1 inch square.

The Polar Axis (P) is made of bright mild steel round rod, $\frac{3}{4}$-inch in diameter and $11\frac{1}{2}$ inches long. This steel is easily obtainable at large tool and material stores. The upper end of the polar axis (P) is driven into a rather smaller hole in the block (Y) which is of hardwood 6 inches long by 2 inches square. Care must be taken to make this hole at right angles to the block. A $\frac{1}{4}$-inch hole is drilled through block and axis, and a bolt inserted.

The Bearings (x, x) may be simply holes ($\frac{3}{4}$-inch) in the hardwood blocks, with a simple split arrangement for taking up wear; but it is more satisfactory to enlarge and square (slightly undercutting) the greater part of each hole, and, with the axis in place, to pour in melted tin or pipe composition (lead and tin) to form more durable bearings. Before pouring the lead, coat the axis with a mixture of black lead and water and allow it to dry. If, when all is cold, the axis cannot be twisted round, when oiled, it should be *gently* hammered endways with a mallet. If there is still trouble, cut with an old saw along the dotted line (Fig. 4), through wood and bearing-metal down to the axis. The upper halves of the split bearings can then be held in place by screws. Similarly for the bearings (y, y).

The Declination Axis (D), another $\frac{3}{4}$ inch steel rod, about 14 inches long, is fixed, like the polar axis, at right angles in an 8 inches long, 2 inches square block, grooved for its whole length on one side to receive the telescope main tube (A). The telescope is fixed to the block by means of leather straps or thin metal bands. Thin $\frac{3}{4}$-inch metal washers are placed between the blocks and the upper bearings of both axes. The balance-weight or counterpoise (w) is formed of a small round tin filled with lead, in which a piece of tube that just slides over the axis has been centrally fixed before the molten lead is poured in. The weight is so adjusted that it will counteract any tendency of the telescope to swing round by its own weight on the polar axis. It would be quite possible to fit graduated circles to this simple head. Celluloid circles can be obtained cheaply, and could be mounted on wooden discs of the same size —an addition which, with a carefully adjusted stand, will make possible the finding of Mercury and Venus in bright daylight and of stars by night from the places given in catalogues. But, even without circles, the advantage of being able to watch a star by only one movement will be found to be a great one.

Alt-azimuth Head.—For this only the parts A, D, Y, W (Fig. 3) are required. The polar axis P is replaced by a $\frac{3}{8}$-inch bolt which passes vertically and without shake through the central hole in the metal top of the tripod. A flat brass plate is screwed to, and protects from wear, the lower side of the block Y, which rests horizontally upon, and can be turned in azimuth about, the metal top. Turn or scrape the top flat, and grease with vaseline.

Adjusting the Equatorial Stand.—The completed stand is set up so that the top of the stand is level, with one of the legs of the tripod placed towards the south, and with the legs set well apart. Three strong cords of equal length should be made taut, one end of each to a central ring and the other end to a screw ring, fixed in the central cross-piece of each leg; this is a precaution against a possible accident.

The telescope tube is next set as nearly as possible parallel to the polar axis, and then, having slightly loosened the clamping screw, it will be sufficient, if no graduated circles are used, to gradually turn the equatorial head till (in the Northern Hemisphere) the Pole Star is seen in the field of view. The head is then clamped. Any slight adjustment in latitude required may be made by moving the southern leg of the tripod either inwards or outwards.

An alternative to the cords, which also renders the stand more rigid, is the addition of three stretcher bars, each made of two parallel metal strips, fixed $\frac{3}{8}$-inch apart, and riveted to a short cross-piece at one end, and to the flap of a firm hinge at the other. The other hinge-flap is screwed to the central cross-piece of the leg, as shown in the illustration. A $\frac{3}{8}$-inch bolt with a wing nut (*c*) passes through the three slots, and clamps the bars together.

When graduated circles are fitted, a more accurate adjustment of the equatorial head is necessary, if it is to be of practical use. With a movable stand it is well to have some means of replacing it in the same position when once it has been carefully adjusted, or much valuable time may be lost in re-adjusting it each night. Three stone slabs, or concrete blocks, having central gun-metal or brass plugs inserted, are set in the ground at the corners of an equilateral triangle equal in size to the most convenient leg base. Each metal plug has a hole or recess in the top, in which rests the previously-mentioned metal spike attached to the lower end of the leg. The adjustment of the head proper may be effected by means of thin wedges under the head, or, better, by three screws passing through the metal top of the tripod and bearing on the under side of the base of the head, which should be protected by a circular metal plate that rests on the points of the adjusting screws.

The true N. pole, towards which the polar axis should be directed as nearly as possible, lies about 1° (two Moon breadths) distant from Polaris, and very nearly on the straight line joining Polaris and η Ursæ Majoris—the last star in the tail of the Great Bear. If the time is chosen when the Pole star transits above or below the pole (see *N.A.*), and the telescope (set as before, parallel to the polar axis) is directed towards the Pole star, so that it appears in the centre of the field of view, then a lowering or a raising of the axis through 1°, by means of the southern adjusting screw, will make the adjustment sufficiently accurate for finding an object when using an eye-piece of low power.

HINTS ON CLEANING.

Refracting Telescope.—A good object glass is so delicately figured that it should be cleaned as rarely and carefully as possible, for fear of affecting the accuracy of its form. (*See below, "Cleaning."*)

The lenses should never be taken out of their cell by an inexperienced person.

The object glass should be held in its cell with just sufficient "play" for a slight rattle to be heard when it is gently shaken. If screwed up tightly, it causes strains in the glass which mar the perfect definition.

Reflecting Telescope.—The silvered mirror requires to be kept with very special care, as the silver is exceedingly liable to tarnish, especially in or near large towns, from the sulphurous fumes in the air. The owner of a reflecting telescope should, therefore, procure and study the "Hints on Reflectors," which have been published by several of the leading makers of these instruments.

A slight stain causes merely an inconsiderable loss of light, but, if badly tarnished, the mirror must be re-silvered. This process may be successfully accomplished by the amateur, with little difficulty, and at no great expense, if he carefully follows the directions given in the books just referred to, and uses pure chemicals.

Care of the Telescope.—Before removing the telescope after the night's work, cover the object glass or mirror with the metal cap provided for that purpose.

Never take the instrument from the cold outer air into a warm room, or the object glass will become dewed. If this should happen, the object glass must not be left in that state; but it should be placed in a warm room, at a safe distance from a fire, until the moisture has vanished. Any stains left on the glass must be removed by gentle polishing. Never wipe an object glass when it is damp.

Cleaning the Lenses.—When it becomes necessary to clean these, any dust should first be removed by means of a *camel's-hair brush*. Then the lens should be wiped very gently with a piece of very fine and clean wash-leather or silk.

When not in use, all brushes and materials employed for this purpose should be carefully protected from dust by keeping them in clean stoppered bottles or air-tight cases.

Solar Eye-pieces.—The use of a silvered or deeply-coloured Barlow lens with an ordinary eye-piece is a simple and effective way of reducing the Sun's light and heat. The chief objection to the silvered lens is that the film is so easily scratched. A special solar diagonal (Sir J. Herschel's), in which only about $\frac{1}{20}$th of the Sun's light is reflected from the first surface of a narrow prism, is procurable. With this, the addition of a light shade-glass is necessary. See illustration in Proctor's *Half-Hours with the Telescope*, new edn.

Helioscopes, or Helioscope eye-pieces, depending upon polarization, reduce the Sun's light sufficiently to enable a dark-glass to be dispensed with, but they are somewhat complicated and expensive appliances.

Spectroscopes.—Small instruments for viewing stellar spectra can be had at a comparatively low price; these screw on to or fit in the eye-piece tube. Those for viewing prominences, however, are much more expensive, as the dispersion required is considerable, and prices are of the order of £7 ($35) upwards. It would be a great boon to amateur astronomers if some enterprising optician could bring out a satisfactory instrument for half that sum, or less.

Astronomical Photography.—Anyone possessing an equatorial telescope with a slow worm-wheel motion on the polar axis, can take good stellar (or cometary) negatives in a box camera attached to the tube of the telescope, using ordinary photographic lenses of *f*/6 or greater aperture, which should be carefully focussed by trial exposures; a driving clock is not essential, though advantageous. The telescope serves as a 'guider,' a star being kept steadily on cross-wires in the eyepiece; these wires can easily be added to a positive eyepiece by anyone accustomed to use tools. Exposures are rather lengthy, from some twenty minutes upwards—to hours for faint stars—and require patience.

Most refractors are not very suitable for taking photographs of the Sun and Moon in the telescope itself, without an eyepiece, as they do not bring the actinic and visual rays to the same focus, and the sharpest position has to be found by trial and error. Reflectors are free from this disadvantage, also 'photo-visual' refractors; but the latter are expensive. The Moon can be taken by a fixed telescope, of ordinary focal length, in about $\frac{1}{4}$-second, but the image is small—in a 3-inch, only $\frac{1}{3}$-inch diameter.

Those desirous of taking up this pursuit should procure 'Astronomical Photography,' by Mr H. H. Waters, F.R.A.S.—a little book which gives all needed information on the subject of apparatus, adjustment, exposure, &c.

A Celestial Globe, adjustable for latitude, is useful for finding the direction and altitude of Mercury, or a comet, in twilight, also the path of the Zodiacal Light. The stars are reversed as regards left and right on the globe, because we view the star sphere from the inside, and the globe is viewed from the outside.

ADJUSTMENTS OF A NEWTONIAN REFLECTOR.

THE elliptical flat mirror, mounted in a short metal tube cut off at an angle of 45° with its axis, is sometimes supported in the centre of the main tube and towards the upper end of it, by a single radial arm fixed to the inside of the tube. More usually the support consists of three, sometimes four, steel strips of spring temper fitted with screwed ends that pass through holes in the main tube, outside which they are held firmly by means of nuts. With the aid of compasses or a scaled ruler set the centre of the flat mounting exactly in the centre of the tube, if it is not already so placed.

When the flat has been centred, its inclination must be adjusted so as to reflect a ray of light passing along the axis of the main tube along the axis of the eyepiece focussing tube. This must be done by means of the adjusting screws fitted to the flat mount. Sometimes these are three in number, but a better arrangement is a hinged flat mount with a single angle-adjusting screw with a knurled head, and an axial screwed pin enabling the flat to be partly rotated and clamped in position by means of a heavy knurled nut.

A brass disc-fitting, with a central hole about $\frac{1}{20}$in. in diameter, is screwed or slid into the eyepiece draw-tube in place of the eyepiece. A special fitting, though convenient, is not indispensable, since the front part of the mount of an eyepiece of high power, with the lenses removed, will do well as a substitute. On looking through this hole, there will be seen the circular end of the eyepiece tube and within it the flat with an apparently circular outline. If the flat is approximately adjusted there will appear, within the circle of the flat, the circular outline of the mirror and its cell. As a help to the eye, the large mirror may be covered with a white circular card of the same size as the mirror. Then, by means of the flat adjusting screws, gradually tilt the flat until the outline of the mirror (or cardboard disc) is concentric with the eyepiece-tube circle. It may be necessary to move the base of the focussing-tube mount slightly up or down the main tube to perfect this adjustment. Remove the card and there will be seen a circular dark spot, the image of the flat. If this is not exactly in the centre of the bright mirror image, it must be brought to that position by means of the three adjusting screws at the base of the large mirror cell. *The dark spot is always most distant from the adjusting screw that must be turned in.* Thus, in Fig. 1, the screw whose position is indicated by the head of the arrow must be turned in to bring the dark spot to the centre. The same result is achieved by turning the two other screws equally outwards. The circular outline of the flat itself should not be exactly concentric with the eyepiece tube and mirror circles, but *slightly* displaced towards the upper end of the tube, as shewn in Fig. 2 where all is in perfect adjustment. EE, the outermost circle represents the far end of the eyepiece tube; T part of the tube which holds the flat; FF the flat itself; MM the bright image of the large mirror; I the dark central image of the flat, and S the images of the four spring supports of the flat mount.

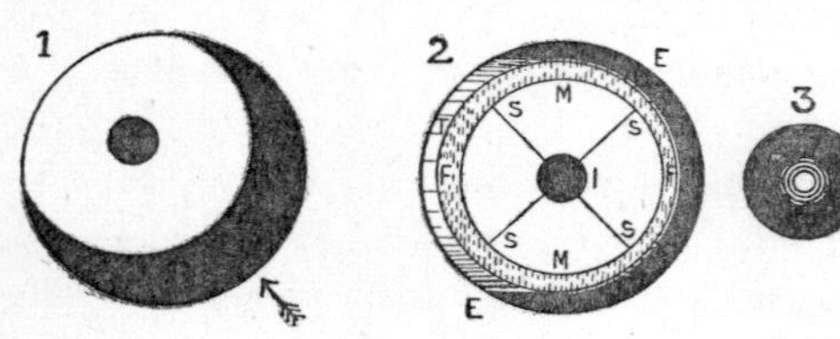

Fig. 3 shows the appearance of a moderately bright star in a good telescope, when the air is steady and the instrument correctly adjusted and carefully focussed—a bright round spot surrounded by two or three concentric rings of light. It is impossible to portray accurately the extreme delicacy of these diffraction rings as they appear on the best observing nights.

EQUATORIAL ADJUSTMENTS.

IT is infeasible here to give full directions for the accurate adjustment of an equatorial. Such instructions are given in Horne and Thornthwaite's "Hints on Reflecting and Refracting Telescopes," and in Chambers' "Handbook of Descriptive and Practical Astronomy," Vol. II. (Clarendon Press, 1890). The chief adjustments are :—

1. *Adjust the vernier-index of the declination circle.* The equatorial being placed in nearly its correct position, read the declination of a star brought to the centre of the field when near its southing with the circle facing E. Repeat with the circle facing W. If the two readings agree, the vernier position is correct; if they are not the same, move the vernier half the difference between them. Other adjustments having been completed, the declination vernier will indicate 0° when the telescope points to the equator.

2. *Adjust the polar axis to the altitude of the Pole.* Read the declination of a star which is on, or nearly on the meridian, and also near the zenith. Compare the reading with the declination of the star as given in the Nautical or Whitaker's Almanac. If the amounts differ, set the circle to the correct reading, and bring the star to the centre of the field by means of the base adjusting screw (S^1 in the drawing on page 51).

3. *Place the polar axis in the meridian.* Point the telescope to a known star about 6 hours from the meridian, either E. or W. of it, but as distant as possible from both Pole and horizon. If the star is E. and its declination as shown on the declination circle exceeds that given in the catalogue, the lower end of the polar axis is W. of its right place and must be moved. A horizontal or azimuth movement given to the equatorial head to correct the declination corrects also the meridian position

Other adjustments necessary are :—

4. *Set the optical axis of the telescope at right angles to the declination axis.*
5. *The polar and declination axes must be set at right angles.*
6. *The index of the hour circle must point to* 0^h *when the telescope is in the meridian and the declination axis horizontal. With a movable hour circle (see opposite), the verniers* V^2 *and* V^3 *should show like readings when the telescope is thus set.*

EQUATORIAL HEAD.

The section drawing represents an equatorial head designed and made by the author. It is suitable for a 4-inch or smaller refractor. It was built up of iron and gunmetal castings from simple wood patterns, and a few mild steel and brass rods. All the work required is within the capacity of a $3\frac{1}{2}$-in. centre foot lathe, with the addition of a single division plate and cutter for the teeth of the R.A. circle, and a circular protractor for the marking of the divisions on the circles.

A. Part of the driving-rod with universal joint U at the upper end, connecting with the worm screw, and a handle (not shewn) at the lower end.
B. Gunmetal coned bearings of the polar axis.
C. Declination circle.
D. Declination axis.
E. Arm screwed to the polar axis tube and adjustable for any latitude.
F. One of two side plates screwed to the base and between which E is held by a $\frac{1}{2}$-in. bolt and nut I.
H. Lever of cam. When pulled down it puts the worm into gear with the fixed toothed ring JJ.
K. Knurled head to turn a pinion engaging with a circle of teeth cut on the inner side of the R.A. ring R.
L. Bolt passing through a hole in the base, slotted to allow for a slight movement in azimuth.
Behind L is a central vertical pin ($\frac{3}{8}$-in. in diameter) about which the whole head can be turned.
M. One of two push screws for exact meridian setting.
N. Knurled declination clamp nut.
P. Polar axis.
R. Right Ascension Ring, marked from 0h. to 24h., from west to east round by south.
S^1. Adjusting screw for the slow adjustment of the tilt of the polar axis.
S^2. One of the two other base screws.
T. Main tube of the telescope.
V^1. Declination Vernier on arm with adjusting push screws at the lower end.
V^2. R.A. Vernier, fixed, for time.
V^3 R.A. Vernier, moving, for R.A. of object.
W. Counterpoise weights with set collars.

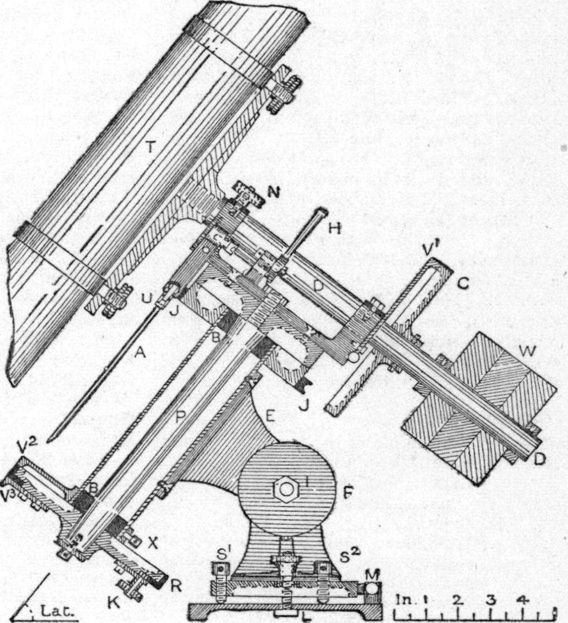

No slow motion in Declination is shewn, but one is a great convenience and could easily be added to the head. For convenience of representation V^2 is shown at right angles to its correct position. It may be rotated about the turned end of the polar axis tube, and clamped in position by the screw X.

A large-faced watch or an ordinary spring clock, regulated to keep sidereal time, with an inner circle of figures, XIII to XXIV added to the face, is a most useful, indeed almost indispensable adjunct. This may be set correctly to sidereal time each day by means of the wireless time signal. The sidereal time for the previous midnight can be obtained from Whitaker's or the Nautical Almanac, and to this $12^h\ 1^m\ 58^s$ (say $12^h\ 2^m$) must be added to get the sidereal time at noon. *

The method of finding a celestial object with an equatorial of this type is simple. (1) Move the telescope so that the declination vernier (V^1) indicates the declination of the object as given in the catalogue. Clamp in declination. (2) By means of the knurled head (K) turn the R.A. ring till the R.A. of the object is shewn by the lower or moving vernier (V^3). (3) Turn the telescope till the sidereal time as read from the clock is shewn also by the upper fixed vernier (V^2).

If a low or medium power is used and the head is in correct adjustment, the object should be in the field of view. The lever (H) is then pulled down, and the object can be followed by slowly turning the driving rod (A).

If the object is not at first in the field of view, a slight movement of the telescope either forwards or backwards in R.A. will generally bring it into sight. If not, the circle readings should be checked and the adjustments of the head corrected if necessary.

The head should be fixed on a strong wooden braced tripod or iron pipe filled with concrete and protected from the weather by a galvanized iron hood, the telescope itself having been removed.

** For places E. of Greenwich a correction of 1m. of time must be added for each 15' of longitude; if W. subtracted.*

PRONUNCIATION OF NAMES

The accents are pronounced as follows:—

Note:—This list follows the so-called English method of pronunciation, which is generally used for Latin and Greek proper names in English context.

ā as in fate	ē as in we	ī as in ice	ō as in go	ū as in unite
ă „ fat	ĕ „ met	ĭ „ ill	ŏ „ odd	ŭ „ up
ä „ arm	é „ water	… …	ô „ orb	û „ urn
á „ sofa	… …	… …	ōō „ food	… …

Constellations.—For the genitives (*g.*) of names ending in *-us -um*, change the *-us* or *-um* into *-i* (pronounced ī), as Lupus, (*g.*) Lupi. Those ending in *a*: change the *a* into *æ* (pronounced ē), as Mensa, Mensæ. Modern Constellations are marked *.

ANDROMEDA, ăn-drŏm′ĕ-dá *Andromeda*
ANTLIA,* ănt′lĭ-ă … *The Air Pump* [1]
APUS,* ā′pŭs (*g.* ā-pōd′is) *Bird of Paradise*
AQUARIUS, á-kwā′rĭ-ŭs *The Water-bearer*
AQUILA, ăk′wĭ-lá … … *The Eagle*
ARA, ā′rā … … *The Altar*
ARGO, är′gō (*g.*, är′gōōs) … *Ship Argo*
ARIES, ā′rĭ-ēz′ (*g.*, ā-rī′ē-tĭs) *The Ram*
AURIGA, ô-rī′gá … *The Charioteer*
BOÖTES, bō-ō′tēz (*g.*, -tĭs) *The Herdsman*
CAELUM,* sē′lŭm … … *The Chisel* [2]
CAMELOPARDUS,* kă-mĕl′ō-pärd-ŭs *Giraffe*
CANCER, kăn′sėr (*g.*, kăn-krī) *The Crab*
CANES VENATICI,* kā′nēz vĕ-năt′-ĭ-sī, or -kī (*g.* kā′nŭm vĕ-năt′ĭ-kō′rŭm) *Greyhounds*
CANIS MAJOR, kā′nĭs mā′-jér, (*g.* má-jō′rĭs)
„ MINOR, kā′nĭs mī′nér (*g.* mī-nō′rĭs) *The Greater and Lesser Dog*
CAPRICORNUS, kăp-rĭ-kôr′nŭs *The Sea-goat*
CARINA,* ká-rī′ná *The Keel (Argo)*
CASSIOPEIA, kăs-ĭ-ō-pē′yá … *Cassiopeia*
CENTAURUS, sĕn-tô′rŭs … *The Centaur*
CEPHEUS, sē′fūs or sē′fē-ŭs … *Cepheus*
CETUS, sē′tŭs *The Sea Monster or Whale*
CHAMAELEON,* kă-mē′lē-ŭn (*g.*, -lē-ŏn′tĭs) *The Chamæleon*
CIRCINUS,* sûr′sĭ-nŭs *The Compasses*
COLUMBA,* kō-lŭm′bá … *The Dove* [3]
COMA BERENICES,* kō′má bĕr-ē-nī′sēz (*g.*, kō′mē bĕrē-nī′sēz) *Berenice's Hair*
CORONA AUSTRALIS, kō-rō′ná ôs-trā′lĭs
„ BOREALIS, „ bō-rē-ā′lĭs *The Southern and Northern Crown*

CORVUS, kôr′vŭs … … *The Crow*
CRATER, krā′tér (*g.*, krăt′ĕr-ĭs) *The Cup*
CRUX,* krŭks, (*g.* krōōsĭs) … *The Cross*
CYGNUS, sĭg′nŭs … *The Swan*
DELPHINUS, dĕl-fī′nŭs … *The Dolphin*
DORADO,* dō-rä′dō (*g.*, -dōōs) *Swordfish*
DRACO, drā′kō (*g.*, drăkō′nĭs) *The Dragon*
EQUULEUS, ē-kwōō′lē-ŭs *The Little Horse*
ERIDANUS, ĕ-rĭd′á-nŭs *The River Eridanus*
FORNAX,* fôr′năks (*g.* fôr-nās′ĭs) *Furnace* [4]
GEMINI, jĕm′ĭ-nī (*g.*, -nō′rŭm) *The Twins*
GRUS,* grŭs (*g.*, grōō′ĭs) … *The Crane*
HERCULES, hûr′kŭ-lēz (*g.* lĭs) *Hercules*
HOROLOGIUM,* hŏr-ō-lō′jĭ-ŭm *The Clock*
HYDRA, hī′drá … *The Water Snake*
HYDRUS,* hī′drŭs … „ „
INDUS,* ĭn′dŭs … … *The Indian*
LACERTA,* lá-sĕr′tá … *The Lizard*
LEO, lē′ō (*g.*, lē-ō′nĭs) *The Lion* [*Lion*
„ MINOR,* mī′nér (*g.* mī-nōr′ĭs) *Lesser*
LEPUS, lē′pŭs (*g.*, lĕp′ŏr-ĭs) *The Hare*
LIBRA, lī′brā … … *The Balances*
LUPUS, lū′pŭs … … *The Wolf*
LYNX,* lĭnks (*g.*, -lĭns′ĭs) *The Lynx*
LYRA, lī′rā … … *The Lyre*
[MALUS,* mā′lŭs, (now PYXIS) *Mast of Argo*]
MENSA,* mĕn′sá … *Table Mountain* [5]
MICROSCOPIUM,* mī-krō-skō′p-ĭ-ŭm *The Microscope*
MONOCEROS,* mō-nŏs′ér-ŏs (*g.*, ĕr-ō′tĭs) [*The Unicorn*]
MUSCA,* mŭs′kă … *The [Southern] Fly* [6]
NORMA,* nôr′má … … *The Square*
OCTANS,* ŏk′tănz (*g.*, ŏk-tăn′tĭs) *Octant* [7]

OPHIUCHUS, ŏf-ĭ-ū′kŭs *The Serpent-bearer*
ORION, ō-rī′ŏn (*g.* ŏr-ĭ-ō′nĭs) *The Hunter*
PAVO,* pā′vō (*g.*, pá-vō′nĭs) *The Peacock*
PEGASUS, pĕg′á-sŭs … *Pegasus*
PERSEUS, pûr′sūs or pûr′sē-ŭs *Perseus*
PHŒNIX,* fē′nĭks (*g.*, fē-nī′cĭs) *The Phœnix*
PICTOR,* pĭk′tŏr (*g.*. -tōr′ĭs) *The Painter* [8]
PISCES, pĭs′ēz (*g.*, pĭs′ĭ-ŭm) *The Fishes*
PISCIS AUSTRINUS, pĭs′ĭs ôs-trī′nŭs *The Southern Fish*
PUPPIS,* pŭp′ĭs (*g.*, pŭp′ĭs) *Poop (of Argo)*
PYXIS,* pĭk′sĭs (*g.*, pĭk′sĭ-dĭs) *The Compass* [9]
RETICULUM,* rē-tĭk′ū-lŭm … *The Net* [10]
SAGITTA, să-jĭt′ă … … *The Arrow*
SAGITTARIUS, săj-ĭ-tā′rĭ-ŭs … *The Archer*
SCORPIO, skôr′pĭ-ō (*g.*, -ō′nĭs) *The Scorpion*
SCORPIUS, skôr′pĭ-ŭs (*g.*, skôr′pĭ-ī)
SCULPTOR,* skŭlp′tĕr (*g.*, -tō′rĭs) *Sculptor* [11]
SCUTUM,* skū′tŭm … … *The Shield* [12]
SERPENS, sér′pĕnz (*g.*, ser-pĕn′tĭs) *Serpent*
SEXTANS,* sĕks′tănz (*g.* -tăn′tĭs) *Sextant* [13]
TAURUS tô′rŭs … … *The Bull*
TELESCOPIUM,* tĕlĕ-skō′pĭ-ŭm *The Telescope*
TRIANGULUM, trī-ang′gū-lŭm *The Triangle*
„ AUSTRALE,* „ -ôstrā′lē *Southern* „
TUCANA,* tōō-kā′ná … *The Toucan*
URSA MAJOR, ûr′să mā′jér (*g.* ûrsē má-jō′rĭs)
„ MINOR, ûr′să mī′nér (*g.*, ûr′sē mī-nō′rĭs) *The Greater and the Lesser Bears*
VELA,* vē′lă (*g.*, vē-lō′rŭm) *Sails (of Argo)*
VIRGO, vûr′gō (*g.*, vûr′jĭ-nĭs) *The Virgin*
VOLANS,* vō′lánz (*g.*, -lăn′tĭs) *Flying Fish* [14]
VULPECULA,* vŭl-pĕk′ū-lá … *The Fox* [15]

Original Forms. [1] Antlia Pneumatica. [2] Caela Sculptoris, *The Sculptor's Chisels.* [3] Columba Noachii, *Noah's Dove.* [4] Fornax Chemica, *The Chemical Furnace.* [5] Mons Mensæ. [6] Apis Musca Australis. [7] Octans Hadleianus, *Hadley's Octant.* [8] Equuleus Pictoris, *The Painter's Easel.* [9] Pyxis Nautica, *The Mariner's Compass.* [10] Reticulum Rhomboidalis, *The Rhomboidal Net.* [11] Apparatus Sculptoris, *The Sculptor's Workshop.* [12] Scutum Sobieskii, *Sobieski's Shield.* [13] Sextans Uraniæ, *Urania's Sextant.* [14] Piscis Volans. [15] Vulpecula et Anser, *The Fox and the Goose.*

Star and Cluster Names. Many of these, transliterated or corrupted from the Arabic, have no standard spellings, as Arneb, Arnab; Caph, Chaph; Cebalrai, Kelbalrai; Tarazed, Trazed, &c. a may = e; an = ain; c = k or kh; ei = ie; f = ph; m = n; s = x or z; sh = sch; t = th.

Achernar, ā′kér-när α Eridani
Acrab, ăk′răb β Scorpii
Adara, ăd-ā′rá ε Canis Maj.
Albireo, ăl-bĭr′ē-ō β Cygni
Alchiba, ăl-kĭ-bä′ α Corvi
Alcor, ăl-kôr′ 80 Urs. Maj.
Alcyone, ăl-sī′ō-nē η Tauri
Aldebaran, ăl-dĕb′á-răn α Tauri
Alderamin, ăl-dĕ-rä′mĭn α Ceph
Algeiba, ăl-jē′bá γ Leonis
Algenib, ăl-jē′nĭb γ Pegasi
Algol, ăl′gŏl, ăl-gŏl′ β Persei
Algorab, ăl-gō-răb′ δ Corvi
Alhena, ăl-hĕn′á γ Gemin.
Alioth, ălĭ-ŏth′ ε Urs. Maj.
Alkaid, ăl-kād′ η „
Alkalurops, ăl-kă-lū′rŏps μ^1 Boöt
Alkes, ăl-kĕz′ α Crateris
Almak, ăl-măk′ γ Androm
Alnilam, ăl-nĭ-lăm′ ε Orionis
Alphard, ăl-färd′ α Hydræ
Alphecca, ăl-fĕk′á α Cor. Bor.
Alpheratz, ăl-fē′răts α Androm
Alphirk, ăl-fûrk′ β Cephei
Alrai, ăl-räī′ γ „
Alruccabah, ăl-rōō-kä′bá α U Min.
Alshain, ăl-shä′ĭn β Aquilæ
Altair, ăl-tär′ α „
Alwaid, ăl-wä′ĭd β Draco
Antares, ăn-tā′rēz α Scorpii
Arcturus, ärk-tū′rŭs α Bootis
Arided, ár-ĭ-ded′ α Cygni
Arneb, är′nĕb α Leporis
Asterope, ăs-tĕr′ō-pē 21 Tauri
Atlas, ăt′lăs 27 „
Azimech, àz-ĭ-mĕk′ α Virginis
Baten Kaitos, bă′t′n-kī′tŏs ζ Ceti
Bellatrix, bĕ-lā′trĭks γ Orionis

Benetnasch, bĕ-nĕt′năsh η Urs Maj
Betelgeuse, bĕt-ĕl-gûz′ α Orionis
Canopus, ká-nō′pŭs α Argûs
Capella, kă-pĕl′ă α Aurigæ
Caph, kăf β Cassiop.
Castor, kás′tér, kăs′tĕr α Gem.
Cor Caroli, kôr kăr′ō-lī α C Ven
Cor Hydræ, kôr hī′drē α Hydræ
Cor Leonis, kôr lē-ō′nis α Leonis
Cor Scorpii, kôr skôr′pĭ-ī (or k. skôr-pĭ-ō′nĭs) α Scorpii
Cor Serpentis, kôr sér-pĕn′tĭs α Serpentis
Cursa, kûr-sä′ β Eridani
Deneb, dĕn′ĕb α Cygni, β Leonis
Deneb Algiedi, dĕn′ĕb ăl-jē′dĭ δ Capricorni
Denebola, dĕ-nĕb′-ō-lá β Leonis
Diphda, dĭf′dá β Ceti
Dubhe, dōōb′hĕ α Ur. Maj.
Electra, ē-lĕk′trā 17 Tauri
Enif, *Eniph*, ĕn′ĭf ε Pegasi
Errai, ăr-räi′ γ Cephei
Etamin, ĕt-á-mĭn′ γ Draconis
Fom, fŏm ε Pegasi
Fomalhaut, fō′măl-hôt, -măl-ō α Piscis Austrini
Gemma, jĕm′á α Corona Bor.
Giedi, Prima & Secunda, jē′dĭ, prī′ma, sē-kŭn′dá α^1, α^2 Cap.
Gomeisa, gō-mī′sä β Can. Min.
Hamal, hăm′ál α Arietis
Homam, hō-măm′ ζ Pegasi
Hyades, hī′ă-dēz (Star Cluster)
Izar, ē-zär′ ε Boötis
Kaitain, kī-tāin′ α Piscium
Kaus Australis, kôs ôs-trā′lĭs ε Sagittarii

Kelb al Rai, kĕlb-ăl-räi′ β Oph.
Kocab, kō′káb β Urs. Min.
Kornephoros, kŏr-nĕf′ō-rŭs β Herculis
Kursa, kûr-sä′ β Eridani
Maia, mā′yă, mī-ä′ 20 Tauri
Markab, mär′kăb α Pegasi
Marsik mär′sĕk κ Herculis
Mebsuta, mĕb-sōō′tá ε Gemin.
Megrez, mē′grĕz δ Urs. Maj.
Mekab, mē′kăb α Ceti
Menkalinan, mĕn-kăl-ĭ-năn′ β Aurigæ
Menkar, *-kab*, mĕn′kär α Ceti
Merak, mē′răk β Urs. Maj.
Merope, mĕr′ō-pē 23 Tauri
Mesarthim, mēs-ăr-tĭm′ γ Arietis
Mintaka, mĭn′tá-kă δ Orionis
Mira, mī′rá ο Ceti
Mirach, mī′răk, mē′răk β Andr.
Mirfak, mĭr′făk α Persei
Mirzam, mĭr′zăm β Can. Maj
Mizar, mī′zär β Andromedæ, ζ Ursæ Majoris, ε Boötis
Muphrid, mōō′frĭd η Boötis
Nath, nàth′ β Tauri
Nekkar, nĕk-kär′ β Boötis
Okda, ŏk′dá α Piscium
Phakt, făkt α Columbæ
Phecda, fĕk′dá γ Urs. Maj
Pleiades, plī′ or plē′ă-dēz
Pleione, plī-ō′nē 28 Tauri
Polaris, pō-lā′rĭs α Urs. Min.
Pollux, pŏl′ŭks β Gemini
Præsepe, prē-sē′pē (Cluster)
Procyon, prō′sĭ-ŏn α Canis Min
Pulcherrima, pŭl-kĕr′ĭmá ε Boötis
Ras Algethi, răs al-jē′tē α Herc.

Ras Alhague, rás ăl-hä′gwĕ α Ophiuchi
Rastaban, răs-tă-băn′ γ Draconis
Regulus, rĕg′ū-lŭs α Leonis
Rigel, rī′gĕl, rī′jĕl β Orionis
Rotanev, rō′tă-nĕv β Delphini
Sadachbia, săd-ăk-bē′á γ Aqr.
Sadalmelik, săd-ăl-mĕl′ĭk α Aqr.
Sadalsud, săd-ăl-sōōd′ β „
Scheat, shē′ăt β Pegasi
Schedar, shĕd′ár α Cassiop.
Sheliak, shĕl′ĭăk β Lyræ
Sheratan, shĕr′ă-tăn′ β Arietis
Sirius, sĭr′ĭ-ŭs α Can. Maj.
Sirrah, sĭr′ā α Andromedæ
Skat, skăt δ Aquarii
Spica, spī′ká α Virginis.
Sulaphat, sōō-lá-făt′ γ Lyræ
Svalocin, svăl′ō-kĭn α Delphini
Talitha, tä-lē′tá ι Ur. Maj.
Tarazed, tăr′á-zĕd γ Aquilæ
Taygeta, tā-ĭj′ĕ-tă 19 Tauri
Thuban, thōō-bán′ α Draconis
Unukalhay, ū-nŭk′ăl-hā′ α Serp.
Vega, vē′gă α Lyræ
Vindemiatrix, vĭn-dē-mĭ-ā′trĭks ε Virginis
Wasat, wä′săt δ Geminorum
Yed, yĕd δ Ophiuchi
Zaurak, zô′răk γ^1 Eridani
Zawijah, ză′vē-jă β Virginis
Zozca, *Zosma*, zŏs′ká, zŏs′má δ Leonis
Zuben el Genubi, zōō-bĕn′ ĕl je-nōō′bē α Libræ
„ *el Hakrabi*, ĕl há-krá′bē γ „
„ *el Chamali*, ĕl shá-mä′lē β „
Zubenesch, zōō-bĕn′ĕsh β „

THE BRIGHTEST AND THE NEAREST STARS.

Name	1950 R.A.	1950 Dec.	Magnitude Apparent	Magnitude Absolute	Parallax	Distance L't. yrs.	Distance Parsecs	Annual P.M.	Luminosity (Sun=1)	Spectral Type
BRIGHTEST STARS.										
Sirius	6^h 43·0^m	−16° 38′	−1·58	1·3	0″·371	9	2·7	1″·32	26	A0
Canopus	6 22·8	−52 40	−0·86	−7·4 ?	0″·005 ?	650 ?	200 ?	0″·02	80,000 ?	F0
α Centauri	14 36·5	−60 38	0·06	4·7, 6·1	0″·758	4	1·3	3″·68	1·1, 0·2	G0, K5
Vega	18 35·2	+38 44	0·14	0·6	0″·124	26	8·3	0″·35	50	A0
Capella	5 12·9	+45 58	0·21	−0·6	0″·069	47	14·5	0″·44	150	G0
Arcturus	14 13·4	+19 28	0·24	−0·2	0″·080	41	12·5	2″·29	100	K0
Rigel	5 12·1	− 8 15	0·34	−5·8 ?	0″·006 ?	540 ?	166 ?	0″·01	18,000 ?	B8
Procyon	7 36·8	+ 5 22	0·48	3·0	0″·312	10	3·2	1″·24	5	F5
Achernar	1 35·9	−57 30	0·60	−0·9	0″·049	66	20·4	0″·09	200	B5
β Centauri	14 0·3	−60 7	0·86	−3·9	0″·011	300	91	0″·04	3,000	B1
Altair	19 48·3	+ 8 43	0·89	2·4	0″·204	16	5·0	0″·66	9	A5
Betelgeuse	5 52·5	+ 7 24	0·92 v.	−2·9	0″·017	190	62	0″·03	1,200	M0
α Crucis	12 23·7	−62 50	1·05	−2·7, −2·2	0″·014	230	71	0″·05	1,000; 650	B1, B1
Aldebaran	4 33·0	+16 25	1·06	−0·1	0″·057	57	17·5	0″·21	90	K5
Pollux	7 42·3	+28 9	1·21	1·2	0″·101	32	10·0	0″·62	28	K0
Spica	13 22·5	−10 54	1·21	−3·1	0″·014	230	71	0″·05	1,500	B2
Antares	16 26·5	−26 20	1·22	−4·0	0″·009	360	111	0″·03	3,400	M0
Fomalhaut	22 54·8	−29 53	1·29	2·0	0″·137	24	7·2	0″·27	13	A3
Deneb	20 39·7	+45 6	1·33	−5·2 ?	0″·005 ?	650 ?	200 ?	0″·00	10,000 ?	A2
Regulus	10 5·7	+12 13	1·34	0·2	0″·058	56	17·2	0″·24	70	B8
β Crucis	12 44·8	−59 25	1·50	−2·5	0″·016	200	62·5	0″·05	850	B1
Castor	7 31·4	+32 0	1·58	1·4, 2·2	0″·076	43	13·2	0″·20	23 ; 11	A0, A0
NEAREST STARS.										
Proxima Centauri	14^h 26·5^m	−62° 29′	10·5	15·5	0″·79	4·2	1·2	3″·85	·0001	M ?
α Centauri	14 36·5	−60 38	0·06	4·7, 6·1	0″·76	4·3	1·3	3″·68	1·1, 0·2	G0, K5
Munich 15040	17 55·3	+ 4 29	9·7	13·4	0″·54	6·2	1·9	10″·29	0·0005	M
Lalande 21185	11 0·6	+36 20	7·6	10·7	0″·42	8·3	2·4	4″·78	0·005	M2
Wolf 359	10 53	+ 7 30	13·5	16·5	0″·40	8·1	2·5	4″·84	0·00002	M4
Sirius A	6 43	−16 38	−1·6	1·3	0″·37	8·7	2·7	1″·32	26·0	A0
Innes' Star	11 14·2	−57 18	11·7	14·4	0″·34	9·6	2·9	2″·69	0·0001	—
B.D. −12° 4523	16 25·4	−12 28	9·5	12·1	0″·33	9·9	3·1	...	0·0015	M5
Corboda Vh.243	5 9·5	−44 57	9·2	11·7	0″·32	10·2	3·2	8″·75	0·0022	M0
Ross 248	23 38	+43 50	13·8	16·3	0″·32	10·2	3·2	...	0·00003	M6
τ Ceti	1 41·8	−16 13	3·6	6·1	0″·32	10·2	3·2	1″·92	0·35	K0
Procyon	7 36·8	+ 5 22	0·5	3·0	0″·31	10·4	3·2	1″·24	5·5	F5
ε Eridani	3 30·6	− 9 38	3·8	6·3	0″·31	10·5	3·2	0″·97	0·31	K0
61 Cygni	21 4·5	+38 29	5·6	8·0	0″·30	10·7	3·3	5″·25	0·06	K5
Lacaille 9352	23 2·4	−36 9	7·4	9·7	0″·29	11·2	3·4	6″·90	0·013	M0
Σ 2398	18 42·3	+59 33	8·8	11·1	0″·29	11·3	3·5	2″·31	0·0036	M4
Groombridge 34	0 15·4	+43 44	8·1	10·4	0″·28	11·6	3·6	2″·89	0·0073	M2
ε Indi	21 59·3	−56 59	4·7	6·9	0″·28	11·6	3·6	4″·69	0·17	K5
Krüger 60	22 26·3	+57 27	9·3	11·4	0″·26	12·5	3·8	0″·87	0·003	K5
Van Maanen's	0 46·2	+ 5 10	12·3	14·3	0″·25	12·8	3·9	3″·01	0·0002	F0
Lalande 8760	4 37	−38 0	6·7	8·6	0″·25	12·9	4·0	3″·53	0·04	M0
O.A. (N) 17415	17 37	+68 23	9·3	11·2	0″·24	13·2	4·1	1″·33	0·003	K
B.D. 51° 658	2 52	+52 12	9·2	11·1	0″·24	13·6	4·2	...	0·004	...

Bayer and Lacaille Letters and Flamsteed Numbers.

Andromeda.	A, 49	b, 60	c, 62							
Aquarius.	A^1, 103	A^2, 104	b^1, 98	b^2, 99	b^3, 101	c^1, 86	c^2, 88	c^3, 89	d, 25	e, 38
	f, 53	g, 66	h, 83	i^1, 106	i^2, 107	i^3, 108	k, 3			
Aquila.	A, 28	b, 31	c, 35	d, 27	e, 36	f, 26	g, 14	h, 15	i, 12	l, 71
Bootes.	b, 46	c, 45	d, 12	e, 6	f, 22	g, 24	h, 38	i, 44	k, 47	
Cancer.	A^1, 45	A^2, 50	b, 49	c, 36	d^1, 20	d^2, 25				
Capricornus.	A, 24	b, 36	c, 46							
Cassiopeia.	A, 48									
Centaurus.	g, 2	h, 4	i, 1	k, 3						
Cygnus.	A, 68	b^1, 27	b^2, 28	b^3, 29	c, 16	d, 20	e, 26	f^1, 59	f^2, 63	g, 71
	P, 34									
Draco.	A, 15	b, 39	c, 46	d, 45	e, 64	f, 27	g, 18	h, 19	i, 10	
Eridanus.	A, 39	b, 62	c, 51	d, 43	l, 53	v, 17	w, 32	S, 64		
Gemini.	A, 57	b, 65	c, 76	d, 36	e, 38	f, 74	g, 81			
Hercules.	A, 104	b, 99	d, 59	e, 69	f, 90	g, 30	h, 29	i, 43	k, 47	l, 45
	m, 36, 37	n, 28	o, 21	r, 5	t, 107	u, 68	w, 72	x, 77	y, 82	z, 88
Hydra.	A, 33	a, 6	k, 51	l, 52	m, 54	D, 12	E, 58	P, 27		
Leo.	A, 31	b, 60	c, 59	d, 58	e, 87	f, 15	g, 22	h, 6	k, 52	l, 53
	m, 51	n, 73	o, 95	p^2, 61	p^3, 62	p^4, 65	p^5, 69			
Lupus.	f, 2	i, 1								
Ophiuchus.	A, 36	b, 44	c, 51	d, 45	f, 53					
Orion.	A, 32	b, 51	c, 42	d, 49	e, 29	f^1, 69	f^2, 72	g, 6	h, 16	i, 14
	k, 74	l, 75	m, 23	n^1, 33	n^2, 38	o, 22	p, 27			
Perseus.	A, 43	c, 48	d, 53	e, 58	f, 52	g, 4	i, 9	l, 32	m, 57	n, 42
	o, 40									
Pisces.	A, 5	b, 7	c, 32	d, 41	e, 80	f, 89	g, 82	h, 68	i, 65	k, 67
	l, 91									
Sagittarius.	A, 60	b, 59	c, 62	d, 43	e^1, 54	e^2, 55	f, 56	g, 61	h^1, 51	h^2, 52
Scorpius.	A, 2	b, 1	c^1, 12	c^2, 13	i, 22	o, 19				
Serpens.	A^1, 11	A^2, 25	b, 36	c, 60	d, 59					
Taurus.	A^1, 37	A^2, 39	b, 79	c, 90	d, 88	e, 30	f, 5	h, 57	i, 97	k, 98
	l, 106	m, 104	n, 109	o, 114	p, 44	q, 19	r, 66	s, 4	t, 6	u, 29
Ursa Major.	A, 2	b, 5	c, 16	d, 24	e, 18	f, 15	g, 80	h, 23		
Virgo.	A^1, 4	A^2, 6	b, 7	c, 16	d^1, 31	d^2, 32	e, 59	f, 25	h, 76	i, 68
	k, 44	l, 74	m, 82	o, 78	p, 90	q, 21				

In this Atlas, Flamsteed numbers are used in preference to Roman letters, since the former generally follow in each constellation in order of Right Ascension, and thus the places of the numbered stars are the more easily found. But, as the letters are sometimes used (occasionally in the italic form), the above table has been prepared as an aid to the speedy identification of the star.

STAR CHARTS

ABBREVIATIONS AND EXPLANATIONS.

Small Crosses (+) indicate the points of intersection of lines of intermediate 20 minutes of R.A. and 5° of Declination.

Marginal Divisions in R.A. denote 5 minutes of sidereal time, and in Declination 1°.

v (small, to a star) denotes variability. A variable star which reaches 6th magnitude or less at its maximum brightness is marked by a small circle only.

R or Ru (small, to a star). A red, orange, or yellow star. In the case of E-B red stars, the letter R is not added as the letters E-B are a sufficient indication of the colour.

Number only (to a star). The number in Flamsteed's Catalogus Britannicus.

Number underlined (to a star), e.g., 56. The hour number in Piazzi's Catalogue.

Greek or Roman Letter (to a star). The letter assigned by Bayer in 1603, and, since Bayer's time, by Lacaille and Gould in southern constellations.

Number only (to a nebula). The number given in the N.G.C., viz., the New General Catalogue, being the General Catalogue of Nebulæ by Sir John Herschel as revised and enlarged by Dreyer (1888).

Number with small number to the right (to a nebula). Sir William Herschel's numbers and the classes into which he divided the nebulæ. Thus, 37^4 = H IV 37.

These classes are :—

I.	Bright nebulæ.	V.	Very large nebulæ.
II.	Faint nebulæ.	VI.	Very compressed and rich clusters of stars.
III.	Very faint nebulæ.	VII.	Compressed clusters of small and large stars.
IV.	Planetary nebulæ.	VIII.	Coarsely scattered clusters of stars.

Abbreviations of the Names of Observers, generally followed by the current number from their Catalogues.

A.	Aitken, R. G.
Ar.	Argelander, F. W. A.
A. C.	Clark, Alvan.
Bar.	Barnard, E.E.
Brs.	Brisbane, T.
Cor.	Cordoba Obs.
Cp.	Cape Obs.
Es.	Espin, T. E. H.
E-B.	Espin-Birmingham.
H.	Herschel, Sir William.
h.	Herschel, Sir John.
Hh.	J. Herschel's Catalogue of W. H.'s double stars.
He.	Howe, H. A.
Hn.	Holden, E. S.
Ho.	Hough, G. W.
Hrg.	Hargreaves, J.
Hu.	Hussey, W. J.
I.	Innes, R. T. A.
Jc.	Jacob, W. S.
L.	Lacaille, N. L. de.
Ll.	Lalande, J. J. de.
Lv.	Leavenworth, F. P.
M.	Messier, C.
Mel.	Melbourne Obs.
R.	Russell, H. C.
Rmk.	Rümker, C. L. C.
S.	South, J.
Sa.	Santiago Obs.
Slr.	Sellors.
U. A.	Uranometria Argentina.
Wnc.	Winnecke.
β	Burnham, S. W.
Δ	Dunlop, J.
λ	Lowell Obs., See.
OΣ	Struve, Otto.
OΣΣ	Pulkova Catalogue. Part II.
Σ	Struve, F. G. W.
σ	Pulkova Obs. Appendix, Vol. III.

INTERESTING OBJECTS. MAPS 1 & 2. (N. OF 60° DEC.)

(CIRCUMPOLAR, NORTH).

Double Stars.

EPOCH 1950.

Star		R.A.	Dec.	Mags.	P.A.	Dist.	Date	Remarks
OΣ67	Camelop.	3ʰ 52·9ᵐ	+60° 58′	5·0, 8·2	47°	1″·9	1925	Gold and green.
Σ485	”	4 3·4	+62 12	6·1, 6·2	304°	18″·3	1925	Relatively fixed.
β	”	4 59·0	+60 22	5·0, 9·0	208°	80″·9	1923	Faint *comes* to B at 14″·8 distance.
Σ634	”	5 14·3	+79 12	4·5, 8·0	62°	9″·1	1926	Optical pair: *d.* diminishing from *p.m.* of A.
19	”	5 32·4	+64 8	6·5, 10·5	47°	1″·3	1921	= Hu. 1107.
Σ1122	”	7 41·2	+65 17	7·1, 7·1	5°	15″·3	1924	Relatively fixed. Rich neighbourhood.
Σ1127	”	7 42·4	+64 11	6·2, 8·0, 9·2	340° 174°	5″·5 11″·4	1926	Triple. No relative motion.
Σ1694	”	12 48·6	+83 41	4·9, 5·4	326°	21″·5	1924	Pale yellow and lilac. Relatively fixed.
ψ	Cassiopeiæ	1 22·4	+67 52	4·4, 8·9	112°	25″·2	1925	*Comes* double, *m.* 9·5: *P.A.* 254°: *d.* 3″·0.
Σ163	”	1 47·6	+64 36	6·2, 8·2	36°	34″·7	1922	Splendid gold and blue. Relatively fixed.
Σ185	”	1 57·3	+75 16	7·0, 8·5	20°	1″·3	1921	Binary.
48	”	1 57·8	+70 40	5·0, 7·5	220°	1″·0	1926	Binary, *P.* 63 y. *d.* 0″·4, 1903; widest abt. 1935.
ι	”	2 24·9	+67 11	4·2, 7·1, 8·1	251° 113°	2″·4 7″·4	1925	Triple star. Fine object in 4-inch.
OΣ52	”	3 13·1	+65 28	6·4, 7·0	94°	0″·5	1924	*P.A.* decreasing.
6	”	23 46·4	+61 57	5·7, 8·2	189°	1″·8	1925	Relatively fixed. *c.p.m.*
Σ3053	”	24 0·0	+65 49	6·0, 7·3	71°	15″·3	1924	Relatively fixed.
Σ320	Cephei	2 59·2	+79 13	6·3, 9·5	231°	4″·8	1925	Orange and blue.
Σ460	”	4 1·4	+80 34	5·2, 6·1	65°	0″·9	1924	Increasing *P.A.*
κ	”	20 10·7	+77 34	4·0, 8·0	122°	7″·4	1922	Bluish *comes.* Relatively fixed.
β	”	21 28·0	+70 20	3·3, 8·0	250°	13″·7	1922	3·3 mag. is a spectroscopic binary. Relatively
OΣ457	”	21 54·2	+65 5	6·3, 8·5	250°	1″·5	1925	... ... [fixed.
Σ2873	”	22 0·4	+82 38	6·2, 7·0	72°	13″·8	1923	Physical pair. *P.A.* slowly decreasing.
ξ	”	22 2·2	+64 23	4·7, 6·5	279°	7″·3	1929	Little relative motion. Probably a slow binary.
Σ2893	”	22 12·0	+73 4	5·5, 7·6	348°	29″·0	1923	Relatively fixed.
Σ2948	”	22 47·8	+66 17	7·0, 8·7	5°	2″·8	1924	Relatively fixed. N. of ι.
Σ2950	”	22 49·4	+61 25	6·0, 7·2	302°	2″·3	1928	*P.A.* slowly decreasing.
o	”	23 16·4	+67 50	5·2, 7·8	205°	3″·0	1926	Binary: orbit doubtful. Test for 2-inch.
OΣΣ123	Draconis	13 25·4	+65 0	6·4, 6·8	147°	69″	...	A fine object. Stars yellow and blue. *c.p.m.*
Σ2054	”	16 23·1	+61 48	5·7, 6·9	355°	1″·2	1931	Near η Draconis.
η	”	16 23·3	+61 38	2·1, 8·1	142°	6″·1	1925	Light-test for 3 in. telescope.
20	”	16 56·2	+65 7	6·5, 7·1	78°	0″·6	1925	Long period binary.
Σ2155	”	17 15·5	+60 46	6·2, 9·5	115°	10″·1	1925	Relatively fixed.
26	”	17 34·5	+61 55	5·5, 10·1	329°	1″·7	1924	Binary, period 111 years.
ψ	”	17 42·8	+72 11	4·0, 5·2	15°	30″·6	1924	Yellow and lilac. *c.p.m.*
40, 41	”	18 3·8	+80 0	5·4, 6·1	234°	19″·8	1925	Relatively fixed.
Σ2403	”	18 43·7	+61 0	6·2, 9·0	271°	1″·6	1926	*P.A.* increasing slowly.
Σ2573	”	19 39·4	+60 23	6·2, 8·5	27°	18″·3	1923	Little change.
ε	”	19 48·3	+70 8	4·0, 7·6	9°	3″·3	1926	Pleasing contrast.
Σ2640	”	20 4·9	+63 45	6·0, 9·9	19°	5″·5	1924	*P.A.* decreasing slowly.
Σ2694	”	20 17·8	+80 23	6·5, 10·5	345°	4″·0	1914	Relatively fixed.
Σ1193	Ursæ Maj.	8 15·2	+72 34	6·0, 9·0	87°	43″·1	1925	Relatively fixed.
σ^2	”	9 6·0	+67 20	5·0, 9·0	90°	1″·5	1925	Binary. Decreasing *P.A.*
23	”	9 27·6	+63 17	3·8, 9·0	271°	22″·8	1924	Relatively fixed.
Σ1415	”	10 13·9	+71 19	6·1, 7·0	167°	16″·7	1925	No change.
OΣ235	”	11 29·5	+61 22	6·0, 7·5	360°	0″·7	1930	Binary, period 72 y. Widening to 1″·0, 1950.
Hu 1136	”	12 3·2	+63 13	6·0, 11·4	223°	2″·0	1921	Relatively fixed.
α	Ursæ Minoris	1 48·8	+89 2	2·0, 9·0	217°	18″·3	1924	*Polaris,* the N. Pole star*. A well-known test.
π^1	”	15 32·1	+80 37	6·1, 7·0	81°	31′·0	1924	Little change, if any. 4° *n* slightly *p* ζ.

Variable Stars.

EPOCH 1950.

		R.A.	Dec.	Var. of mag.	Spectrum	Period	
RZ	Cassiopeiæ	$2^h\ 44{\cdot}4^m$	+69° 26′	6·4 - 7·8	A	1·19 days	Algol type.
SU	„	2 47·5	+68 41	5·9 - 6·3	F5	1·95 „	Cepheid type.
T	Cephei	21 8·8	+68 17	5·5 - 9·5	Me	391 „	Long period variable.
V	„	23 54·0	+82 55	6·2 - 7·1	A	360 „	„ „
R	Ursæ Majoris	10 41·2	+69 3	6·0 - 13·0	Me	298 „	„ „

Nova.

Nova 1572 Cassiopeiæ. $0^h\ 22^m{\cdot}0$, +63° 53′.

The new star first seen by Tycho Brahé on Nov. 11, 1572, when it was brighter than Jupiter, then in opposition and near perihelion. It soon became as bright as Venus, and was seen by some even in broad daylight. At the end of the month, it began to fade gradually, and underwent a succession of changes in colour—white, yellowish, ruddy, and finally leaden. At length, in March 1574, it ceased to be visible. Tycho's instruments were too rough for him to determine its place with great accuracy, so that it is uncertain whether one of two faint stars, near the position that he gave, is identical with the Nova.

Nebulæ and Clusters. (Maps 1 and 2) *(Unlettered Nos. are those of the N.G.C.)*

225, H.VIII 78 **Cassiop.**, $0^h\ 40^m{\cdot}6$, +61° 31′. A fine cluster, somewhat W shaped. Half way from γ to κ.

581, M103, „ $1^h\ 29^m{\cdot}8$, +60° 26′. Beautiful field 1°f and slightly N. of δ: contains Σ131 and a red star.

663, H.VI 31 „ $1^h\ 42^m{\cdot}5$, +61° 0′. A fine open cluster, visible in finder. Includes Σ153.

7654, M52, „ $23^h\ 22^m{\cdot}0$, +61° 19′. Irregular cluster about 20′ diam., containing an orange star.

6543, H.IV 37, **Draconis**, $17^h\ 58^m{\cdot}6$, +66° 38′. Planetary nebula. A remarkable object: very bright oval disc like a star out of focus, with a central $9^m{\cdot}6$ star. Bluish; nearly at the N. Pole of the Ecliptic.

3031, M81, **Ursæ Majoris**, $9^h\ 51^m{\cdot}5$, +69° 18′. Bright, with almost stellar nucleus grouped with small stars: Spiral, with rather faint arms.

3034, M82, „ $9^h\ 51^m{\cdot}8$, +69° 58′. A narrow curved ray 7′ × 1′·5, with rifts. Really a Spiral seen almost edgewise. Within ¾° of M81, which is included with a very low power.

5322, H.I 256 „ $13^h\ 47^m{\cdot}9$, +60° 25′. A bright, roundish nebula, with a brighter central part.

* *Polaris.* Easily found by the *Pointers* (α and β Ursæ Maj.). 1° from the N. Celestial Pole in 1950; nearest in 2095, within 26′. It is easy with 2½ inch; companion bluish. The large star is a spectroscopic binary and slightly variable.

MAP I

EPOCH 1950

For Abbreviations and Contractions see page 55

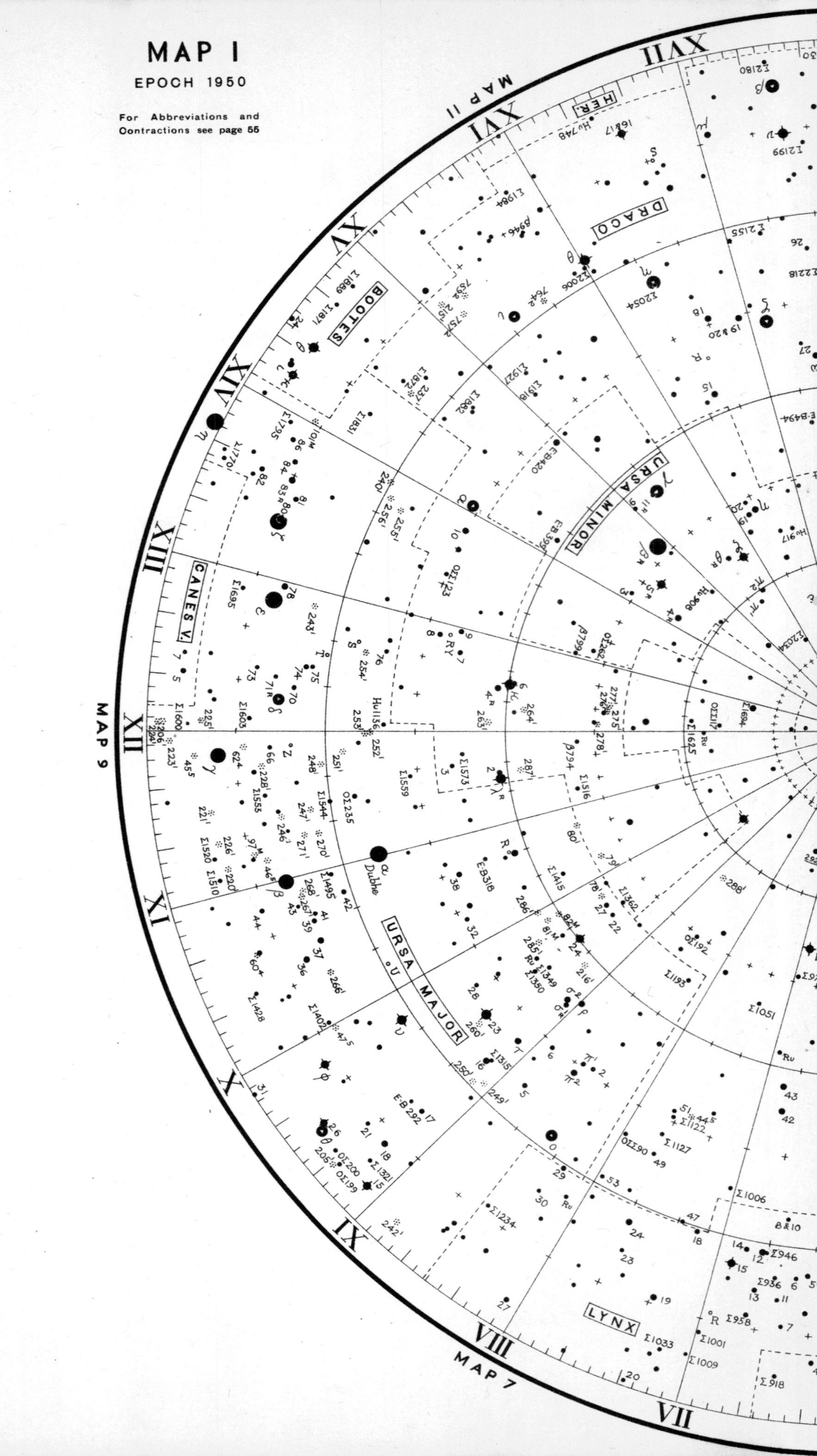

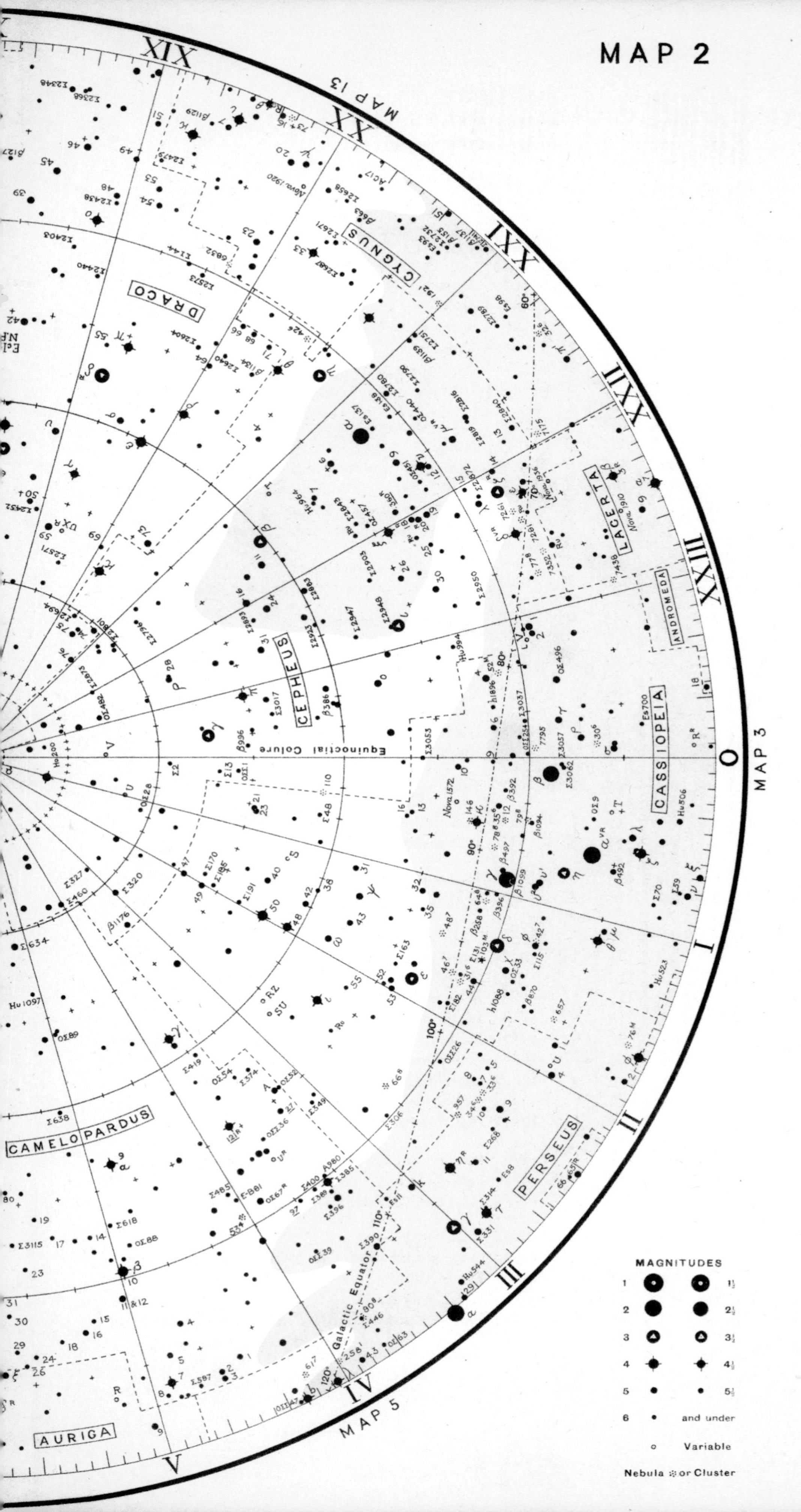
MAP 2
MAP 13
MAP 3
MAP 5
DRACO
CYGNUS
CEPHEUS
LACERTA
ANDROMEDA
CASSIOPEIA
PERSEUS
CAMELOPARDUS
AURIGA
Equinoctial Colure
Galactic Equator
Nova 1572
Nova 1910
Nova 1936
Nova 1920
MAGNITUDES
1
1½
2
2½
3
3½
4
4½
5
5½
6
and under
Variable
Nebula or Cluster

Interesting Objects. Maps 3 & 4.

(R.A. XXII. Hrs. to II. Hrs. Dec. 60° N. to 60° S.).

Double Stars.

Epoch 1950.

		R.A.	Dec.	Mags.	*P.A.*	Dist.	Date	Notes
36	Andromedæ	0h 52m·3	+23° 22′	6·1, 6·7	113°	0″·6	1938	Binary. Period 124 years. *n.p.* η.
γ	„	2 0·8	+42 6	3·0, 5·0	61°	9″·7	1927	Gold and blue. Magnificent object.
γ²	„	2 0·8	+42 6	5·4, 6·6	103°	0″·4	1937	Very close binary, *P.* 55y. Closing till 1945.
OΣ500	„	23 35·1	+44 9	6·1, 7·0	333°	0″·6	1925	Binary. [Widest 0″·6, 1971.
Σ3042	„	23 49·3	+37 37	7·0, 7·0	87°	5″·2	1931	No appreciable change.
Σ3050	„	23 56·9	+33 27	6·0, 6·0	242°	1″·9	1935	Binary. *P.A.* increasing, distance decreasing.
41	Aquarii	22 11·5	−21 19	5·6, 7·6	116°	4″·9	1926	Little change.
51	„	22 21·5	− 5 6	5·6, 5·7	351°	0″·7	1926	Binary.
53	„	22 23·9	−17 0	6·0, 6·5	313°	5″·8	1924	*P.A.* slowly increasing, distance diminishing.
ζ	„	22 26·2	− 0 17	4·4, 4·6	291°	2″·6	1935	Slow binary. *P.A.* and *d.* decreasing. Test for
94	„	23 16·4	−13 44	5·2, 7·2	348°	13″·3	1922	Relatively fixed. Yellowish and blue. [2-in.
107	„	23 43·4	−18 57	5·3, 6·5	137°	6″·2	1925	Slow retrograde motion; increasing distance.
1	Arietis	1 47·4	+22 2	6·2, 7·4	166°	2″·8	1937	Test for 2-in. telescope.
γ	„	1 50·8	+19 3	4·2, 4·4	360°	8″·4	1924	Beautiful fixed pair. Fine for small telescope.
λ	Cassiopeiæ	0 29·0	+54 15	5·6, 5·9	168°	0″·6	1932	Binary. Increasing *P.A.*
η	„	0 46·1	+57 33	3·7, 7·4	278°	8″·7	1936	Binary of long period, 500 ± years.
σ	„	23 56·4	+55 29	5·4, 7·5	327°	3″·1	1926	No change. Grand low power field.
δ	Cephei	22 27·3	+58 10	var., 7·5	192°	41″·0	1924	Yellow and blue: A is variable, see footnote.
42	Ceti	1 17·2	− 0 46	6·2, 7·2	1°	1″·4	1935	Direct angular movement.
Σ147	„	1 39·3	−11 34	6·0, 7·3	89°	2″·9	1925	*c.p.m.*
p	Eridani	1 37·9	−56 27	6·0, 6·1	207°	9″·6	1935	Binary, period 219 years. Distance increasing.
θ	Gruis	23 4·0	−43 48	4·5, 7·0	49°	1″·4	1934	*P.A.* increasing.
Δ246	„	23 4·4	−50 58	6·1, 6·8	257°	8″·4	1927	Little change.
Σ2894	Lacertæ	22 16·7	+37 31	6·0, 8·2	194°	15″·8	1925	Relatively fixed. White and blue.
8	„	22 33·6	+39 23	6·0, 6·5	186°	22″·3	1923	Multiple system; distant stars mags. 10 and 11.
Σ2877	Pegasi	22 11·9	+16 57	6·4, 9·6	10°	14″·1	1924	Optical. Distance increasing from *p.m.*
Σ2878	„	22 12·0	+ 7 44	6·8, 8·3	123°	1″·3	1934	Long period binary. *P.A.* slowly decreasing.
32	„	22 19·0	+28 5	5·0, 9·3	127°	72″·0	1924	B has 11 mag. *comes* at 2″·9 distance.
33	„	22 21·2	+20 36	6·0, 10·0	177°	1″·1	1923	*P.A.* and distance slowly decreasing.
34	„	22 24·0	+ 4 8	5·8, 11·7	218°	3″·1	1923	Little change.
37	„	22 27·4	+ 4 11	5·8, 7·2	98°	0″·5	1926	Binary, with orbit in line of sight. Widening.
ξ	„	22 44·2	+11 55	4·0, 12·0	108°	11″·9	1924	*P.A.* slowly decreasing. [*P.* abt. 150 yrs.
52	„	22 56·7	+11 27	6·2, 7·7	248°	0″·7	1936	Close double. *P.A.* increasing.
57	„	23 7·0	+ 8 24	5·9, 10·2	198°	32″·9	1923	Relatively fixed.
78	„	23 41·4	+29 6	5·0, 8·1	208°	1″·2	1924	*P.A.* increasing.
β	Phœnicis	1 3·9	−46 59	4·1, 4·2	357°	1″·3	1936	Binary. *P.A.* decreasing. 11th mag. star at 57″,
ζ	„	1 6·3	−55 31	4·1, 8·4	245°	6″·8	1913	Little change. A is variable. [1920.
θ	„	23 36·8	−46 55	6·3, 6·9	272°	4″·2	1921	Relatively fixed.
35	Piscium	0 12·4	+ 8 33	6·2, 7·8	149°	11″·8	1926	Relatively fixed.
55	„	0 37·3	+21 10	5·5, 8·2	193°	6″·6	1920	Orange and blue. Relatively fixed.
65	„	0 47·2	+27 26	6·0, 6·0	297°	4″·5	1926	Little change.
ζ	„	1 11·1	+ 7 19	4·2, 5·3	63°	23″·6	1921	Relatively fixed. [Test for 2-in.
α	„	1 59·4	+ 2 31	4·3, 5·2	306°	2″·5	1935	Pale green and blue: *P.A.* and *d.* diminishing.
β	Piscis Aus.	22 28·7	−32 36	4·4, 7·8	172°	30″·4	1918	Relatively fixed.
γ	„	22 49·8	−33 7	4·5, 8·5	266°	4″·3	1926	*P.A.* slowly decreasing.
δ	„	22 53·2	−32 47	4·3, 10·5	240°	5″·3	1925	Relatively fixed.

INTERESTING OBJECTS. MAPS 3 & 4 — *Continued.*

(R.A. XXII. HRS. TO II. HRS. DEC. 60°N. TO 60°S.).

Variable Stars.

EPOCH 1950.

		R.A.	Dec.	Var. of mag.	Spectrum	Period	Notes
R	Andromedæ	$0^h\ 21^m{\cdot}4$	+38° 18′	5·6 - 14·9	Me	410 days	Long period variable.
R	Aquarii	23 41·2	−15 33	6·0 - 11	Me	380 „	„ „
α	Cassiopeiæ	0 37·6	+56 15	2·2 - 3·1	Ko	...	Irregular variable.
R	„	23 55·8	+51 7	5·3 - 12	Me	432 days	Long period variable.
δ	Cephei *	22 27·3	+58 10	3·6 - 4·3	G	5·37 „	Cepheid. 7m. *comes* at 41″.
T	Ceti	0 19·2	−20 20	5·1 - 7·0	Mb	...	Irregular type.
β	Pegasi	23 1·3	+27 48	2·2 - 2·7	Ma	...	... ...
R	Sculptoris	1 24·7	−32 49	6·2 - 8·8	N	376 days	Long period variable.

Nebulæ and Clusters. (Maps 3 and 4) *(Unlettered Nos. are those of the N.G.C.)*

224, M31 Andromedæ, $0^h\ 40^m{\cdot}0$, +41° 0′. The 'Great Nebula in Andromeda,' visible as a hazy spot to the naked eye. Long, oval, and brightening towards the centre, with almost star-like nucleus; photos by the 100-in. telescope resolve the outer parts into stars. Assuming 'red-shift' as due to velocity, like all other extra-galactic nebulæ it is receding, though apparently approaching owing to the Galactic rotation. Distance 700,000 - 800,000 light-years: it is the nearest Spiral except M33 in Triangulum, which is probably rather nearer.

7662, H.IV 18, Androm. $23^h\ 23^m{\cdot}4$, +42° 12′. A remarkably bright, slightly elliptical, planetary nebula, 32″ × 28″, bluish. With a low power almost starlike; in a 10-in. telescope the dusky centre makes it annular. A 14 mag. nucleus is visible in very large telescopes, and clear in photographs.

457, H.VII 42 Cassiop., $1^h\ 16^m{\cdot}0$, +58° 3′. A condensed cluster of moderately bright stars 18′ in diameter. Attending φ, which is, however, probably much nearer us than is the cluster.

7789, H.VI 30 „ $23^h\ 54^m{\cdot}5$, +56° 26′. Between ρ and σ. A large cluster of very faint stars.

7243, H.VIII 75 Lacer. $22^h\ 13^m{\cdot}1$, +49° 38′. A fine, open, irregular cluster, followed by a beautiful field.

650, M76, Persei, ... $1^h\ 38^m{\cdot}3$, +51° 20′. A double nebula, like the 'Dumb-bell Nebula' in Vulpecula (Map 13), but much smaller. It is a gaseous nebula, and therefore belongs to our System.

598, M33, Trianguli, $1^h\ 31^m{\cdot}0$, +30° 24′. Very large, faint, ill-defined nebula: central portions the brightest; irregular nodosities give it a curdled appearance. Use very low power on a dark, clear night. Spiral in photographs.

* *δ Cephei.* This star is typical of Class IV. short-period Cepheid variables. Its magnitude varies from about 3·6 to 4·3 (range 0·7 mag.), and its period is 5·37 days. Its rise from minimum to maximum occurs in about 1½ days, and is, therefore, more rapid than its decline, which occupies about 4 days, and is not uniform, but subject to slight oscillations. These changes are repeated with great regularity. The variations are thought to be due to pulsations in the atmosphere of the star, but the cause of the variability is still in doubt.

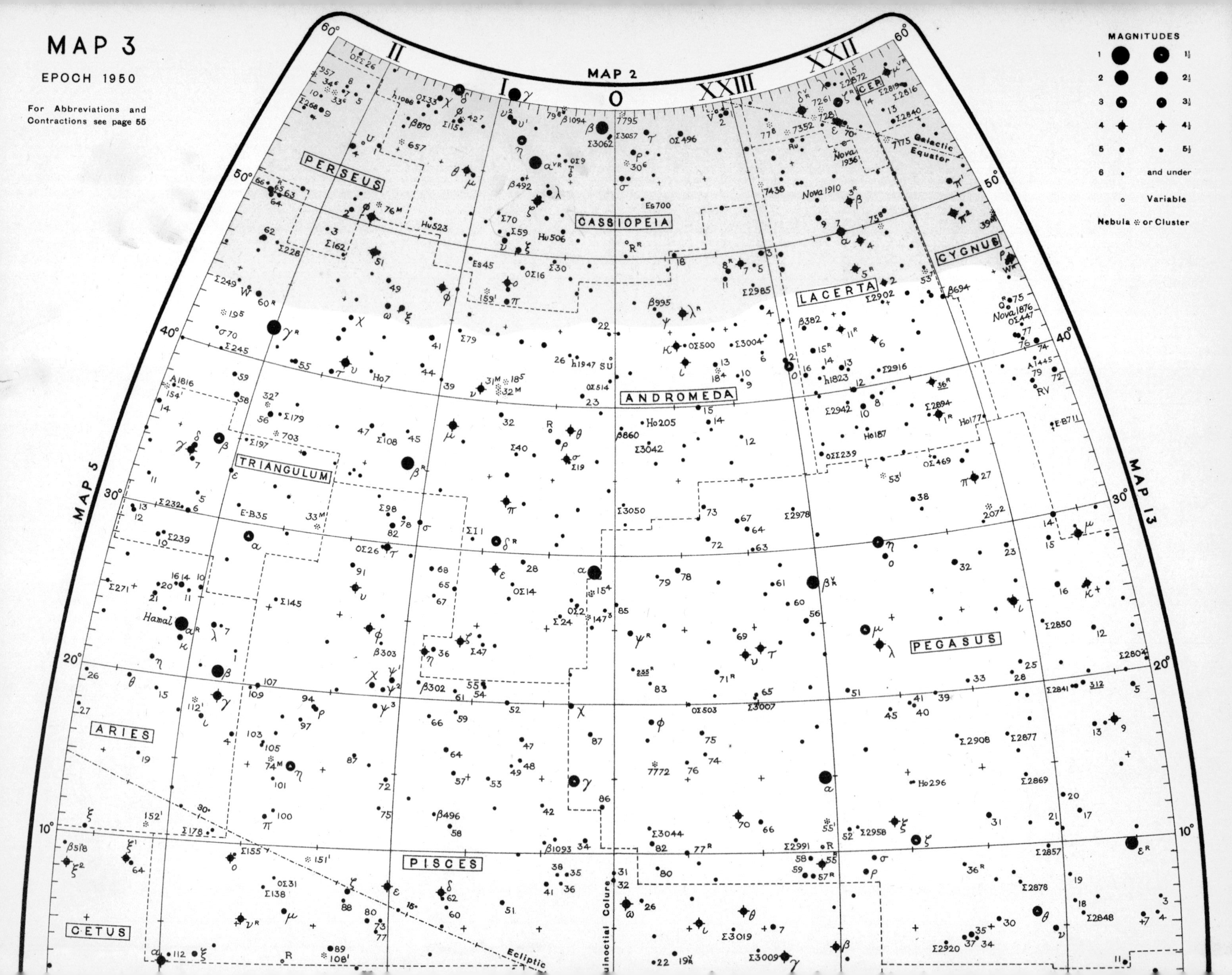
MAP 3
EPOCH 1950
For Abbreviations and Contractions see page 55
MAGNITUDES
1 1½ 2 2½ 3 3½ 4 4½ 5 5½ 6 and under
Variable
Nebula or Cluster
MAP 2
MAP 5
MAP 13
II
I
0
XXIII
XXII
60°
50°
40°
30°
20°
10°
PERSEUS
CASSIOPEIA
CEP
CYGNUS
LACERTA
ANDROMEDA
TRIANGULUM
PEGASUS
ARIES
PISCES
CETUS
Galactic Equator
Nova 1936
Nova 1910
Nova 1876
Hamal
Ecliptic
Equinoctial Colure

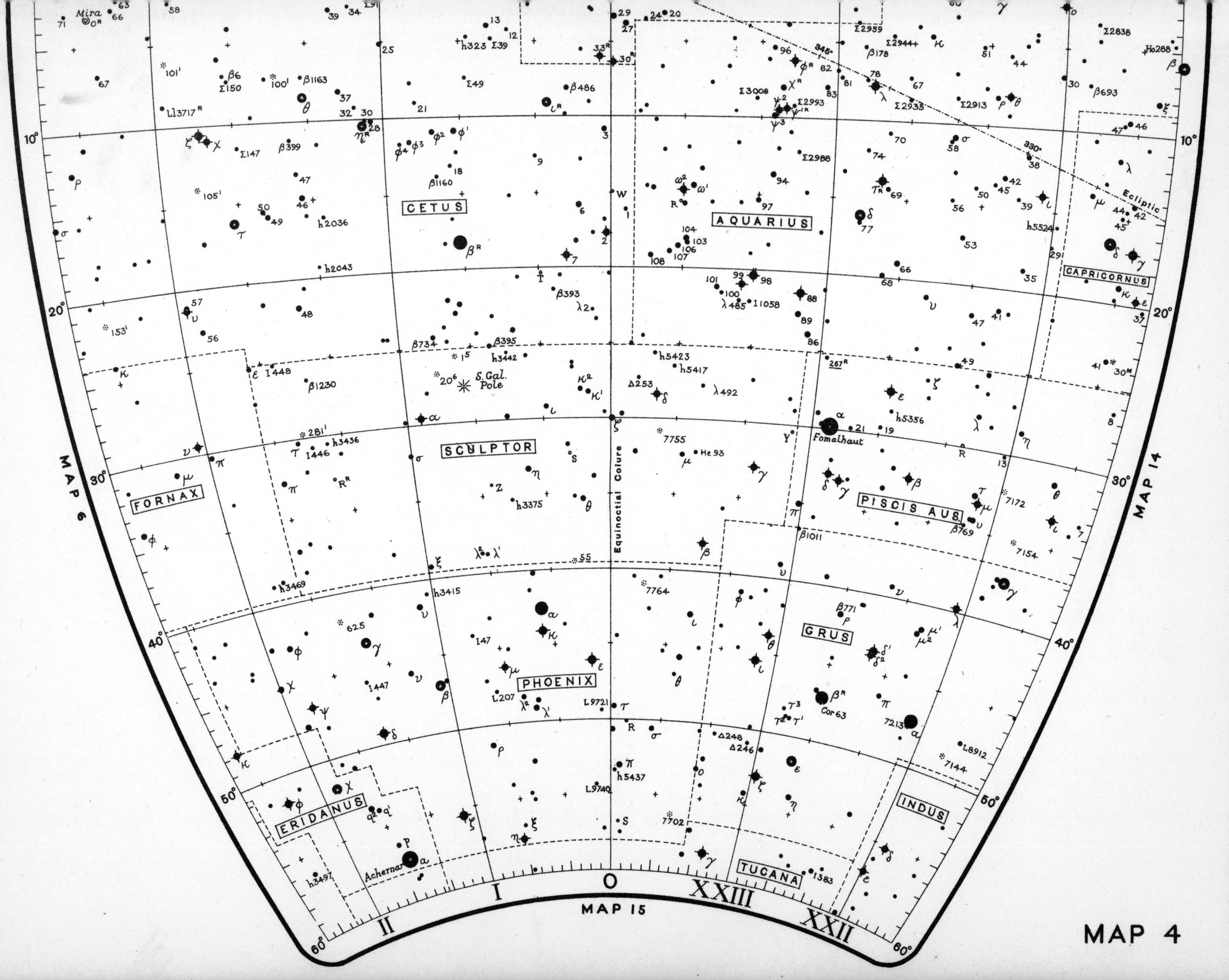

MAP 4
MAP 14
MAP 15
MAP 6
CETUS
AQUARIUS
CAPRICORNUS
SCULPTOR
FORNAX
PISCIS AUS
GRUS
PHOENIX
ERIDANUS
TUCANA
INDUS
Ecliptic
Equinoctial Colure
Fomalhaut
Achernar
Mira
S. Gal. Pole
XXII
XXIII
O
I
II

Interesting Objects. Maps 5 & 6.

(R.A. II. Hrs. to VI. Hrs. Dec. 60° N. to 60° S.).

Double Stars.

Epoch 1950.

Star	Constellation	R.A.	Dec.	Mags.	P.A.	Dist.	Date	Notes
59	Andromedæ	$2^{h}\ 7^{m}{\cdot}8$	+38° 48′	6·7, 7·2	35°	16″·6	1923	Relatively fixed.
30	Arietis	2 34·1	+24 26	6·1, 7·1	274°	38″·7	1920	White and blue. Relatively fixed.
π	,,	2 46·5	+17 15	4·9, 8·4	119°	3″·2	1923	There is a 10·2 mag. star at 110°; *d.* 25″ (1915).
ε	,,	2 56·4	+21 8	6·0, 6·4	205°	1″·5	1936	Test for 3-inch telescope.
52	,,	3 2·5	+25 4	6·0, 6·0, 10·8	277° 356°	0″·3 5″·2	1922	Triple.
ω	Aurigæ	4 55·8	+37 49	5·0, 8·0	357°	5″·8	1925	*P.A.* very slowly increasing.
14	,,	5 12·2	+32 38	5·0, 7·2	225°	14″·5	1922	11 mag. star at 11″·1 distance.
θ	,,	5 56·3	+37 13	2·7, 7·2	332°	2″·8	1924	Test for 4-inch telescope.
γ	Cæli	5 2·6	−35 33	4·7, 8·5	310°	2″·9	1935	... ...
1	Camelopardi	4 28·1	+53 48	5·1, 6·2	308°	10″·2	1924	Relatively fixed.
66	Ceti	2 10·2	− 2 38	6·0, 7·8	232°	16″·3	1925	Yellow and blue. Relatively fixed. *c.p.m.*
γ	,,	2 40·7	+ 3 2	3·7, 6·2	293°	3″·0	1935	3·7 mag. star yellowish. Little relative movement.
h 3527	Eridani	2 41·4	−40 44	7·0, 7·1	42°	2″·0	1935	... ...
θ	,,	2 56·4	−40 30	3·4, 4·4	87°	8″·2	1924	Very slow increase of *P.A.*
ρ^2	,,	3 0·2	− 7 53	6·2, 9·2	84°	2″·9	1923	Little change.
h 3556	,,	3 10·7	−44 37	5·9, 9·5	208°	3″·1	1926	The 5·9 star is a close double, 0″·5 (1926).
f, Δ16	,,	3 46·6	−37 47	4·9, 5·4	209°	7″·8	1919	*P.A.* slowly increasing.
32	,,	3 51·8	− 3 6	4·0, 6·0	347°	7″·0	1922	Topaz and green. Fine contrast.
39	,,	4 12·0	−10 23	6·0, 8·8	148°	6″·5	1922	Little change.
55	,,	4 41·2	− 8 53	6·2, 6·7	317°	9″·3	1923	Relatively fixed.
ι	Leporis	5 10·0	−11 56	4·2, 10·5	335°	12″·8	1903	Relatively fixed.
κ	,,	5 10·9	−13 0	5·0, 7·5	360°	2″·6	1926	Yellowish and bluish. Relatively fixed.
β	,,	5 26·1	−20 48	3·0, 9·6	313°	2″·5	1926	*P.A.* increasing.
α	,,	5 30·5	−17 51	4·0, 9·5	156°	35″·5	1920	Fine field.
ρ	Orionis	5 10·7	+ 2 48	4·7, 8·5	63°	7″·0	1921	No change. Other stars in field.
β	,,	5 12·1	− 8 15	0·3, 6·7	202°	9″·4	1925	*Rigel.* The attendant is bluish. Test for 2-in.
η	,,	5 22·0	− 2 26	3·8, 4·8	79°	1″·4	1927	*P.A.* slowly decreasing. Test for 4-inch.
33	,,	5 28·6	+ 3 15	6·0, 7·3	26°	2″·0	1922	Relatively fixed.
δ	,,	5 29·4	− 0 20	2·0, 6·8	360°	52″·8	1922	Relatively fixed.
λ	,,	5 32·4	+ 9 54	4·0, 6·0	43°	4″·2	1934	Relatively fixed. Very fine region.
θ	,,	5 33·0	− 5 27	6·0, 7·0, 7·5, 8·0	...	...	...	The *Trapezium* in Orion. Two other stars a test for 4-in.
ι	,,	5 33·0	− 5 56	3·2, 7·3	141°	11″·4	1925	Relatively fixed. Nebulous glow.
σ	,,	5 36·2	− 2 36	4·0, 10·0, 7·5, 7·0	236° 85°	11″·1 12″·9	...	Fine group with striking colours. 8 stars in 4-in.
ζ	,,	5 38·2	− 1 57	2·0, 5·0	157°	2″·8	1929	*P.A.* slowly increasing. Test for 2-inch.
52	,,	5 45·3	+ 6 26	6·2, 6·2	207°	1″·4	1934	Test for 3-inch telescope.
η	Persei	2 47·0	+55 41	4·0, 8·5	301°	28″·4	1925	Yellow and blue. Several faint *comites.*
20	,,	2 50·6	+38 8	5·5, 10·0	237°	14″·0	1917	Closely *f* 16 Persei. Test for 3-inch.
ε	,,	3 54·5	+39 52	3·1, 8·3	10°	9″·0	1924	... ...
ι	Pictoris	4 49·8	−53 33	5·6, 6·4	58°	12″·0	1917	Relatively fixed.
Σ422	Tauri	3 34·2	+ 0 26	6·0, 8·2	253°	6″·5	1924	Slow change. Probably a binary.
χ	,,	4 19·5	+25 31	5·7, 7·8	25°	19″·9	1924	Relatively fixed.
Σ559	,,	4 30·6	+17 55	7·0, 7·1	277°	3″·0	1924	... ...
α	,,	4 33·0	+16 25	1·0, 11·2	34°	121″	1923	*Aldebaran.* Distance increasing from *p.m.* of A.
Σ572	,,	4 35·4	+26 51	6·5, 6·5	198°	4″·1	1937	*P.A.* decreasing; distance increasing slowly.
118	,,	5 26·2	+25 7	5·8, 6·6	203°	4″·8	1929	*P.A.* very slowly increasing.
ι, 6	Trianguli	2 9·5	+30 4	5·0, 6·4	74°	3″·9	1923	Yellow and blue. Fine pair.

INTERESTING OBJECTS. MAPS 5 & 6 — *Continued.*

(R.A. II. HRS. TO VI. HRS. DEC. 60° N. TO 60° S.).

Variable Stars.

EPOCH 1950.

		R.A.	Dec.	Var. of mag.	Spectrum	Period	Notes
ε	Aurigæ	$4^h\ 58^m \cdot 4$	+43° 44′	3·3 - 4·1	F5p	27·14 yrs.	Spectroscopic Binary.
o	Ceti	2 16·8	− 3 12	1·7 - 9·6	Me	331 days	*Mira.* Long period variable.*
R	Leporis	4 57·3	−14 53	6·0 - 10·4	N	430 „	Hind's 'Crimson Star.'
α	Orionis	5 52·5	+ 7 24	0·5 - 1·1	M1	...	*Betelgeuse.* Irregular variable.†
U	„	5 52·9	+20 11	5·4 - 12·3	Me	374 days	Long period variable.
ρ	Persei	3 2·0	+38 39	3·3 - 4·1	M2	...	Irregular variable.
β	„	3 4·9	+40 46	2·3 - 3·5	B8	2·87 days	*Algol.* The typical Algolid.‡
λ	Tauri	3 57·8	+12 20	3·3 - 4·2	B3	3·9 „	Algol eclipsing type.
R	Trianguli	2 34·0	+34 3	5·8 - 12·0	Me	270 „	Long period variable.

Nebulæ and Clusters. **(Maps 5 and 6)** *(Unlettered Nos. are those of the N.G.C.)*

1912, M38, Aurigæ, $5^h\ 25^m \cdot 3$, +35° 48′. A striking, loose, cruciform cluster, in a glorious neighbourhood.

1960, M36, „ $5^h\ 33^m \cdot 0$, +34° 7′. An open cluster of stars of mag. 8-14, regularly arranged. 2° *f φ* Aurigæ.

2099, M37, „ $5^h\ 49^m \cdot 0$, +32° 33′. Fine open cluster. Ruddy 9th magnitude star near the centre.

1068, M77, Ceti, $2^h\ 40^m \cdot 1$, − 0° 15′. Small, round, faintish nebula, centrally condensed. 1° *f* δ, slightly S.

1976, M42, Orionis, $5^h\ 32^m \cdot 5$, − 5° 25′. The Great Nebula in Orion, visible to the naked eye as θ Orionis. A greenish, irregular, fan-shaped mass, best seen with a low power. With higher powers, the bright 'Huygenian' region shows a mottled appearance 'like the breaking up of a mackerel sky' (Sir J. Herschel). Includes the 'Trapezium' (see previous page).

869, H.VI 33, Persei, $2^h\ 17^m \cdot 2$, +56° 55′.
884, H.VI 34, „ $2^h\ 20^m \cdot 4$, +56° 53′.
} Two magnificent clusters, visible to the naked eye, and fine objects even in small telescopes; the diameter of each is about 45′. There is a fine ruby star near the centre of 884.

1039, M34, „ $2^h\ 38^m \cdot 8$, +42° 32′. A fine loose cluster, just visible to the naked eye; it contains the double star OΣ44. A low power is required to cover the large field.

1435, Tauri, $3^h\ 43^m \cdot 2$, +23° 37′. Faint nebula, near *Merope* in the Pleiades—a cluster which requires a very large field; well seen in finder. Ordinary eyes see six or seven stars, but some can count many more.

1952, M1, Tauri, $5^h\ 31^m \cdot 5$, +21° 59′. The 'Crab Nebula,' near ζ, a faint, oval, gaseous nebula. Its serrated outline is visible only in large instruments. Discovered 1731, and forgotten; its rediscovery by Messier in 1758, led him to make his catalogue of 103 nebulæ.

* *Mira.* 'The Wonderful.' It was seen as a new star for a few weeks by Fabricius in 1596, and by Bayer in 1603, who catalogued it as *o* Ceti. It is invisible except in a telescope for about 5 months, sinking to a minimum of 8·5 to 9·6 mag.; then it becomes visible to the naked eye for about 6 months, rising at maximum usually to 3rd or 4th mag., but sometimes to 5th or 2nd mag. Its rise is more rapid than its fall. At maximum the light increases some 1400 times, apparently as the result of outbursts of hydrogen gas. Mean period 330 days, with large variations.

† *Betelgeuse* is one of the reddest of the bright stars. Its angular diameter, measured by the interferometer with the 100-in. telescope, is about 0″·045, giving an actual diameter of about 300,000,000 miles—large enough to include easily the whole orbit of the earth. Since the measures vary, it appears that pulsatory changes in the star's diameter may be connected with its variability. Betelgeuse has a mean density about 1 millionth that of water or $\frac{1}{1000}$ that of air.

‡ *Algol.* Its name, 'The Demon Star,' suggests that its variability was known to the Arabs centuries ago. It is typical of the 'dark-eclipsing' variables. Its magnitude for about 2d. 11h. is substantially constant at 2·3, but with a slight secondary fall and rise, of $\frac{1}{20}$ mag. at half-way; it then decreases rapidly to mag. 3·5 in about 5 hours, and in another 5 hours regains its original brightness. Period about 69 hours. The change of light is due to two stars, one bright, the other faint, very close together, revolving round their common centre of gravity, and mutually eclipsing each other. A third star is included in the system.

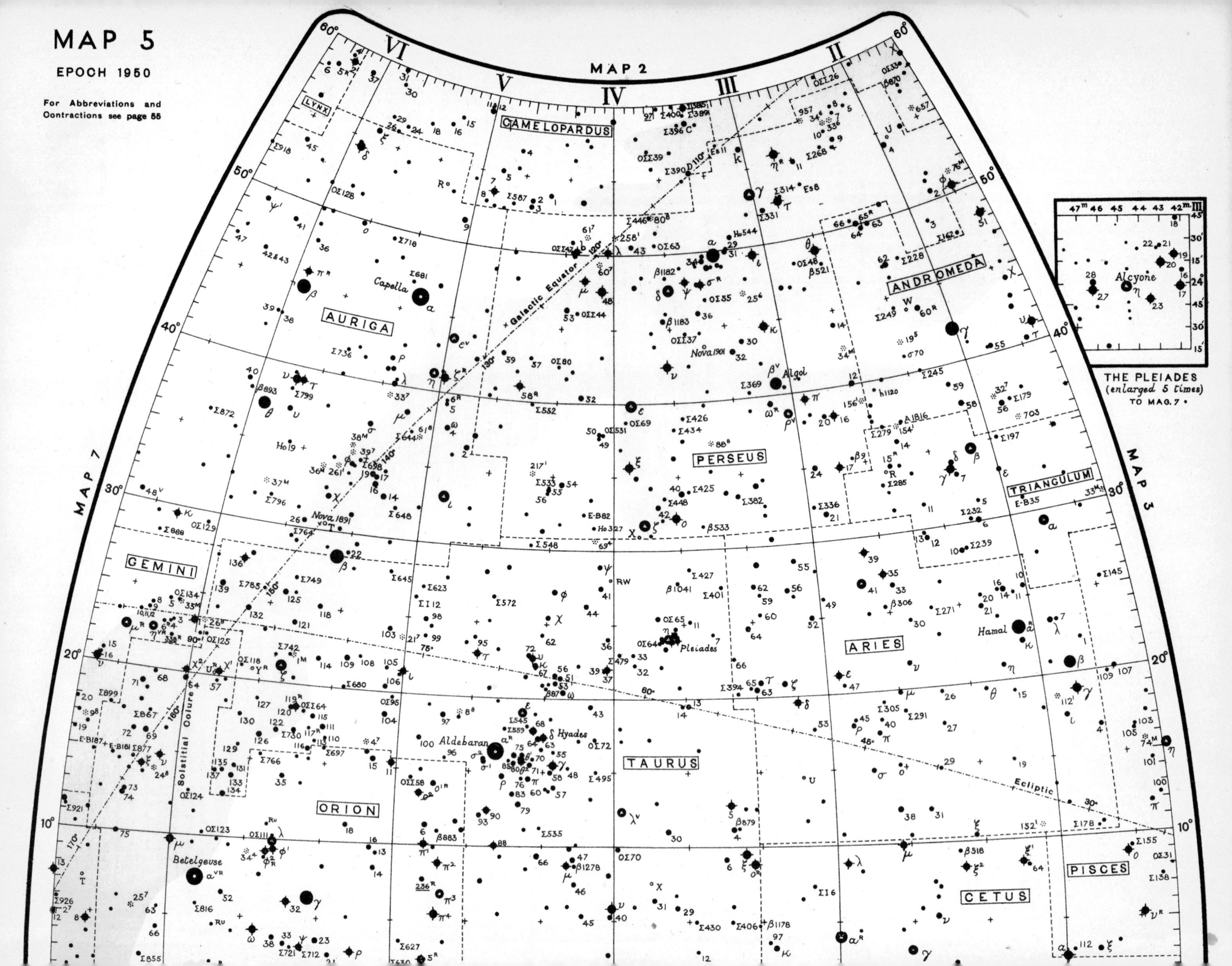

MAP 5
EPOCH 1950
For Abbreviations and Contractions see page 55
MAP 2
MAP 3
MAP 7
CAMELOPARDUS
LYNX
AURIGA
Capella
PERSEUS
Algol
Nova 1901
ANDROMEDA
TRIANGULUM
ARIES
Hamal
TAURUS
Pleiades
Hyades
Aldebaran
GEMINI
Nova 1891
ORION
Betelgeuse
CETUS
PISCES
Galactic Equator
Ecliptic
Solstitial Colure
THE PLEIADES (enlarged 5 times) TO MAG. 7 •
Alcyone

MAP 6
MAP 4
MAP 8
MAP 15
CETUS
ERIDANUS
FORNAX
PHOENIX
LEPUS
COLUMBA
CAELUM
HOROLOGIUM
RETICULUM
DORADO
PICTOR
PUPPIS
CANIS MAJ.
MONOCEROS
Solstitial Colure
Mira
Rigel
Achernar
Canopus
MAGNITUDES
and under
Variable
Nebula or Cluster

INTERESTING OBJECTS. MAPS 7 & 8.

(R.A. VI. HRS. TO X. HRS. DEC. 60° N. TO 60° S.).

Double Stars.

EPOCH 1950.

		R.A.	Dec.	Mags.	*P.A.*	Dist.	Date	Notes
ζ^1	Antliæ	9h 28m·6	−31° 40′	5·9, 6·7	211°	8″·2	1919	Relatively fixed.
41	Aurigæ	6 7·8	+48 44	5·2, 6·4	355°	7″·8	1923	Relatively fixed. *c.p.m.*
Σ872	,,	6 12·3	+36 10	6·0, 7·0	217°	11″·2	1924	Relatively fixed.
54	,,	6 36·4	+28 19	6·0, 7·8	36°	0″·9	1927	*c.p.m.*
ζ	Cancri	8 9·3	+17 48	5·0, 5·7	108°	0″·7	1937	{ Binary, *P.* 60 years. Widest 1″·1 in 1960. { Third star 5·5 mag. at 5″·4 distance.
υ^1, 30	,,	8 23·7	+24 42	6·0, 7·1	47°	5″·9	1926	*P.A.* slowly increasing. *d.* constant.
ϕ^2	,,	8 23·8	+27 6	6·3, 6·3	216°	5″·0	1934	Little change.
ι	,,	8 43·7	+28 57	4·4, 6·5	307°	30″·7	1922	Yellow and blue: fine contrast. No change.
57	,,	8 51·2	+30 46	5·9, 6·4	320°	1″·4	1937	*P.A.* slowly decreasing. Test for 4-inch.
66	,,	8 58·3	+32 27	6·1, 8·2	136°	4″·6	1923	Relatively fixed.
ν^1	Canis Maj.	6 34·2	−18 37	6·0, 8·0	263°	17″·5	1926	Relatively fixed.
α	,,	6 43·0	−16 38	−1·6, 8·4	47°	9″·7	1931	*Sirius*, The Dog Star. Widest 11″·5 in 1975.*
μ	,,	6 53·8	−13 59	4·7, 8·0	339°	3″·0	1926	Yellow and blue. Little change.
ϵ	,,	6 56·7	−28 54	1·6, 8·0	160°	7″·7	1926	Relatively fixed.
β755	Columbæ	6 33·7	−36 44	6·1, 6·8	257°	1″·3	1925	11·2 mag. star at 21″ distance.
20	Geminorum	6 29·4	+17 49	6·0, 6·9	211°	20″·0	1922	Yellow and blue. No change.
38	,,	6 51·8	+13 15	5·4, 7·7	156°	6″·7	1922	*P.A.* decreasing. Increase in distance.
λ	,,	7 15·2	+16 38	3·2, 10·3	33°	9″·9	1914	Relatively fixed. Light test for 3-inch.
δ	,,	7 17·1	+22 5	3·2, 8·2	211°	6″·7	1925	3·2 mag. star is yellowish. Test for 2-inch.
α	,,	7 31·4	+32 0	2·0, 2·8	204°	3″·9	1937	*Castor.* Very fine object.†
κ	,,	7 41·4	+24 31	4·0, 8·5	236°	6″·8	1924	Relatively fixed. Delicate pair.
Σ1245	Hydræ	8 33·2	+ 6 48	6·0, 7·0	26°	10″·2	1925	1° *np* δ Hydræ. Relatively fixed.
ϵ	,,	8 44·2	+ 6 36	3·8, 7·8	253°	3″·6	1929	*P.A.* increasing. A a close 15 year binary.
θ	,,	9 11·8	+ 2 32	5·0, 10·8	185°	38″·3	1924	Distance decreasing. Light test for 3-inch.
ω	Leonis	9 25·8	+ 9 17	5·9, 6·7	141°	0″·9	1936	Close binary. Period 117 years.
3	,,	9 25·8	+ 8 24	6·0, 10·7	81°	25″·7	1908	Light test for 4-inch telescope.
6	,,	9 29·3	+ 9 56	5·0, 9·5	75°	37″·4	1921	... ...
4	Lyncis	6 17·6	+59 24	6·4, 7·9	113°	0″·8	1924	Direct movement. Orbit doubtful.
12	,,	6 41·8	+59 30	5·2, 6·1, 7·4	107° 308°	1″·7 8″·6	1926	5·2 and 6·1 form a binary; very long period,
19	,,	7 18·8	+55 23	5·3, 6·6	315°	14″·7	1923	Relatively fixed. [retrograde. Test for 3-in.
β758	,,	7 25·1	+48 17	6·2, 10·2	94°	17″·1	1906	Light test for 3-inch telescope.
38	,,	9 15·8	+37 1	4·0, 6·7	233°	2″·9	1925	*P.A.* decreasing.
8	Monocerotis	6 21·1	+ 4 37	4·0, 6·7	27°	13″·2	1923	Yellow and blue. Grand low power field.
11	,,	6 26·4	− 7 0	5·0, 5·5, 6·0	132° 105°	7″·4 2″·8	1926	Beautiful fixed triple star.
Δ23	Puppis	6 3·5	−48 27	7·0, 7·4	82°	1″·8	1937	Binary. Direct movement.
k	,,	7 36·8	−26 41	4·5, 4·6	318°	9″·9	1927	Relatively fixed.
2	,,	7 43·2	−14 34	6·2, 7·0	340°	16″·9	1923	... ...
5	,,	7 45·6	−12 4	5·3, 7·4	9°	3″·4	1929	*P.A.* diminishing slowly. Test for 2-inch.
ι	Ursæ Majoris	8 55·8	+48 14	3·1, 10·3	2°	7″·4	1922	*P.A.* increasing. *d.* decreasing. Test for 4-in.
ϕ	,,	9 48·7	+54 19	5·1, 5·5	331°	0″·5	1926	Binary. Period 112½ years.
δ	Velorum	8 43·3	−54 31	2·0, 6·6	160°	3″·0	1935	10th mag. star at 69″ *d.* makes with A., h4136.
H	,,	8 54·8	−52 32	4·9, 7·7	339°	2″·7	1927	Fine contrast in colours.
h4165	,,	9 0·2	−51 59	5·6, 7·1	107°	1″·3	1925	*P.A.* slowly increasing.
ψ	,,	9 28·8	−40 15	3·8, 5·8	307°	0″·4	1934	Binary. Period 34 years.
h4220	,,	9 32·0	−48 47	5·8, 6·4	210°	2″·1	1925	*P.A.* slowly increasing.

INTERESTING OBJECTS. MAPS 7 & 8 — *Continued.*

(R.A. VI. HRS. TO X. HRS. DEC. 60° N. TO 60° S.).

Variable Stars.

EPOCH 1950.

	R.A.	Dec.	Var. of mag.	Spectrum	Period	Notes
RT, 48 Aurigæ	6h 25m·3	+30° 33′	4·9 - 5·9	G	3·73 days	Cepheid variable.
R Cancri	8 13·7	+11 53	6·0 - 11·3	Me	362 „	Long period variable.
R Canis Majoris	7 17·2	−16 18	5·9 - 6·7	F	1·14 „	Algol type.
η Geminorum	6 11·9	+22 31	3·2 - 4·2	M1	231 „	Long period variable.
ζ „	7 1·2	+20 39	3·7 - 4·3	G	10·2 „	Cepheid variable.
R „	7 4·3	+22 48	5·9 - 13·8	G	370 „	Long period variable.
R Leonis	9 44·9	+11 40	5·0 - 10·5	Me	312 „	„ „
R Leonis Min.	9 42·6	+34 45	6·2 - 12·0	Me	370 „	„ „
T Monocerotis	6 22·5	+ 7 7	5·8 - 6·8	G5	27·0 „	Cepheid variable.
L^2 Puppis	7 12·0	−44 34	4·6 - 6·2	Me	140 „	Long period variable.
V „	7 56·7	−49 6	4·1 - 4·9	B1p	1·45 „	Lyrid type.

Nebulæ and Clusters. (Maps 7 and 8) *(Unlettered Nos. are those of the N.G.C.)*

2632, M44, Cancri, 8h 37m ·2, +20° 10′. *Præsepe* (the Bee-hive) of the ancients. A large scattered cluster almost resolved by the naked eye; contains some orange stars. Best seen in finder, or with very low power.

2682, M67 „ 8h 48m ·5, +12° 0′. A roughly circular, open cluster of faint stars, diam. 27′. Low power object.

2287, M41, Canis Maj., 6h 44m ·9, −20° 42′. A fine open cluster of bright stars in curves. Just visible to the naked eye. There is a ruddy star near the centre.

2168, M35, Geminorum, 6h 5m ·7, +24° 21′. Fine open cluster of bright stars in streams, with many fainter stars. Between ε Geminorum and ζ Tauri, a little to N.

2392, H.IV 45 „ 7h 26m ·2, +21° 2′. Oval planetary nebula, about 25″ in diameter, with 9·5 mag. central star.

2244, H.VII 2, Monocer. 6h 30m·0, + 4° 54′. Beautiful open cluster of 7th to 14th mag. stars, visible to the naked eye. Includes the 6th mag. 'giant' yellow star 12 Monocerotis, probably nearer than the cluster.

2506, H.VI 37 „ 7h 57m·5, −10° 27′. Fine cloud of faint stars, mag. 10 downwards in grand region. Best seen with low power.

2437, M46 Puppis, 7h 39m·5, −14° 42′. A beautiful cluster of small stars, about 30′ in diameter. On its northern edge is the irregular planetary ring nebula 2438.

2440, H.IV 64 „ 7h 39m·6, −18° 5′. A bright, bluish, planetary nebula, in a rich neighbourhood, best seen with a moderately high power. A 10th mag. ruddy star follows.

* *Sirius.* The brightest star. Between 1834 and 1844, Bessel found that it had wavy irregularities in its proper motion, and came to the conclusion that the visible star must be revolving round the centre of gravity of itself, and an invisible companion star, in a period of about 50 years. The *comes*, of about 8th magnitude, was discovered by Clark in 1862 near its predicted place. Unless atmospheric conditions are good, it is difficult, or impossible, to see it even when widest, though it is sometimes visible in a 6-inch telescope. In 1894, when closest (about 2″) the faint star was invisible. It was next seen by Burnham in 1896 (*d.* 3″·8), and widened to its maximum distance of 11″·5 about 1925. It is now (1939) rapidly closing, and from 1940 to 1950 will be invisible in all except the largest telescopes. The *comes* is a 'white dwarf' (Spectrum about F7), only about 1/10,000th as bright as its primary, but with a mass ⅘ as great. Its density is 36,000 times that of the Sun, or 50,000 times that of water. Its diameter is only about 26,000 miles, but it contains almost as much matter as the Sun, whose diameter is 864,000 miles. Vyssotsky (1930) obtained different results, a mean magnitude of 7·1, a diameter of 48,000 miles, and a density only ⅛ of that usually adopted.

† *Castor.* A very fine double and binary star, in slow retrograde motion, with a period of about 350 years. The component stars were at their widest distance apart, 6″·5, about 1880; they are now closing and will continue to do so for some years. Both of the stars are spectroscopic binaries, with periods of about 3 and 9 days respectively. A third faint star, also a close binary, forms part of the same system.

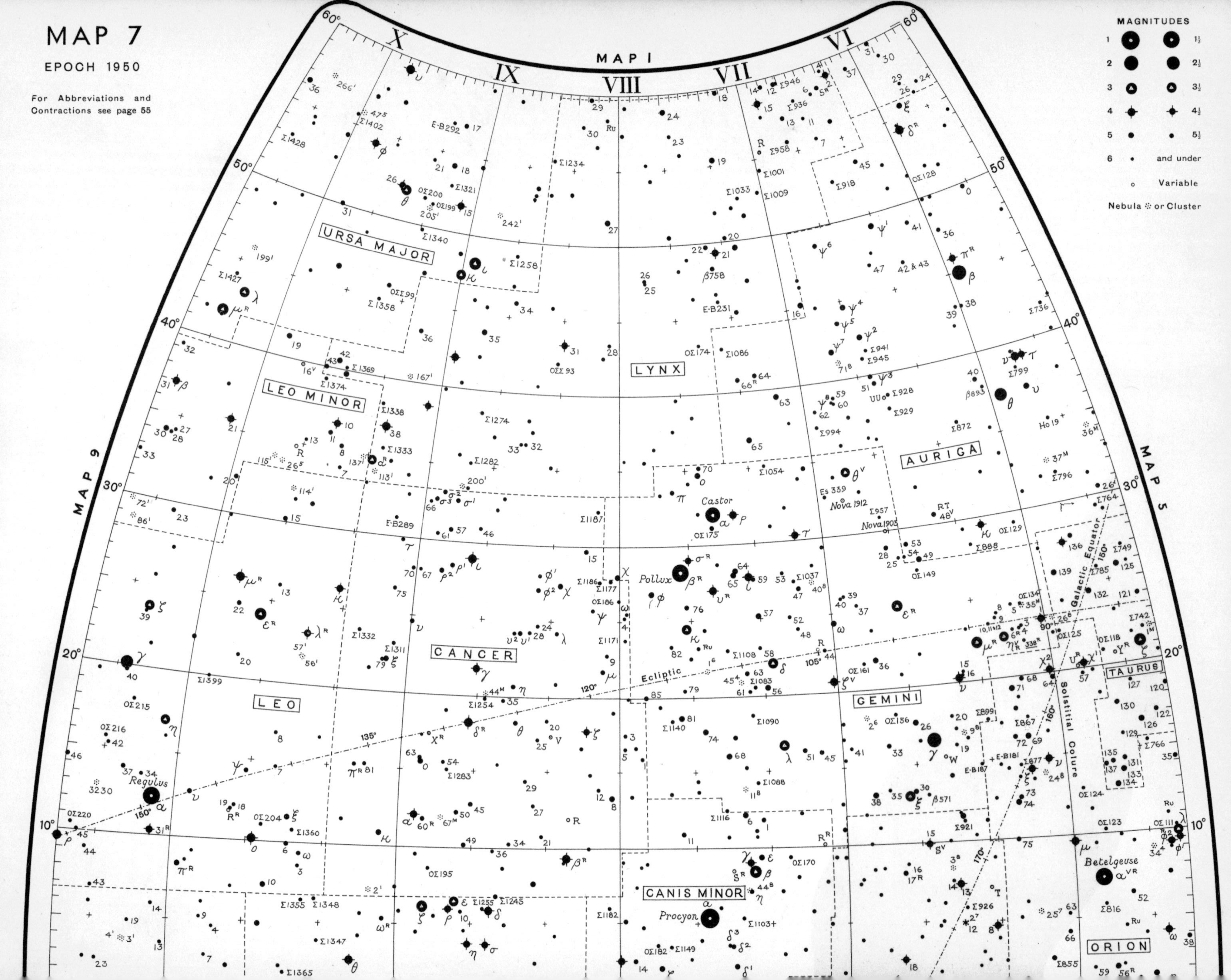
MAP 7
EPOCH 1950
For Abbreviations and Contractions see page 55
MAGNITUDES
1
2
3
4
5
6
and under
Variable
Nebula or Cluster
MAP I
MAP 5
MAP 9
X
IX
VIII
VII
VI
URSA MAJOR
LEO MINOR
LYNX
AURIGA
CANCER
LEO
GEMINI
TAURUS
CANIS MINOR
ORION
Castor
Pollux
Procyon
Regulus
Betelgeuse
Ecliptic
Galactic Equator
Solstitial Colure
Nova 1912
Nova 1903

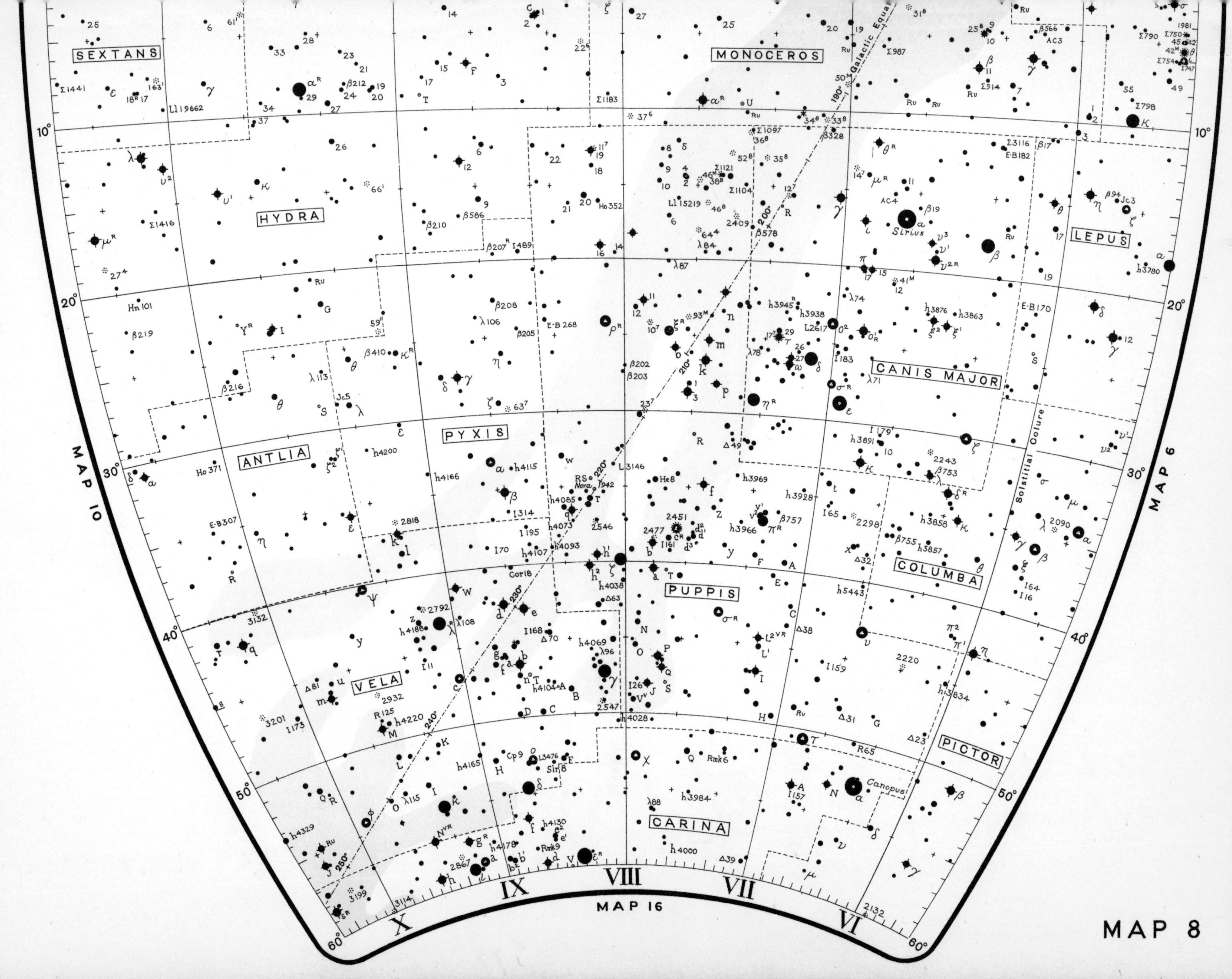
SEXTANS
HYDRA
MONOCEROS
LEPUS
CANIS MAJOR
PYXIS
ANTLIA
COLUMBA
PUPPIS
VELA
PICTOR
CARINA
Sirius
Canopus
Galactic Equator
Solstitial Colure
MAP 6
MAP 10
MAP 16
VI
VII
VIII
IX
X

MAP 8

Interesting Objects. Maps 9 & 10.

(R.A. X. Hrs. to XIV. Hrs. Dec. 60° N. to 60° S.).

Double Stars.

Epoch 1950.

Star	Constellation	R.A.	Dec.	Mags.	P.A.	Dist.	Date	Notes
1	Boötis	13ʰ 38ᵐ·3	+20° 12′	6·2, 9·1	140°	4″·7	1925	*P.A.* slowly decreasing. Stars bluish
Σ1606	CanumVen.	12 8·2	+40 10	6·3, 7·0	323°	1″·0	1925	*P.A.* decreasing.
2	,,	12 13·6	+40 56	5·7, 8·0	260°	11″·5	1925	Relatively fixed.
α, 12	,,	12 53·7	+38 35	3·2, 5·7	228°	19″·7	1925	*Cor Caroli.* Relatively fixed.
25	,,	13 35·2	+36 33	5·7, 7·6	119°	1″·6	1926	Binary, period 220 years. *P.A.* decreasing.
h 4409	Centauri	11 5·0	−42 22	5·4, 8·5	267°	1″·9	1926	*P.A.* slowly decreasing.
I 78	,,	11 31·2	−40 19	6·3, 6·3	94°	1″·0	1937	Little change.
D	,,	12 11·4	−45 27	5·3, 6·5	245°	2″·9	1926	Relatively fixed.
γ	,,	12 38·8	−48 41	3·1, 3·1	23°	0″·5	1938	Binary, period 80 years.
Q	,,	13 38·5	−54 18	5·4, 6·8	164°	5″·2	1915	Relatively fixed.
N	,,	13 48·8	−52 34	5·7, 7·7	288°	18″·1	1919	Relatively fixed.
k	,,	13 48·9	−32 45	4·5, 5·9	110°	7″·6	1922	Little change.
h	,,	13 50·3	−31 41	4·8, 6·3	186°	15″·1	1919	Relatively fixed.
y	,,	13 50·6	−35 26	5·6, 5·8	102°	1″·2	1927	*P.A.* increasing.
2	Comæ Ber.	12 1·7	+21 44	6·0, 7·5	237°	3″·9	1924	Little change.
Σ1639	,,	12 21·9	+25 52	6·7, 7·9	332°	0″·9	1937	Binary, *P.* 361 y. Widening, *P.A.* decreasing.
24	,,	12 32·6	+18 39	4·7, 6·2	271°	20″·1	1922	Yellow and greenish white. Relatively fixed.
35	,,	12 50·8	+21 31	5·0, 7·8	118°	0″·9	1937	Long period binary. *P.A.* increasing.
β920	Corvi	12 13·2	−23 4	6·5, 7·8	285°	1″·2	1936	*P.A.* is increasing.
δ	,,	12 27·3	−16 15	3·0, 8·5	212°	24″·2	1926	Relatively fixed. A is yellow.
Σ1669	,,	12 38·7	−12 44	6·1, 6·2	306°	5″·4	1926	Slow increase of *P.A.*
μ	Crucis	12 51·7	−56 54	4·5, 5·5	17°	34″·9	1913	Relatively fixed.
N	Hydræ	11 29·8	−28 59	5·8, 5·9	210°	9″·1	1926	*c.p.m.*
β	,,	11 50·4	−33 38	4·4, 4·8	358°	1″·2	1932	*P.A.* slowly increasing.
OΣ215	Leonis	10 13·5	+17 59	7·0, 7·2	193°	1″·1	1938	*P.A.* decreasing.
γ	,,	10 17·2	+20 6	2·4, 3·8	119°	4″·0	1934	Binary, *P.* 407 y. *P.A.* and distance increasing.
49	,,	10 32·5	+ 8 55	6·0, 8·7	158°	2″·4	1923	Little change.
54	,,	10 52·9	+25 1	5·0, 7·0	108°	6″·3	1925	Slow increase of *P.A.*
ι	,,	11 21·3	+10 48	3·9, 7·1	15°	0″·7	1937	Binary of uncertain period. Closing.
83	,,	11 24·3	+ 3 17	6·3, 7·3	150°	28″·9	1922	Relatively fixed.
88	,,	11 29·2	+14 39	6·4, 8·2	326°	15″·4	1924	Yellow and lilac. *c.p.m.*
90	,,	11 32 1	+17 4	6·0, 7·3	209°	3″·4	1922	9·0 magnitude star at 63″ distance.
35	Sextantis	10 40·8	+ 5 1	6·1, 7·2	236°	6″·4	1923	Little change.
41	,,	10 47·8	− 8 38	6·0, 11·7	306°	27″·3	1925	Little change.
ξ	Ursæ Majoris	11 15·6	+31 50	4·4, 4·9	292°	1″·5	1937	Binary, *P.* 60 y. Closest 0″·9 in 1933. Widen-[ing to 2″·9, 1980.
ν	,,	11 15·8	+33 22	3·7, 10·1	147°	7″·2	1926	Relatively fixed.
57	,,	11 26·4	+39 37	5·2, 8·2	1°	5″·5	1924	*P.A.* slowly decreasing. *Comes* variable?
ζ	,,	13 21·9	+55 11	2·1, 4·2	150°	14″·5	1926	*Mizar.* Naked eye pair with *Alcor.*
s	Velorum	10 29·8	−44 49	6·2, 6·5	219°	13″·5	1913	Relatively fixed.
μ	,,	10 44·6	−49 9	3·0, 6·8	80°	1″·1	1937	Closing; *P.A.* increasing. Fine contrast.
Σ1627	Virginis	12 15·6	− 3 40	5·9, 6·4	196°	19″·9	1925	Relatively fixed.
17	,,	12 20·0	+ 5 35	6·2, 9·0	337°	19″·6	1925	Relatively fixed.
γ	,,	12 39·1	− 1 10	3·6, 3·7	317°	5″·7	1938	A splendid binary star.*
θ	,,	13 7·4	− 5 16	4·0, 9·0	343°	7″·2	1921	Test for 3-inch. 10th mag. star at 71″ distance.
81	,,	13 35·0	− 7 37	7·5, 7·5	40°	2″·6	1926	Relatively fixed.
84	,,	13 40·6	+ 3 47	5·8, 8·2	230°	3″·3	1924	Test for 3-inch telescope.
Σ1788	,,	13 52·4	− 7 49	6·7, 7·9	83°	3″·1	1927	Binary. *P.A.* increasing.

Variable Stars.

EPOCH 1950.

		R.A.	Dec.	Var. of mag.	Spectrum	Period	Notes
R	Canum Ven.	13h 46m·8	+39° 47′	6·1 - 12·5	Me	333 days	Long period variable.
η	Carinæ	10 43·0	−59 25	>1·0 - 7·8	Pec.	...	or η Argûs. Irregular.†
T	Centauri	13 38·9	−33 21	5·2 - 10·0	Me	90 days	Long period variable.
U	Hydræ	10 35·1	−13 7	4·5 - 6·0	N	...	Irregular variable.
R	„	13 26·9	−23 1	4·0 - 10·1	Me	415 days	Long period variable.
W	„	13 46·2	−28 7	6·5 - 8·0	Me	384 „	„ „
T	Ursæ Majoris	12 34·1	+59 46	5·5 - 13·1	Me	254 „	„ „
R	Virginis	12 35·9	+ 7 16	6·0 - 12·0	Me	145 „	„ „
S	„	13 30·4	− 6 56	5·6 - 12·3	Me	372 „	„ „

Nebulæ and Clusters. (Maps 9 and 10) *(Unlettered Nos. are those of the N.G.C.)*

4258, H.V 43, Canum V., 12h 16m·5, +47° 34′. A large pear-shaped nebula, with nucleus in the southern part. It is actually a Spiral with two main arms, and many condensations.

5055, M63 „ 13h 13m·6, +42° 18′. A bright, oval nebula, 8′ × 3′, with central nucleus. An 8th mag. star closely precedes. In photographs it appears as a Spiral, with compact whorls.

5194, M51 „ 13h 27m·8, +47° 27′. The larger of two nebulæ nearly in contact. Spiral as seen in 12-inch telescope.

5272, M3 „ 13h 39m·9, +28° 38′. A beautiful, bright, condensed globular cluster. The outer parts can be resolved into stars with a 4-inch telescope, and the whole cluster in a 6-inch, with high power.

3372, Δ309, Carinæ, 10h 43m·0, −59° 25′. The 'Keyhole Nebula,' a diffused branching nebula round η Argûs. Gaseous.

3532, Δ323 „ 11h 4m·3, −58° 24′. A magnificent cluster of stars from 8th-12th magnitude.

5139, ω, Centauri, 13h 23m·7, −47° 3′. A noble globular cluster. Like a tailless comet, nearly 4th mag. to the naked eye. It is 30′ in diameter, and contains thousands of 12th and 15th mag. stars.

4501, M88, Comæ Ber., 12h 29m·5, +14° 42′. A long, bright nebula, 5′ × 2′, with bright centre and condensations. Many nebulæ in this region.

4565, H.V 24, „ 12h 33m·9, +26° 16′. A much elongated nebula, 15′ × 1′, with bright centre, and dark longitudinal centre streak. The largest edgewise Spiral.

4826, M64 „ 12h 54m·3, +21° 57′. The 'Black-eye Nebula.' A bright, oval nebula, with a dark central area of absorbing matter, visible in large telescopes.

3242, H.IV 27 Hydræ 10h 22m·3, −18° 23′. Planetary nebula, 40″ × 35″, with brighter inner ring. Pale blue tint. 2° S. of μ.

3587, M97 Ursæ Majoris 11h 11m·8, +55° 17′. The 'Owl Nebula.' A large, faint planetary nebula, 3′ in diameter. Large aperture, low power and clear night are required for a good view.

* γ *Virginis.* A fine binary star with a period of about 180 years. Its orbit is very eccentric. In 1780 its distance was 5″·7. It closed up till in 1836 (0″·3–0″·5 *d.*), it appeared single in all but the Great Dorpat refractor (9½-in. aperture), which elongated the star. The pair then widened, becoming an easy telescopic object, and reaching its widest (6″·2) about 1920. It is now (1939) slowly closing, and will again appear single, except in large instruments, about the year 2016.

† η *Carinæ.* It was seen as a 4th magnitude star by Halley in 1677, and oscillated between that magnitude and 2nd till 1814, when it began to rise, reaching 1st magnitude in 1827. It fell to 2nd magnitude for about 5 years, rose to mag. 0 in 1838, outshining *Rigel*, faded somewhat, and then, in 1843, became mag. −1·0, about as bright as *Canopus.* From that maximum it declined till it became invisible to the naked eye about 1866-68, 7th mag. 1870. Since then it has not changed much in brightness. It has a peculiar spectrum with bright lines, and should, perhaps, be classed with the Novæ.

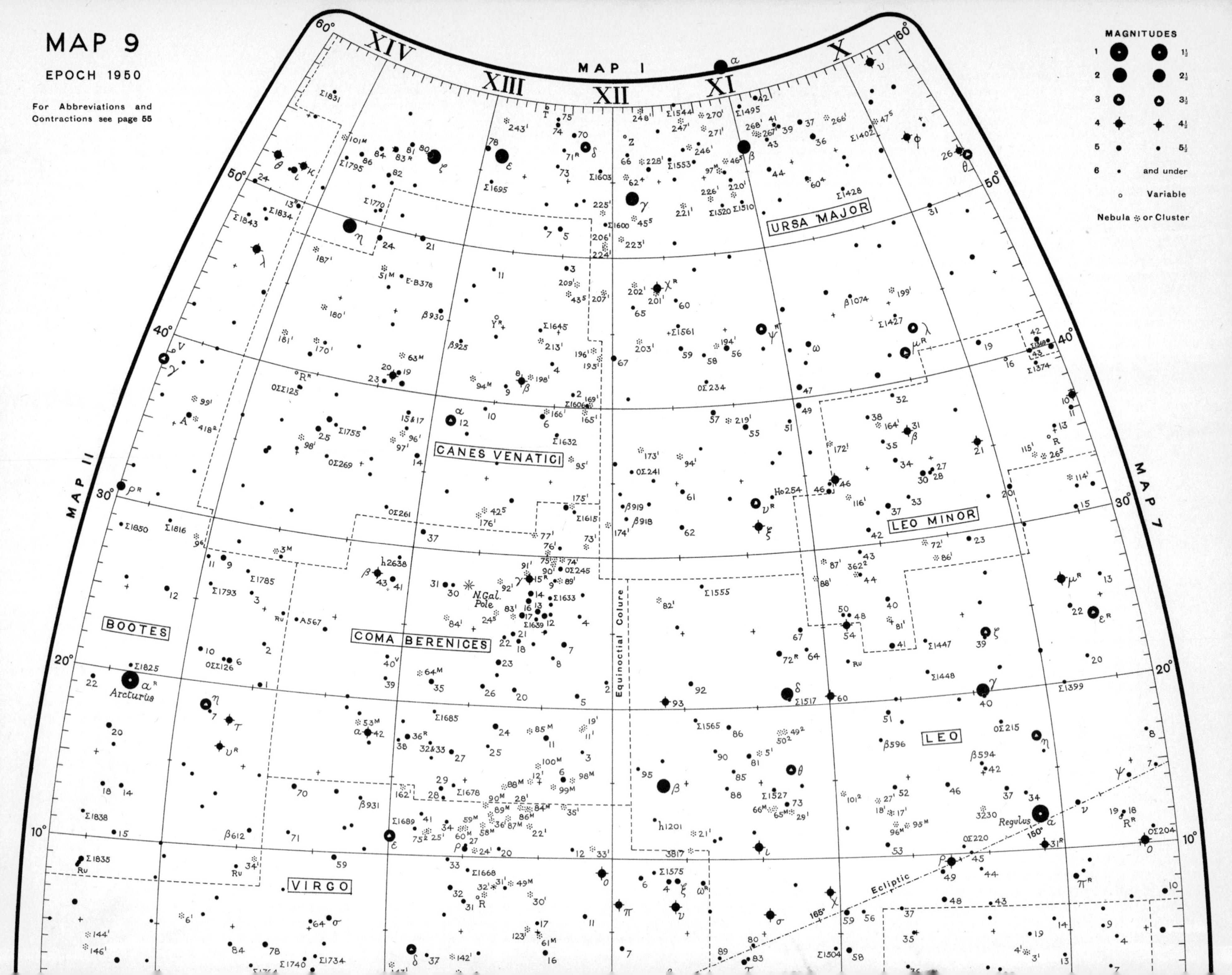

MAP 9
EPOCH 1950
For Abbreviations and Contractions see page 55
MAGNITUDES
1 1½
2 2½
3 3½
4 4½
5 5½
6 and under
Variable
Nebula or Cluster
MAP I
MAP II
MAP 7
XIV
XIII
XII
XI
X
URSA MAJOR
CANES VENATICI
LEO MINOR
COMA BERENICES
BOOTES
LEO
VIRGO
N.Gal. Pole
Arcturus
Regulus
Equinoctial Colure
Ecliptic

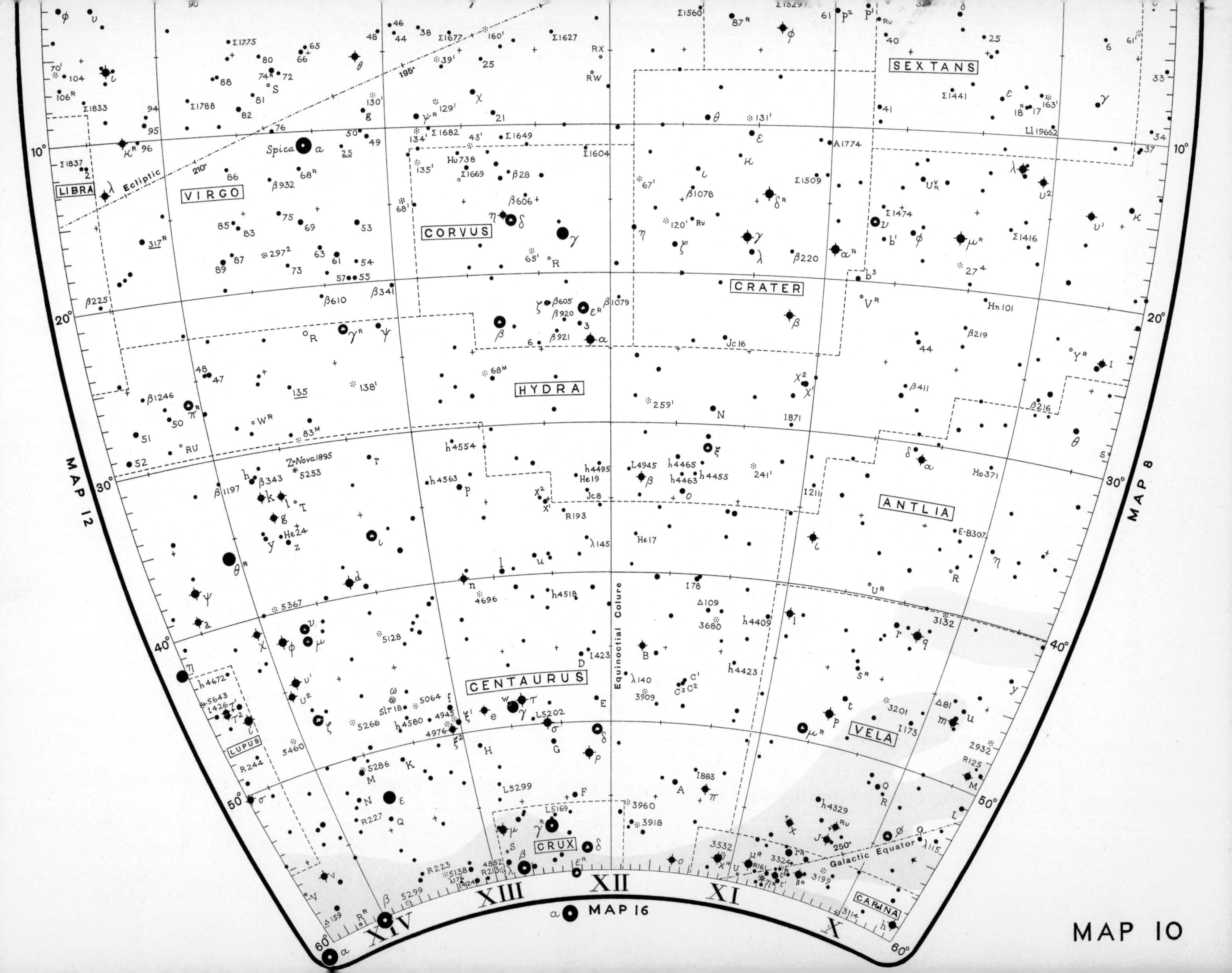
SEXTANS
CRATER
HYDRA
CORVUS
VIRGO
LIBRA
ANTLIA
CENTAURUS
VELA
CRUX
CARINA
LUPUS
Spica
Ecliptic
Equinoctial Colure
Galactic Equator
MAP 8
MAP 12
MAP 16
X
XI
XII
XIII
XIV
MAP 10

INTERESTING OBJECTS. MAPS 11 & 12.

(R.A. XIV. HRS. TO XVIII. HRS. DEC. 60° N. TO 60° S.).

Double Stars.

EPOCH 1950.

		R.A.	Dec.	Mags.	*P.A.*	Dist.	Date	Notes
κ	Boötis	$14^{h}11^{m}{\cdot}7$	+52° 1′	5·1, 7·2	237°	13″·2	1925	Little change.
ι	,,	14 14·4	+51 36	4·9, 7·5	33°	38″·4	1922	Relatively fixed.
Σ1835	,,	14 20·9	+ 8 40	5·5, 6·8	190°	6″·4	1925	*Comes* a close binary. Period 40½ years.
π	,,	14 38·4	+16 38	4·9, 6·0	106°	5″·8	1936	*P.A.* slowly increasing. Probably a physical pair.
ζ	,,	14 38·8	+13 57	4·4, 4·8	133°	1″·1	1936	Binary with very eccentric orbit. *P.* 130 yrs.
ε	,,	14 42·8	+27 17	3·0, 6·3	334°	2″·8	1931	{ *Pulcherrima* of Struve. Yellow and blue. *P.A.* slowly increasing. Test for 2-inch.
39	,,	14 48·0	+48 55	5·8, 6·5	45°	3″·3	1922	... ...
ξ	,,	14 49·0	+19 19	4·8, 6·8	13°	4″·8	1937	Binary, *P.* 152 yrs. *d.* increasing to 7″·2 in 1982.
44	,,	15 2·2	+47 50	5·2, 6·1	248°	2″·6	1937	Binary. *P.* 205 years. Highly inclined orbit.
δ	,,	15 13·5	+33 30	3·2, 7·4	79°	105″	1923	No change since 1822. [Closing.
μ^2	,,	15 22·7	+37 32	6·7, 7·3	36°	1″·8	1938	Binary. Period about 230 years. μ^1 at 109″ *d.*
L5893	Centauri	14 19·0	−58 14	4·9, 6·9	161°	9″·6	1913	= Δ159. Relatively fixed.
η	Coronæ Bor.	15 21·1	+30 28	5·2, 5·7	288°	0″·4	1937	Binary. *P.* 42 yrs. Widening to 1″·1 in 1950.
ζ	,,	15 37·5	+36 48	4·0, 4·9	304°	6″·3	1925	Beautiful object. Little change.
σ	,,	16 12·8	+33 59	5·0, 6·1	224°	5″·5	1937	Binary. Very long period.
17	Draconis	16 35·0	+53 2	5·0, 6·0	111°	3″·5	1925	16 Draconis, 5·0 mag., 90″·4 distant.
μ	,,	17 4·3	+54 32	5·0, 5·1	102°	2″·3	1938	Binary of very long period. *P.A.* decreasing.
ν	,,	17 31·2	+55 13	4·6, 4·6	312°	61″·9	1924	ν^1 and ν^2. *c.p.m.* Fine object.
κ	Herculis	16 5·8	+17 11	5·0, 6·0	12°	29″·5	1925	Little change since 1822.
ζ	,,	16 39·4	+31 41	3·0, 6·5	234°	0″·8	1935	Binary. Period 34 years. Widest 1″·6, 1954.
Σ2107	,,	16 49·8	+28 45	6·5, 8·0	50°	0″·9	1930	Long period binary. Widening since 1900.
α	,,	17 12·4	+14 27	3·0, 6·1	112°	4″·4	1934	Orange and green; A is variable. Little change.
δ	,,	17 13·0	+24 54	3·0, 7·5	208°	11″·0	1928	An optical pair. Distance diminishing.
ρ	,,	17 22·0	+37 11	4·0, 5·1	315°	3″·8	1926	Very slow increase of *P.A.*
Σ2215	,,	17 44·9	+17 43	5·9, 7·9	289°	0″·8	1924	*P.A.* slowly decreasing.
90	,,	17 51·7	+40 1	5·9, 9·2	123°	1″·7	1924	Gold and blue.
95	,,	17 59·4	+21 36	4·9, 4·9	259°	6″·2	1936	Very little change in either *P.A.* or distance.
μ	Libræ	14 46·6	−13 57	5·4, 6·3	348°	1″·8	1936	Test for 2½-inch telescope.
π	Lupi	15 1·7	−46 51	4·7, 4·8	78°	1″·5	1934	*P.A.* decreasing.
μ	,,	15 15·0	−47 42	4·8, 5·2	150°	1″·6	1925	*P.A.* decreasing. 7·2 mag. star 24″ *sf.*
ρ	Ophiuchi	16 22·6	−23 20	5·7, 6·4	350°	3″·4	1924	Binary.
λ	,,	16 28·4	+ 2 6	4·0, 6·1	181°	0″·5	1938	Binary. Period 135 years. Closest in 1945.
21	,,	16 48·9	+ 1 18	6·0, 8·0	148°	0″·8	1926	Test for 6-inch telescope. [tance.
A, 36	,,	17 12·3	−26 30	5·6, 5·7	180°	4″·3	1925	Binary of very long period; slow change of dis-
39	,,	17 15·0	−24 14	5·5, 6·0	355°	10″·8	1925	Orange and blue. Fixed optical pair.
τ	,,	18 0·4	− 8 11	5·0, 5·7	266°	2″·0	1936	Binary. Period 224 years.
ξ	Scorpii	16 1·6	−11 14	4·9, 5·2	205°	1″·2	1937	Binary. *P.* 44½ yrs. 7·2 mag. star at 7″·4, 1925.
β	,,	16 2·5	−19 40	2·9, 5·2	23°	13″·8	1925	A has a close *comes*, mag. 8·5, at 0″·8, 1927.
ν	,,	16 9·1	−19 21	4·2, 6·5	336°	41″·5	1925	Both A and B are close doubles.
σ	,,	16 18·1	−25 29	3·1, 7·8	272°	20″·3	1916	No change since 1822.
α	,,	16 26·5	−26 20	1·2, 6·8	275°	3″·0	1935	*Antares.* Red and green. No certain change.*
Σ1919	Serpentis	15 10·6	+19 28	6·1, 7·0	10°	24″·2	1936	Relatively fixed.
5	,,	15 16·8	+ 1 58	5·0, 10·0	37°	11″·0	1923	Very near the nebula M5.
δ	,,	15 32·4	+10 42	3·0, 4·0	181°	3″·6	1927	Binary. *P.A.* decreasing, distance increasing.
β	,,	15 43·9	+15 35	3·0, 9·2	265°	30″·8	1925	Relatively fixed. Test for 2½-inch.
Σ1833	Virginis	14 20·0	− 7 33	7·0, 7·0	174°	5″·9	1926	Little relative motion.
φ	,,	14 25·6	− 2 0	5·2, 9·7	110°	4″·7	1924	Test for 3-inch telescope.

INTERESTING OBJECTS. MAPS 11 & 12—*Continued.*

(R.A. XIV. HRS. TO XVIII. HRS. DEC. 60° N. TO 60° S.).

Variable Stars.

EPOCH 1950.

	R.A.	Dec.	Var. of mag.	Spectrum	Period	Notes
R Boötis	$14^h\ 35^m{\cdot}0$	+26° 52′	6·0 - 13·0	Me	222 days	Long period variable.
34, W ,,	14 41·2	+26 44	5·2 - 6·1	K5	...	Irregular variable.
R Centauri	14 13·0	- 59 41	5·3 - 13	Me	560 days	Long period variable.
S Coronæ Bor.	15 19·3	+31 33	6·1 - 12	Me	361 ,,	,, ,,
R ,,	15 46·4	+28 19	5·8 - 12·5	Pec	...	Irregular variable.†
T ,,	15 57·4	+26 4	2·0 - 9·5	Pec	...	,, ,, ‡
30, g Herculis	16 27·0	+41 59	4·7 - 6·0	M2	...	,, ,,
S ,,	16 49·7	+15 2	5·9 - 12·5	Me	300 days	Long period variable.
α ,,	17 12·4	+14 27	3·1 - 3·9	M2	...	Irregular variable.
68, u ,,	17 15·5	+33 9	4·8 - 5·4	B3	2·05 days	β Lyræ type.
δ Libræ	14 58·3	- 8 19	4·8 - 6·2	A0	2·33 ,,	Algol type.
U Ophiuchi	17 14·0	+ 1 16	5·7 - 6·7	B8	1·68 ,,	,, ,,
Y ,,	17 50·0	- 6 8	6·1 - 6·5	G0	17·1 ,,	Cepheid type.
X Sagittarii	17 44·5	-27 49	4·3 - 5·0	F8	7·01 ,,	,, ,,
RR Scorpii	16 53·4	-30 30	5·6 - 11·3	Me	279 ,,	Long period variable.
R Serpentis	15 48·4	+15 17	5·5 - 13·4	Me	357 ,,	Long period variable.

Nebulæ and Clusters. (Maps 11 and 12) *(Unlettered Nos. are those of the N.G.C.)*

6205, M13, Herculis, $16^h\ 39^m{\cdot}9$, +36° 33′. The 'Great Cluster in Hercules'—a grand globular cluster of thousands of stars, just visible to the naked eye, about ⅓ the distance from η to ζ. Centrally resolved in 6-inch telescope.

6210, Σ5N ,, $16^h\ 42^m{\cdot}4$, +23° 54′. A small, bright, planetary nebula, with a bluish disc about 8″ in diameter, and surrounded by a faint glow. *sp* 51 Herculis.

6341, M92 ,, $17^h\ 15^m{\cdot}6$, +43° 12′. A very fine globular cluster, about 8′ in diameter, resembling M13, but smaller and closer. It forms a triangle with π and η.

6067, Δ360, Normæ, $16^h\ 9^m{\cdot}4$, - 54° 5′. A large rich cluster, 20′ in diameter, composed of stars of 10th-15th magnitude.

6273, M19, Ophiuchi, $16^h\ 59^m{\cdot}5$, - 26° 12′. A fine globular cluster, 5′ in diameter. Very low in the latitude of British Isles.

6494, M23, Sagittarii, $17^h\ 54^m{\cdot}0$, - 19° 1′. An open cluster, 47′ in diameter, with stars of 9th-13th mag. Fine low power field.

6093, M80, Scorpii, $16^h\ 14^m{\cdot}1$, - 22° 51′. A bright, and much condensed globular cluster. A mass of faint stars.

6121, M4 ,, $16^h\ 20^m{\cdot}5$, - 26° 24′. Easily resolved cluster of rather faint stars, 13′ in diameter.

6405, M6 ,, $17^h\ 36^m{\cdot}7$, - 32° 10′. A most beautiful open cluster of stars 'like a butterfly with open wings.'

6475, M7 ,, $17^h\ 50^m{\cdot}7$, - 34° 48′. A brilliant open cluster of bright stars, visible to the naked eye.

5904, M5, Serpentis, $15^h\ 15^m{\cdot}9$, + 2° 16′. A fine globular cluster, 15′ in diameter, composed of 11th-15th mag. stars, with much-compressed centre. Closely *np* 5 Serpentis.

* *Antares* was so named by the Greeks from its similarity to the ruddy Mars (Greek, Ares) in regard to colour. It is a very luminous 'super-giant' star (Spectrum M0), with a diameter of about 370,000,000 miles. Its *comes*, green in colour, is not usually seen except when atmospheric conditions are favourable.

† R *Coronæ Borealis.* For several years, sometimes as many as nine, this star remains at its normal brightness of about 6th magnitude. Then it decreases rapidly by several magnitudes to a minimum magnitude of 12·5. After a short time, or after several years, during which minor fluctuations occur, it rises again to its normal brightness.

‡ T *Coronæ Borealis*—the 'Blaze Star.' In May 1866 this star rose suddenly from 9·5 to 2nd magnitude. Nine days later it became invisible to the naked eye, and after a few weeks it fell to the 9th magnitude. It revived to 7th magnitude and then decreased to 9·5 and after being invisible to the naked eye for nearly 80 years, it rose to 3rd mag. on Feb. 8, 1946, but again faded rapidly.

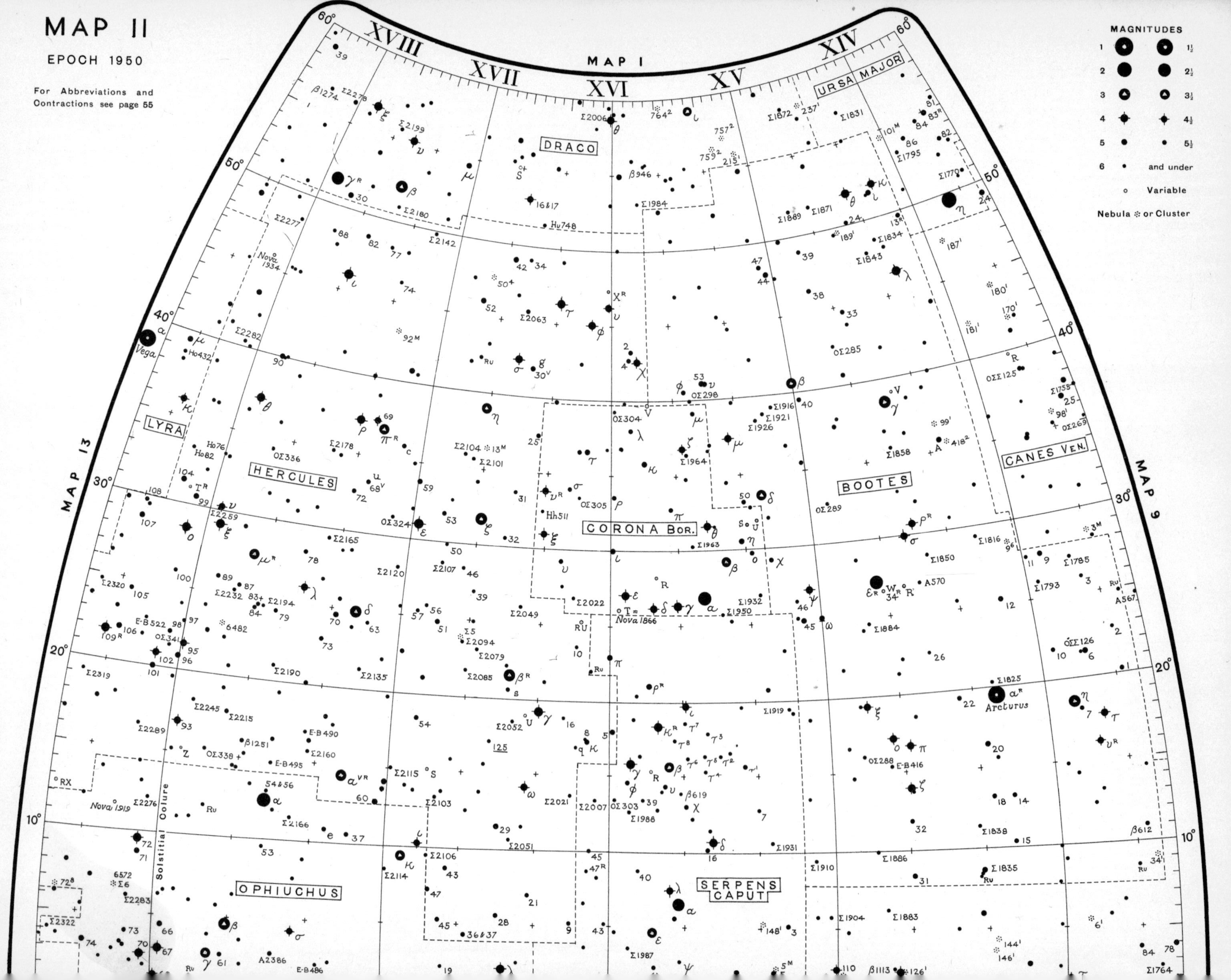
MAP II
EPOCH 1950
For Abbreviations and Contractions see page 55
MAGNITUDES
1 1½
2 2½
3 3½
4 4½
5 5½
6 and under
Variable
Nebula or Cluster
MAP I
MAP 9
MAP 13
XVIII
XVII
XVI
XV
XIV
DRACO
URSA MAJOR
LYRA
HERCULES
CORONA BOR.
BOOTES
CANES VEN.
OPHIUCHUS
SERPENS CAPUT
Vega
Arcturus
Nova 1934
Nova 1866
Nova 1919
Solstitial Colure

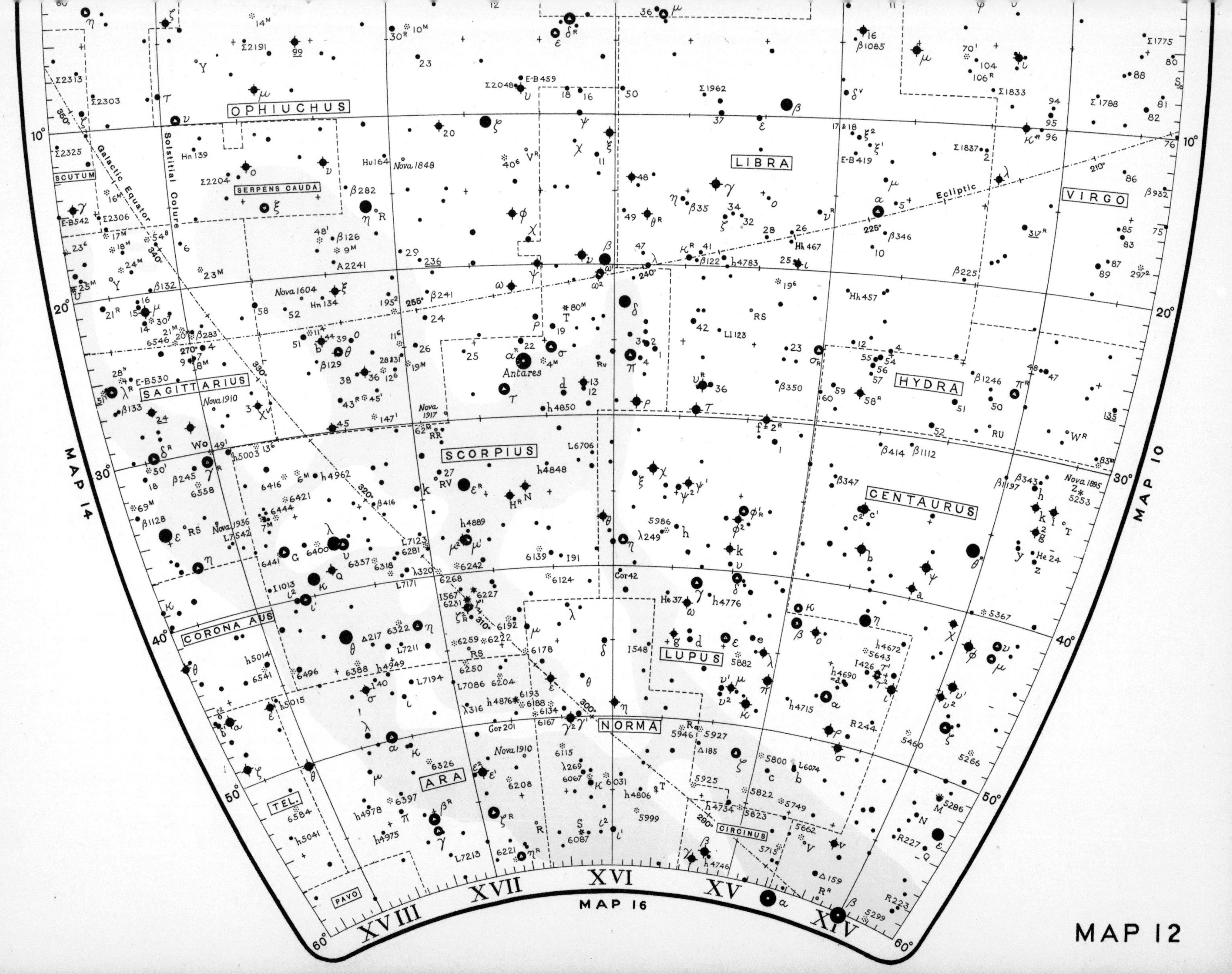
OPHIUCHUS
LIBRA
VIRGO
SERPENS CAUDA
SCUTUM
SAGITTARIUS
HYDRA
SCORPIUS
Antares
CENTAURUS
CORONA AUS
LUPUS
NORMA
ARA
TEL.
CIRCINUS
PAVO
Ecliptic
Galactic Equator
Solstitial Colure
Nova 1848
Nova 1604
Nova 1910
Nova 1917
Nova 1936
Nova 1885
MAP 14
MAP 10
MAP 16
XVIII
XVII
XVI
XV
XIV
MAP 12

INTERESTING OBJECTS. MAPS 13 & 14.

(R.A. XVIII. HRS. TO XXII. HRS. DEC. 60°N. TO 60°S.).

Double Stars.

EPOCH 1950.

		R.A.	Dec.	Mags.	*P.A.*	Dist.	Date	Notes
12	Aquarii	21ʰ 1ᵐ·4	− 6° 1′	6·0, 8·1	192°	2″·8	1924	Test for 2-inch telescope.
Σ2404	Aquilæ	18 48·4	+10 55	5·8, 7·0	182°	3″·4	1936	Relatively fixed.
11	,,	18 56·8	+13 33	5·7, 9·2	275°	16″·2	1925	Optical pair. Test for 2-inch telescope.
23	,,	19 16·0	+ 1 0	5·5, 9·5	8°	3″·4	1920	*Comes* best seen with high power.
Σ2532	,,	19 27·7	+ 2 48	6·0, 10·2	4°	33″·5	1923	Light-test for 2½-inch telescope.
π	,,	19 46·4	+11 41	6·0, 6·8	113°	1″·4	1937	Little change. Test for 3-inch telescope.
α^1, α^2	Capricorni	20 14·9	−12 40	3·2, 4·2	291°	376″	...	Naked eye pair. α^1, 9 mag. *comes* at 45″.
α^2	,,	20 15·3	−12 42	3·8, 11·0	158°	7″·1	1924	B is a close double. Test for 6-inch.
π	,,	20 24·5	−18 22	5·1, 8·7	145°	3″·4	1926	Relatively fixed.
ρ	,,	20 26·0	−17 59	5·0, 7·8	168°	2″·2	1925	Distance and *P.A.* slowly decreasing.
o	,,	20 27·0	−18 45	6·3, 6·8	239°	21″·9	1923	Relatively fixed. *c.p.m.*
Σ2780	Cephei	21 10·5	+59 47	6·0, 7·0	219°	1″·1	1933	Test for 4-inch. *P.A.* slowly decreasing.
h5014	CoronæAus.	18 3·2	−43 26	5·8, 5·8	221°	1″·6	1933	Binary, period about 200 years.
κ	,,	18 29·9	−38 46	6·0, 6·6	359°	21″·6	1913	Relatively fixed.
γ	,,	19 3·1	−37 8	5·0, 5·0	67°	2″·4	1935	Binary, period about 120 years. Test for 2-in.
Σ2486	Cygni	19 10·8	+49 45	6·0, 6·5	216°	8″·9	1926	Beautiful field. *c.p.m.*
β	,,	19 28·7	+27 51	3·0, 5·3	55°	34″·6	1924	Yellow and blue. Grand contrast.
16	,,	19 40·6	+50 24	5·1, 5·3	134°	38″·5	1924	*c.p.m.*
δ	,,	19 43·5	+45 0	3·0, 7·9	263°	1″·9	1936	Long period binary, 321 years. Test for 4-in.
ψ	,,	19 54·4	+52 18	5·0, 7·5	179°	3″·1	1927	Slow decrease of *P.A.* and distance.
Σ2671	,,	20 17·2	+55 14	6·0, 7·4	338°	3″·4	1924	Test for 2-inch telescope.
49	,,	20 39·0	+32 8	6·0, 8·1	46°	2″·8	1925	Yellow and blue.
52	,,	20 43·6	+30 32	4·0, 9·2	65°	6″·4	1925	In the branching nebula 6960.
Σ2741	,,	20 56·9	+50 16	6·0, 7·3	31°	2″·1	1926	Test for 2½-inch telescope.
61	,,	21 4·4	+38 28	5·3, 5·9	134°	25″·1	1928	Distance increasing from 16″, 1780.*
τ	,,	21 12·8	+37 49	3·8, 8·0	160°	0″·9	1926	Binary, period 49 years.
γ	Delphini	20 44·4	+15 57	4·0, 5·0	270°	10″·4	1931	Yellow and emerald.
39	Draconis	18 23·2	+58 46	4·7, 7·7, 7·1	353° 21°	3″·8 89″·2	1926	Triple star.
ϵ, 1	Equulei	20 56·6	+ 4 6	5·7, 7·0, 7·1	322° 72°	0″·2 10″·9	1925	Triple. A + B form a close binary. *P.* 101 yrs.
100	Herculis	18 5·8	+26 5	5·9, 5·9	183°	14″·1	1923	Two faint *comites.*
Σ2289	,,	18 7·9	+16 28	6·0, 7·1	225°	1″·2	1936	Decreasing *P.A.*
θ	Indi	21 16·3	−53 40	4·7, 7·1	279°	5″·4	1936	*P.A.* decreasing, distance increasing.
α	Lyræ	18 35·2	+38 44	0·2, 10·5	169°	56″·4	1925	*Vega.* An optical pair. Distance increasing.
ϵ^1	,,	18 42·7	+39 37	4·6, 6·3	5°	2″·9	1935	{ The "Double-double." ϵ^1 and ϵ^2 are at 208″
ϵ^2	,,	18 42·7	+39 34	4·9, 5·2	111°	2″·3	1935	{ distance; each is a binary.
ζ	,,	18 43·0	+37 33	4·2, 5·5	150°	43″·7	1924	Relatively fixed.
η	,,	19 12·0	+39 3	4·0, 8·1	83°	28″·2	1925	Three other small pairs in a low power field.
70	Ophiuchi	18 2·9	+ 2 32	4·3, 6·0	118°	6″·6	1937	Binary, *P.* 88 yrs. Widest 6″·7, 1933. Closing.
Σ2276	,,	18 3·4	+12 0	6·0, 7·0	258°	7″·1	1924	Relatively fixed.
κ	Pegasi	21 42·4	+25 25	3·9, 10·8	296°	12″·9	1924	A is an extremely close binary. *P.* 11·4 years.
κ^2	Sagittarii	20 20·5	−42 35	6·0, 7·3	228°	1″·1	1936	*P.A.* increasing.
59	Serpentis	18 24·6	+ 0 10	5·5, 7·8	317°	3″·9	1921	Relatively fixed.
Σ2375	,,	18 43·0	+ 5 26	6·2, 6·6	116°	2″·4	1936	Test for 2½-inch telescope.
θ	,,	18 53·7	+ 4 8	4·0, 4·2	103°	22″·3	1926	Fine pair. *c.p.m.*

INTERESTING OBJECTS. MAPS 13 & 14—*Continued.*

(R.A. XVIII. HRS. TO XXII. HRS. DEC. 60° N. TO 60° S.).

Variable Stars.

EPOCH 1950.

		R.A.	Dec.	Var. of mag.	Spectrum	Period	Notes
R	Aquilæ	19h 4m·0	+ 8° 9′	5·8 - 12·0	Me	310 days	Long period variable.
U	„	19 26·6	− 7 9	6·2 - 6·9	G0	7·02 „	Cepheid type.
η	„	19 50·0	+ 0 53	3·7 - 4·5	G0	7·18 „	„ „
μ	Cephei	21 41·9	+58 33	3·7 - 4·7	M1	...	Irregular variable.
SU	Cygni	19 42·8	+29 8	6·2 - 7·0	F5	3·8 days	Short period variable.
χ	„	19 48·6	+32 48	4·2 - 13·7	Mep	409 „	Long period. Mira type.
X	„	20 41·5	+35 25	5·9 - 7·0	F5p	16·4 „	Short period variable.
W	„	21 34·1	+45 9	5·0 - 6·7	M3	132 „	Long period variable.
β	Lyræ	18 48·2	+33 18	3·4 - 4·1	B2p	12·91 „	The typical Lyrid variable.†
R	„	18 53·9	+43 53	4·0 - 4·7	M2	46·4 „	Irregular variable.
S	Sagittæ	19 53·8	+16 30	5·4 - 6·1	G0	8·38 „	Cepheid type.
W	Sagittarii	18 1·8	−29 35	4·8 - 5·8	F5	7·59 „	„ „
Y	„	18 18·5	−18 53	5·4 - 6·5	G0	5·77 „	„ „
R	Scuti	18 44·9	− 5 46	4·7 - 7·8	G5p	...	Irregular variable.
T	Vulpeculæ	20 49·3	+28 3	5·2 - 6·4	F8	4·44 days	Cepheid type.

Nebulæ and Clusters. (Maps 13 and 14) *(Unlettered Nos. are those of the N.G.C.)*

7009, H.IV 1, Aquarii, 21h 1m·4, −11° 34′. The 'Saturn Nebula.' A very bright, bluish, planetary nebula, 25″ × 17″. The thin rays or ansae are seen with large telescopes only. Precedes ν.

7089, M2 „ 21h 30m·9, − 1° 4′. A globular cluster about 7′ in diameter. A fine object in large telescopes.

7092, M39, Cygni, 21h 30m·5, +48° 13′. A large, open cluster of bright stars, well seen with low powers.

6720, M57, Lyræ, 18h 52m·0, +32° 58′. The 'Ring Nebula.' ⅓ the distance from β towards γ. An oval, planetary, 80″ × 60″, which bears magnifying well. A faint star *f* is seen in a 4-inch. The fainter central star is visible in large instruments only.

6572, Σ6, Ophiuchi, 18h 10m·2, + 6° 50′. A small, but extremely bright, elliptical planetary nebula, 7″ in diameter, of a bluish colour. It is, perhaps, the brightest of its kind.

7078, M15, Pegasi, 21h 27m·6, +11° 57′. A grand, bright, condensed globular cluster, 6′ in diameter, blazing in the centre.

6523, M8, Sagittarii, 18h 0m·6, −24° 23′. The 'Lagoon Nebula,' visible to the naked eye. An ill-defined nebulosity with dark patches and stars, followed by an irregular open cluster.

6618, M17 „ 18h 18m·0, −16° 12′. The 'Omega' (Ω) or 'Horseshoe' Nebula. A bright and large nebula, in shape something like a figure 2, with a long, bright bottom streak.

6656, M22 „ 18h 33m·3 −23° 57′. A large, bright, globular cluster, about 15′ in diameter, between μ and σ. The larger stars are ruddy.

6705, M11, Scuti, 18h 48m·2, − 6° 20′. A grand, fan-shaped cluster, with bright star at apex. Dark structures to the south.

6853, M27, Vulpeculæ, 19h 57m·4, +22° 35′. The 'Dumb-bell Nebula.' An ellipse with faintly luminous notches. Seven stars—probably unconnected—are visible in a 10-inch instrument.

* 61 *Cygni.* The first star to have its parallax determined, by Bessel in 1838. The two stars probably form a long period binary system, since they have the same parallax, and the path of B relative to A is slightly concave.

† β *Lyræ.* The typical 'Lyrid' or 'Bright-eclipsing' variable. It has two unequal minima (mags. 3·8 and 4·1), separated by two equal maxima (mag. 3·4). The variations of light are due to the mutual eclipse of two unequally bright stars, very close together, and ellipsoidal in shape as the result of tidal distortion. Period 12·91 days.

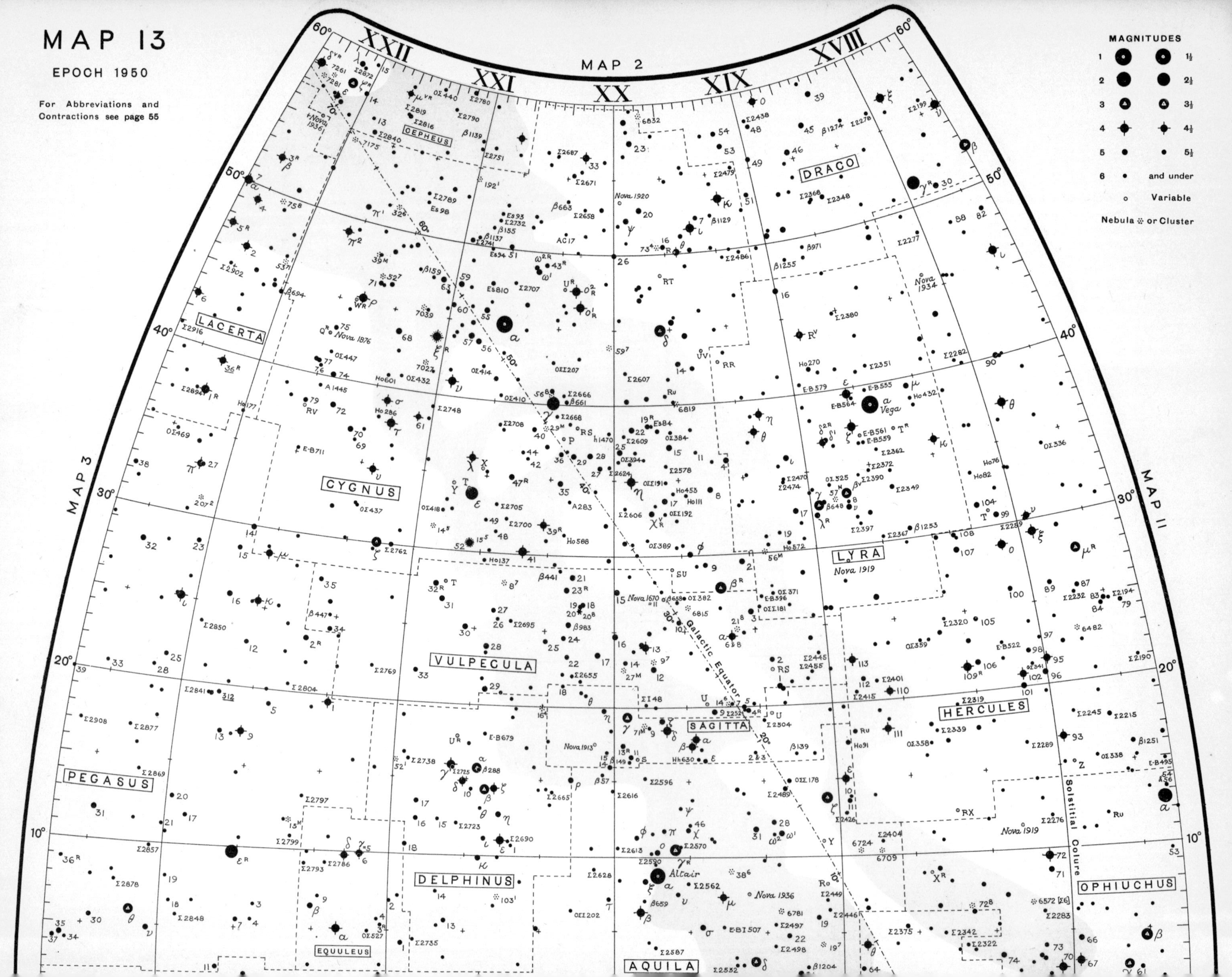
MAP 13
EPOCH 1950
For Abbreviations and Contractions see page 55
MAGNITUDES
1
1½
2
2½
3
3½
4
4½
5
5½
6
and under
Variable
Nebula or Cluster
MAP 2
MAP 3
MAP 11
XXII
XXI
XX
XIX
XVIII
60°
50°
40°
30°
20°
10°
CEPHEUS
LACERTA
CYGNUS
DRACO
LYRA
VULPECULA
SAGITTA
HERCULES
PEGASUS
DELPHINUS
EQUULEUS
AQUILA
OPHIUCHUS
Vega
Altair
Nova 1876
Nova 1920
Nova 1934
Nova 1919
Nova 1670
Nova 1913
Nova 1936
Galactic Equator
Solstitial Colure

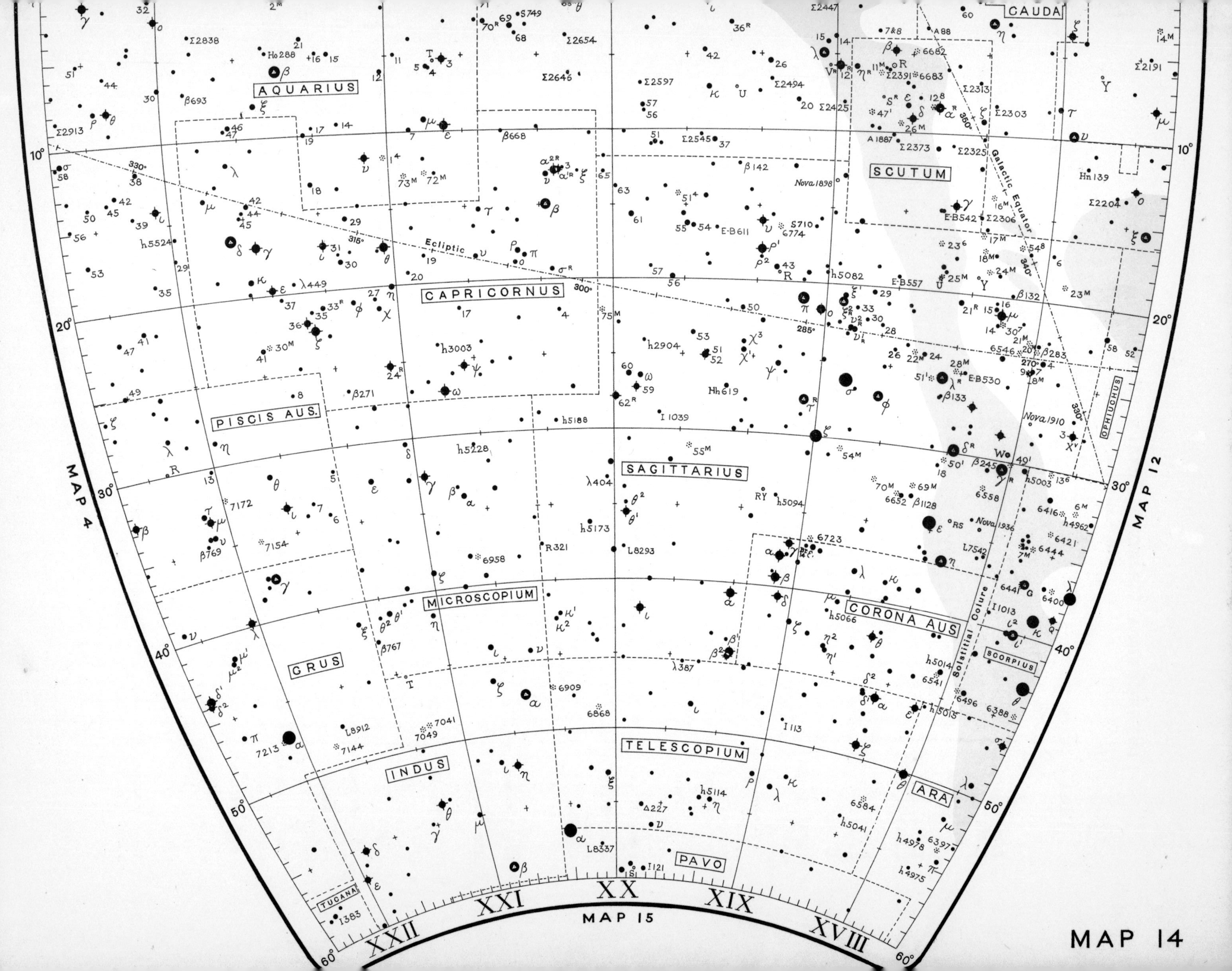

MAP 14
MAP 12
MAP 4
MAP 15
AQUARIUS
CAPRICORNUS
PISCIS AUS.
SAGITTARIUS
SCUTUM
CAUDA
OPHIUCHUS
MICROSCOPIUM
GRUS
CORONA AUS
TELESCOPIUM
INDUS
PAVO
ARA
SCORPIUS
TUCANA
Ecliptic
Galactic Equator
Solstitial Colure
Nova 1898
Nova 1910
Nova 1936
XXII
XXI
XX
XIX
XVIII

INTERESTING OBJECTS. MAPS 15 & 16. (S. OF −60° DEC.)

(CIRCUMPOLAR, SOUTH).

Double Stars.

EPOCH 1950.

Star	Constellation	R.A.	Dec.	Mags.	*P.A.*	Dist.	Date	Notes
I236	Apodis	$14^{h}48^{m}$·1	−73° 0′	5·7, 8·5	107°	1″·9	1926	*P.A.* increasing.
L7507	„	18 6·3	−73 41	5·9, 9·5	242°	2″·0	1926	*P.A.* increasing.
C	Carinæ	8 14·5	−62 46	5·3, 8·0	64°	3″·8	1917	Little change, if any.
h4128	„	8 38·2	−60 9	6·4, 7·1	213°	1″·5	1934	*P.A.* and distance slowly decreasing.
L3846	„	9 17·6	−74 41	5·4, 10·5	343°	7″·0	1926	A is a close double; distance 0″·4, 1927.
h4213	„	9 24·3	−61 44	6·0, 9·4	327°	8″·8	1917	Relatively fixed.
υ	„	9 45·9	−64 50	3·2, 6·0	128°	5″·0	1926	*c.p.m.* Relatively fixed.
h4306	„	10 17·5	−64 25	7·0, 7·0	135°	2″·3	1918	Little change.
h4383	„	10 52·0	−70 27	6·6, 7·2	285°	1″·6	1917	Little change, if any.
R164	„	10 57·2	−61 3	6·4, 10·2	79°	3″·9	1927	Little change, if any.
Cor 33	Centauri	14 11·4	−61 28	6·7, 8·7	160°	3″·0	1920	= Cor. 167 (Innes).
α	„	14 36·6	−60 38	0·3, 1·7	310°	4″·1	1936	Splendid binary. *P.* 80 yrs., 2nd nearest star.
δ	Chamæleontis	10 45·2	−80 12	6·1, 6·4	68°	0″·5	1926	*P.A.* increasing.
ε	„	11 57·0	−77 57	5·4, 6·2	183°	1″·1	1922	Slowly increasing *P.A.*
α	Circini	14 38·5	−64 45	3·4, 8·8	235°	15″·8	1925	Yellow and red. *c.p.m.* *P.A.* slowly decreasing.
α	Crucis	12 23·7	−62 49	1·4, 1·9	119°	4″·7	1926	Relatively fixed. Test for 1-inch.
ι	„	12 42·7	−60 42	4·7, 7·8	27°	26″·4	1922	Decreasing *P.A.*
h3568	Hydri	3 9·0	−79 11	5·7, 7·7	224°	15″·4	1919	Relatively fixed.
h4432	Muscæ	11 21·4	−64 40	5·7, 6·5	300°	2″·5	1918	*P.A.* increasing slowly.
L4920	„	11 49·4	−64 56	5·2, 7·8	159°	1″·8	1915	... ...
h4498	„	12 3·8	−65 26	6·2, 7·9	61°	8″·7	1918	Little change, if any.
β	„	12 43·2	−67 49	3·9, 4·2	4°	1″·3	1934	*P.A.* increasing.
θ	„	13 4·9	−65 2	5·8, 8·0	186°	5″·7	1922	Relatively fixed.
h4813	Normæ	15 51·3	−60 2	6·1, 9·8	99°	3″·8	1927	Relatively fixed.
R38	Octantis	3 50·8	−85 26	6·7, 8·2	246°	2″·1	1914	No change since 1877.
λ	„	21 43·5	−82 57	5·5, 7·7	69°	3″·1	1926	*P.A.* decreasing.
ξ	Pavonis	18 18·6	−61 31	4·3, 8·1	154°	3″·5	1936	Little change. Colour contrast.
R314	„	18 43·6	−73 3	6·3, 8·7	269°	2″·0	1913	*P.A.* and distance increasing.
L8550	„	20 47·5	−62 37	5·8, 5·8	93°	2″·7	1926	= Rmk 26. *P.A.* slowly decreasing.
L8625	„	21 4·0	−73 22	5·8, 6·1	136°	8″·1	1901	A doubled by Innes 1898. Not seen, 1900.
I5	Pictoris	6 37·5	−61 28	6·4, 8·5	269°	2″·9	1925	*c.p.m.*
θ	Reticuli	4 17·1	−63 23	6·2, 8·0	4°	4″·5	1917	... ...
h3670	„	4 33·1	−62 56	5·9, 8·4	99°	32″·0	1917	Little change, if any.
L6477	Triang. Aus.	15 43·6	−65 17	6·4, 6·6	151°	2″·1	1926	= Rmk 20.
h4809	„	15 50·7	−60 36	6·5, 8·3	97°	1″·4	1924	= Sellors 11. h's *comites* 9th mag. at 43″ and [49″.
β	Tucanæ	0 29·3	−63 14	4·5, 4·5	170°	27″·1	1916	'Superb Object.' 6th mag. star at 0″·2, 1925.
κ	„	1 14·0	−69 9	5·1, 7·3	346°	5″·4	1920	Low power field includes I27, a close binary.
h3426	„	1 15·3	−66 40	6·3, 9·3	337°	2″·7	1920	*c.p.m.*
δ	„	22 23·8	−65 13	4·8, 8·1	282°	7″·0	1916	Relatively fixed. Colour contrast.
I340	„	22 49·0	−63 27	6·1, 9·1	6°	1″·1	1927	*P.A.* decreasing.
γ	Volantis	7 9·2	−70 25	3·9, 5·8	299°	13″·7	1922	No appreciable change.
h3997	„	7 36·4	−74 10	7·2, 7·3	117°	2″·0	1930	*P.A.* slowly increasing.
ζ	„	7 42·3	−72 29	3·9, 9·0	116°	16″·7	1917	Relatively fixed.
ε	„	8 7·8	−68 28	4·5, 8·0	22°	6″·1	1922	Little change. A is a spectroscopic binary.

Variable Stars.

EPOCH 1950.

		R.A.	Dec.	Var. of mag.	Spectrum	Period	Notes
θ	Apodis	$14^h\ 0^m{\cdot}5$	−76° 33′	5·1 - 6·6	M3	...	Irregular variable.
R	Carinæ	9 31·0	−62 34	4·5 - 10·0	Me	309 days	Long period variable.
l	„	9 43·9	−62 17	3·6 - 5·0	G0	35·5 „	Cepheid type.
S	„	10 7·8	−61 19	5·8 - 9·0	Me	149 „	Long period variable.
R	Doradûs	4 36·3	−62 10	5·7 - 6·8	M3	360 „	„ „
R	Muscæ	12 39·0	−69 8	6·5 - 7·6	G5	0·88 „	Short period variable.
κ	Pavonis	18 51·8	−67 18	4·0 - 5·5	F5	9·10 „	Cepheid type.

Nova.

Nova Pictoris, 1925. $6^h\ 35^m{\cdot}2$ −62° 35′.

Discovered by R. Watson, in South Africa, in the early morning of May 25th, 1925. From its magnitude of 2·3 on that date, it rose to mag. 1·7 on May 26th, but by next day had fallen to below 3rd mag. It then brightened again, reaching mag. 1·1 on June 9th, fell to mag. 4 on July 4th, and rose again to mag. 1·9 on August 9th. From that brightness it fell, with minor fluctuations of light, till on Dec. 25th it was about 6th mag. In 1935 it was about 9th mag., at which it had been for some years. In March, 1928, it was found to consist of two nebulous components about 0″·5 distant from centre to centre.

An examination of photographic plates, that had been taken before its discovery as a Nova, shewed that it had been of about 12th mag. (1911-1925), and had risen to 3rd mag. on April 13th, 1925.

The position of the Nova is about 7° from the N.E. edge of Nubecula Major and in Galactic Latitude −26°.

Nebulæ and Clusters. (Maps 15 and 16) *(Unlettered Nos. are those of the N.G.C.)*

2808, Δ265, Carinæ, $9^h\ 11^m{\cdot}0$, −64° 39′. A large, rich, globular cluster of 13th to 15th mag. stars 'like the finest dust,' 5′ in diameter. The centre is a blaze of closely-packed stars.

3766, Δ289, Centauri, $11^h\ 33^m{\cdot}9$, −61° 20′. A fine cluster, visible in a binocular, containing at least 200 stars of 8th to 13th magnitude.

4755, Δ301, Crucis, $12^h\ 50^m{\cdot}7$, −60° 5′. Surrounding κ Crucis, a fine red star. A brilliant and beautiful cluster of over 100 stars of various colours 'like a superb piece of jewellery.'

2070, Δ142, Doradûs, $5^h\ 39^m{\cdot}1$, −69° 9′. The 'Great Looped Nebula' round 30 Doradûs. A large and bright nebula, extremely complex in structure. It is visible to the naked eye in the larger Magellanic Cloud, or the Nubecula Major.

6752, Δ295, Pavonis, $19^h\ 6^m{\cdot}4$, −60° 4′. A large, bright, globular cluster, 18′ in diameter; stars from 11th to 16th mag.

6025, Δ304, Triang. Aus. $15^h\ 59^m{\cdot}4$, −60° 21′. A bright, open cluster of stars from the 7th magnitude downwards.

104, Δ18, Tucanæ, $0^h\ 21^m{\cdot}9$, −72° 22′. 47 Tucanæ. A most glorious cluster of 12th to 14th magnitude and fainter stars, the central portion being much compressed. Visible to the naked eye as a hazy 5th magnitude star near the Nubecula Minor.

362, Δ62, „ $1^h\ 0^m\ 7$, −71° 6′. A globular cluster, 10′ in diameter, of 13th to 14th magnitude stars, with a central blaze of closely-packed stars. It is just visible to the naked eye as a 6th magnitude star.

MAP 15

EPOCH 1950

For Abbreviations and Contractions see page 55

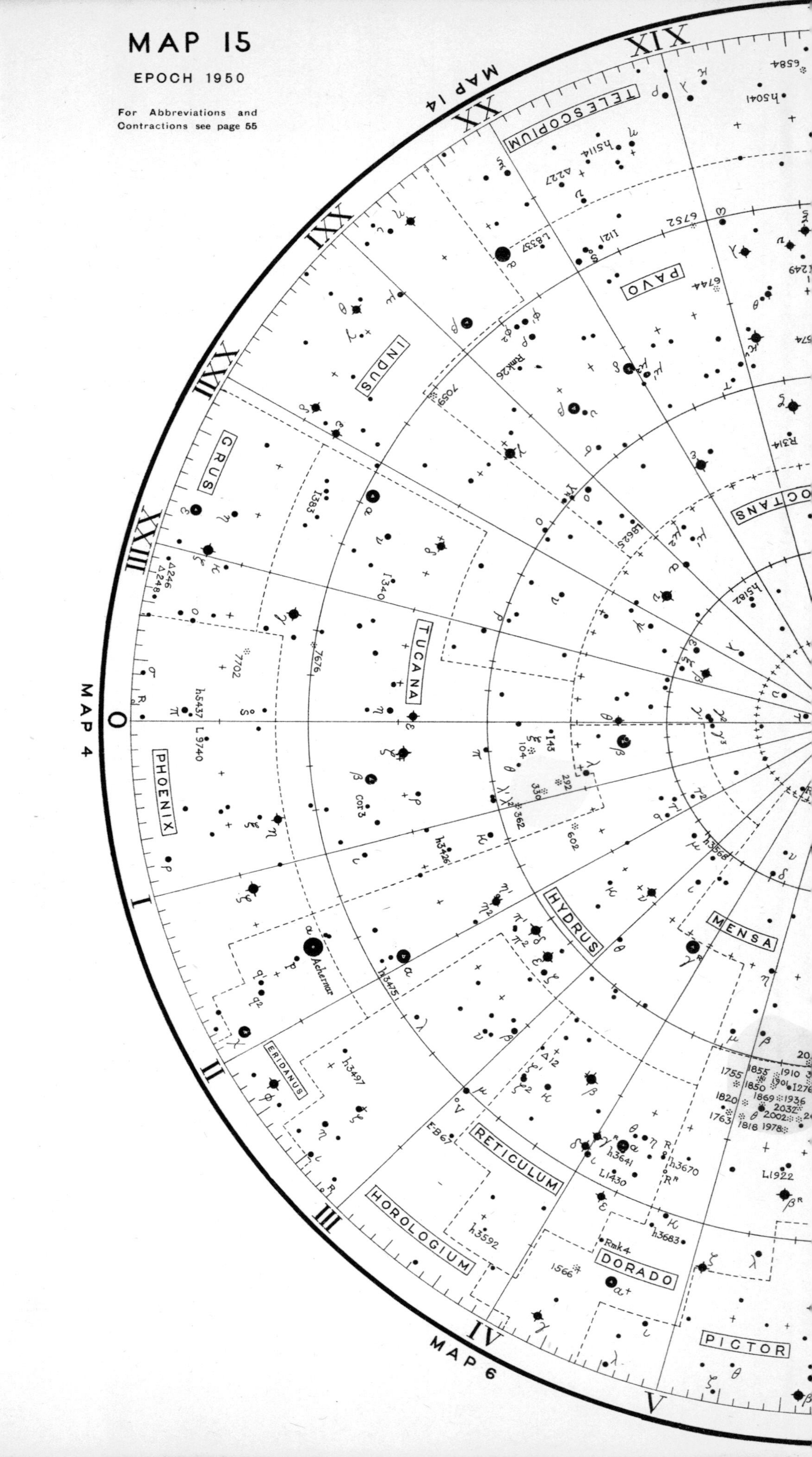

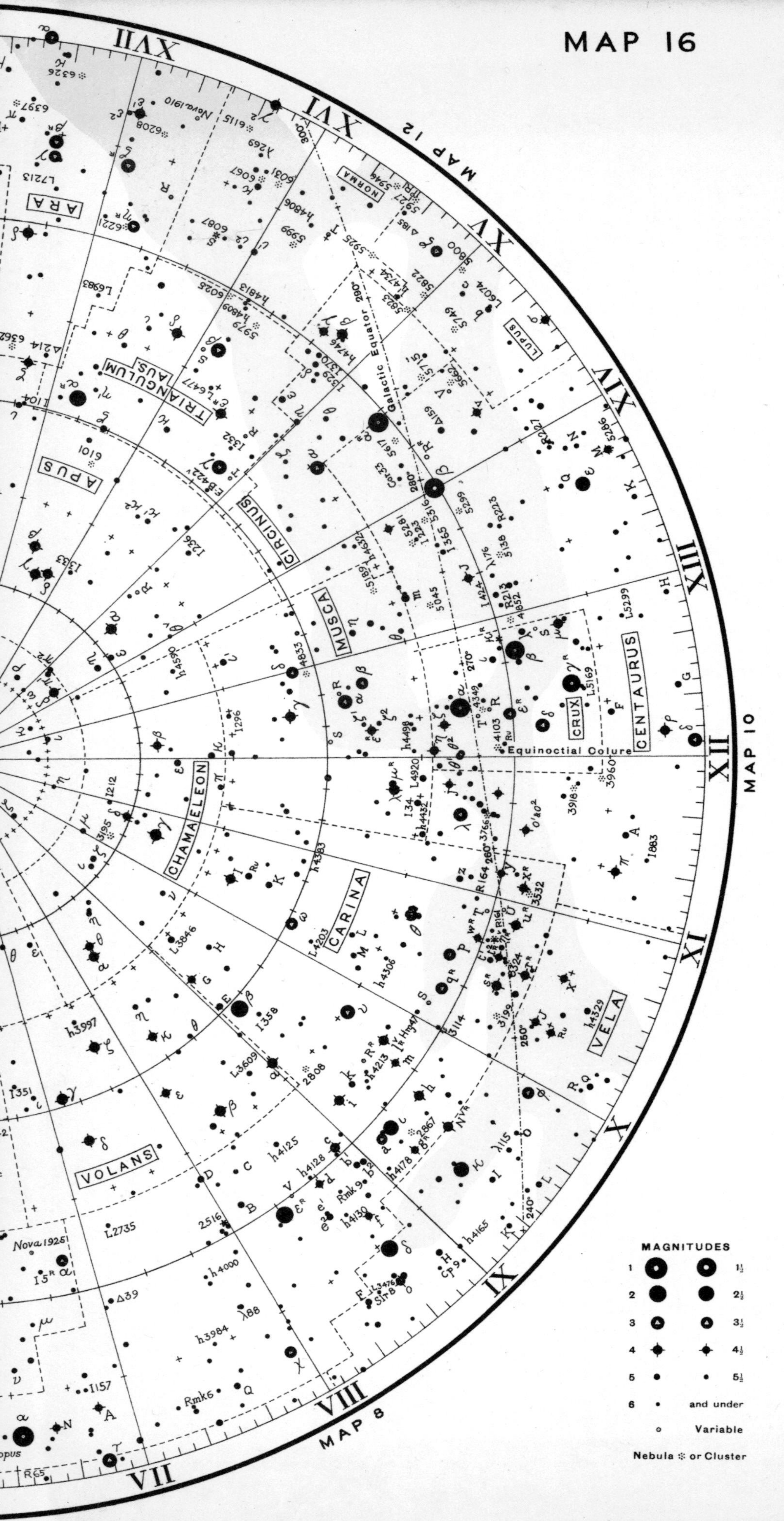

MAP 16
MAP 12
MAP 10
MAP 8
ARA
NORMA
LUPUS
TRIANGULUM AUS.
APUS
CIRCINUS
MUSCA
CRUX
CENTAURUS
CHAMAELEON
CARINA
VELA
VOLANS
Galactic Equator
Equinoctial Colure
Nova 1910
Nova 1925
XVII
XVI
XV
XIV
XIII
XII
XI
X
IX
VIII
VII
MAGNITUDES
1
1½
2
2½
3
3½
4
4½
5
5½
6
and under
Variable
Nebula or Cluster

GALACTIC CHART (Galactic Longitude 0° to 180°; Galactic Latitude 50°N. to 50°S.) MAP 17

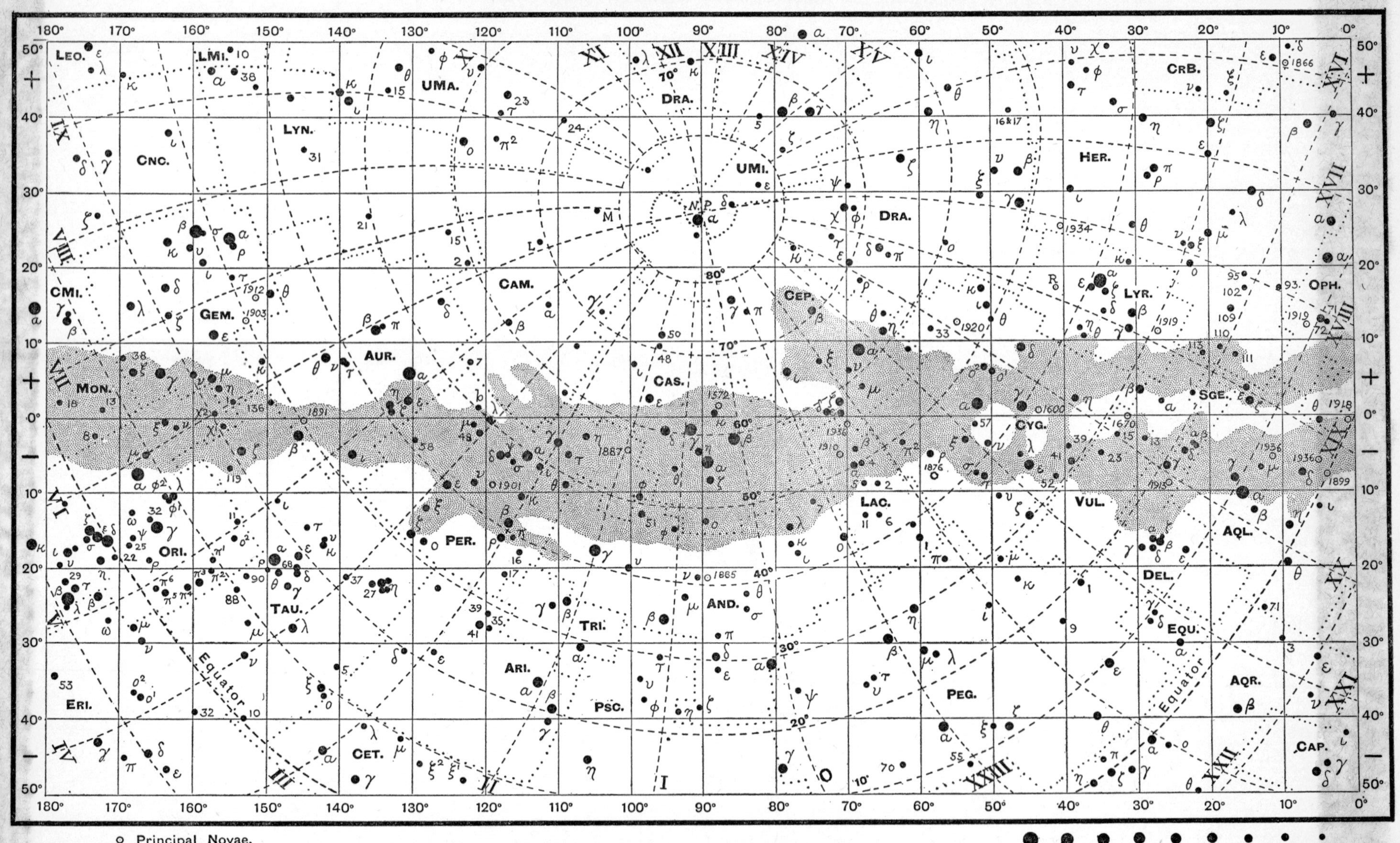

o Principal Novae.

The stippled area represents the general position of the Milky Way.

Magnitudes. 0 1 15 2 25 3 35 4 45

Galactic Chart (Galactic Longitude 180° to 360°; Galactic Latitude 50°N. to 50°S.)

Map 18

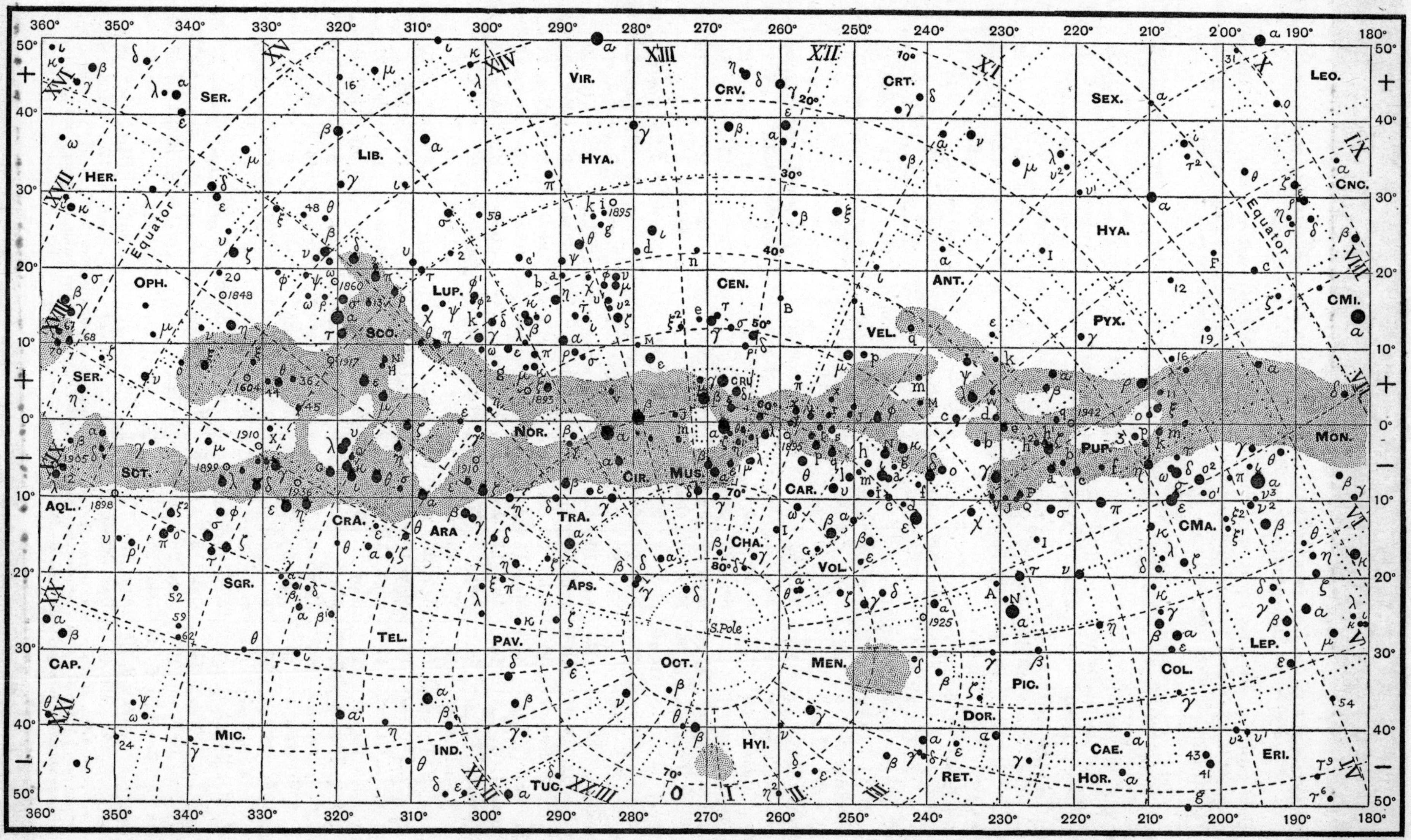

⊙ Principal Novae.

The stippled area represents the general position of the Milky Way.

Magnitudes. 0 1 15 2 25 3 35 4 45

INDEX TO THE CONSTELLATIONS.

With the number of the Map in which each is shown, and the approximate date of culmination of a point on its central hour of Right Ascension at 9 p.m. and Midnight.

For each Hour earlier or later than 9 p.m. or midnight—
Earlier—Add 15 days to dates given below.
Later—Subtract 15 days from ,, ,,

For each Week earlier or later than dates below—
Earlier—Add 28 minutes to 9 p.m. or midnight
Later—Subtract ,, from ,, ,,

Name of Constellation	Genitive	See Map No.	Approx. Date Culmination 9 p.m.	Approx. Date Culmination Midnight
Andromeda	Andromedæ	**3**	Nov. 23	Oct. 9
Antlia† ...	... Antliæ	**8, 10**	Apr. 10	Feb. 24
Apus† ...	... Apodis	**16**	July 5	May 21
Aquarius	... Aquarii	**4, 14**	Oct. 9	Aug. 25
Aquila ...	... Aquilæ	**13, 14**	Aug. 30	July 16
Ara ...	... Aræ	**12, 16**	July 25	June 10
Argo* (See Carina, Vela, and Puppis)		**8, 10, 16**	...	...
Aries ...	... Arietis	**5**	Dec. 14	Oct. 30
Auriga ...	... Aurigæ	**5, 7**	Feb. 4	Dec. 21
Boötes ...	... Boötis	**11**	June 16	May 2
Caelum† ...	... Cæli	**6**	Jan. 15	Dec. 1
Camelopardus†	Camelopardi	**1, 2**	Feb. 6	Dec 23
Cancer ...	... Cancri	**7**	Mar. 16	Jan. 30
Canes Venatici†	Canum Venaticorum	**9**	May 22	Apr. 7
Canis Major	Canis Majoris	**8**	Feb. 16	Jan. 2
Canis Minor	Canis Minoris	**7**	Feb. 28	Jan. 14
Capricornus	Capricorni	**14**	Sept. 22	Aug. 8
Carina† ...	... Carinæ	**8, 16**	Mar. 17	Jan. 31
Cassiopeia	Cassiopeiæ	**2, 3**	Nov. 23	Oct. 9
Centaurus	...Centauri	**10, 16**	May 14	Mar. 30
Cepheus ...	... Cephei	**2**	Nov. 13	Sept. 29
Cetus ...	... Ceti	**4, 5**	Nov. 29	Oct. 15
Chamaeleon†	Chamæleontis	**16**	Apr. 15	Mar. 1
Circinus†	... Circini	**16**	June 14	Apr. 30
Columba†	Columbæ	**6**	Feb. 1	Dec. 18
Coma Berenices†	Comæ Berenices	**9**	May 17	Apr. 2
Corona Australis	Coronæ Australis	**14**	Aug. 14	June 30
Corona Borealis	Coronæ Borealis	**11**	July 3	May 19
Corvus ...	... Corvi	**10**	May 12	Mar. 28
Crater ...	... Crateris	**10**	Apr. 26	Mar. 12
Crux† ...	... Crucis	**16**	May 12	Mar. 28
Cygnus ...	... Cygni	**13**	Sept. 13	July 30
Delphinus	...Delphini	**13**	Sept. 14	July 31
Dorado† ...	...Doradûs	**15, 16**	Jan. 31	Dec. 17
Draco ...	...Draconis	**1, 2**	July 8	May 24
Equuleus	... Equulei	**13**	Sept. 22	Aug. 8
Eridanus...	... Eridani	**6**	Dec. 25	Nov. 10
Fornax† ...	...Fornacis	**6**	Dec. 17	Nov. 2
Gemini ...	Geminorum	**7**	Feb. 19	Jan. 5
Grus† ...	... Gruis	**4**	Oct. 12	Aug. 28
Hercules	...Herculis	**11**	July 28	June 13
Horologium†	Horologii	**6, 15**	Dec. 25	Nov. 10
Hydra ...	... Hydræ	**8, 10**	Apr. 29	Mar. 15
Hydrus† ...	... Hydri	**15**	Dec. 10	Oct. 26

Name of Constellation	Genitive	See Map No.	Approx. Date Culmination 9 p.m.	Approx. Date Culmination Midnight
Indus† ...	... Indi	**14, 15**	Sept. 26	Aug. 12
Lacerta†	... Lacertæ	**3**	Oct. 12	Aug. 28
Leo ...	... Leonis	**7, 9**	Apr. 15	Mar. 1
Leo Minor†	Leonis Minoris	**9**	Apr. 9	Feb. 23
Lepus ...	... Leporis	**6**	Jan. 28	Dec. 14
Libra ...	... Libræ	**12**	June 23	May 9
Lupus ...	... Lupi	**12**	June 23	May 9
Lynx† ...	... Lyncis	**1, 7**	Mar. 5	Jan. 19
Lyra ...	... Lyræ	**13**	Aug. 18	July 4
Mensa† ...	... Mensæ	**15, 16**	Jan. 28	Dec. 14
Microscopium†	Microscopii	**14**	Sept. 18	Aug. 4
Monoceros†	Monocerotis	**7, 8**	Feb. 19	Jan. 5
Musca† ...	... Muscæ	**16**	May 14	Mar. 30
Norma† ...	... Normæ	**12**	July 3	May 19
Octans† ...	... Octantis	**15, 16**	Circum	polar
Ophiuchus	Ophiuchi	**11, 12**	July 26	June 11
Orion ...	... Orionis	**5, 6**	Jan. 27	Dec. 13
Pavo† ...	... Pavonis	**15**	Aug. 29	July 15
Pegasus ...	... Pegasi	**3**	Oct. 16	Sept. 1
Perseus ...	... Persei	**5**	Dec. 22	Nov. 7
Phoenix†	Phœnicis	**4**	Nov. 18	Oct. 4
Pictor† ...	... Pictoris	**6, 16**	Jan. 30	Dec. 16
Pisces ...	... Piscium	**3**	Nov. 11	Sept. 27
Piscis Austrinus	Piscis Austrini	**4**	Oct. 9	Aug. 25
Puppis† ...	... Puppis	**8**	Feb. 22	Jan. 8
Pyxis† ...	... Pyxidis	**8**	Mar. 21	Feb. 4
Reticulum†	... Reticuli	**15**	Jan. 3	Nov. 19
Sagitta ...	... Sagittæ	**13**	Aug. 30	July 16
Sagittarius	Sagittarii	**14**	Aug. 21	July 7
Scorpius	... Scorpii	**12**	July 18	June 3
Sculptor†	Sculptoris	**4**	Nov. 10	Sept. 26
Scutum† ...	... Scuti	**14**	Aug. 15	July 1
Serpens ...	Serpentis	**11**	July 21	June 6
Sextans†	Sextantis	**9, 10**	Apr. 8	Feb. 22
Taurus ...	... Tauri	**5**	Jan. 14	Nov. 30
Telescopium†	Telescopii	**14**	Aug. 24	July 10
Triangulum	Trianguli	**3**	Dec. 7	Oct. 23
Triangulum Australe†	Trianguli Australis	**16**	July 7	May 23
Tucana† ...	... Tucanæ	**15**	Nov. 1	Sept. 17
Ursa Major	Ursæ Majoris	**1, 9**	Apr. 25	Mar. 11
Ursa Minor	Ursæ Minoris	**1**	June 27	May 13
Vela† ...	Velorum	**8, 10**	Mar. 30	Feb. 13
Virgo ...	... Virginis	**9, 10**	May 26	Apr. 11
Volans† ...	...Volantis	**16**	Mar. 4	Jan. 18
Vulpecula†	Vulpeculæ	**13**	Sept. 8	July 25

* The ancient constellation of Argo Navis is now divided into the separate constellations of Carina, Vela, and Puppis, but only one sequence of Greek letters is used in the three constellations. Camelopardus is given as Camelopardalis in the I.A.U list.

† Constellations so marked have been added since the time of Ptolemy (about A.D. 150).